The Traces
of Thomas Hariot

The Traces of Thomas Hariot

MURIEL RUKEYSER

RANDOM HOUSE *New York*

All rights reserved under International
and Pan-American Copyright Conventions.
Published in the United States by Random House, Inc.,
New York, and simultaneously in Canada
by Random House of Canada Limited, Toronto.

ISBN: 0-394-44923-1

Library of Congress Catalog Card Number: 69-16452

Hariot's signature on cover, facsimile of Crown Copyright material
in the Public Record Office is reproduced by permission of
the Controller of Her Majesty's Stationery Office.

Manufactured in the United States of America
by the Haddon Craftsmen, Inc., Scranton, Pennsylvania

2   4   6   8   9   7   5   3

First Edition

To Monica McCall

A new light was struck by Hariot.
— *Coleridge*

This world, a sacred holy animal, to be loved.
— *Bruno, in* DE IMMENSO

. . . . Employed in discovering.
— *Said of Hariot on the title-page*
of A BRIEF AND TRUE REPORT

LOST, PERISHED, & DISCOVERED
— *Motto on the title-page of Hariot's book*
on America A BRIEF AND TRUE REPORT

TRACE (treis), sb.[1] M E. The track made by the passage of any person or thing, whether beaten by feet or indicated in any other way.

Vestiges of marks remaining and indicating the former presence, existence, or action of something.

An indication of the presence of a minute amount of some constituent in a compound; a quantity so minute as to be inferred but not actually measured.

A non-material indication or evidence of the presence or existence of something, or of a former event or condition; a sign, mark.

O E D

Psychol. An engram. (Engram, A lasting trace left in an organism by psychic experience.)

Webster

CONTENTS

ILLUSTRATIONS

INTRODUCTION:
The Questions

T o stand in this moment, in a city in history, thinking of a lost man who was great. And if he is great, what is his greatness? If he is great, why is he lost? Thinking, rather, of his traces among us who hardly know his name. You will find reminders among the stories of early America : Thomas Hariot, the friend of Sir Walter Ralegh who as a young man came to the New World to live his year; scientist, mathematician, experimental observer, who voyaged with the 1585 expedition to "Virginia," exploring and record-ing in that unknown wildness. Friend of Marlowe, accused with him of heresy. Linked with poets and pioneer scientists, gone down, almost forgotten among great waves of crushing powers. Caught indeed in all the heresies of his time, scientific, political, philosophical, sexual.

Scientist, then, who adventured into his sciences, into Virginia when America stood to England as the moon stands to us. Naturalist, mathematician, originator and founder in these languages of the world; expert in ships and navigation, and master-teacher to the sea-captains of the Elizabethan time. Astronomer, who lived among the wars of vision and the Copernican struggle, among the grinding of lenses at the begin-ning of the telescope, and indeed had the telescope at the same moment as Galileo.

Man whose ramifying thought links him with Kepler in an exchange of letters and questions; with the young Descartes, dreaming a chain of dreams one crucial winter night. Hariot, the lost man — and that name can be spelled Harriot, Harriott, Heriots, Heriot; any way you choose, for we are in the late

1500's, when spelling is not yet a mark of education and caste, when Lady Ralegh spells as she pleases. The questions come to this threshold life, whose marks and traces hide curiously; it is a threshold of all things, for in England the old style of religion, calendar, the sea, and essential being, England itself, have all broken open into another life.

What is this life and who is Thomas Hariot? It is not that we go into the past, live in the past, to find him, but that his print, his traces, are around us. Indeed, if one searches the past for him, the search will lead to fiery details; a stroke here and then an airy space, another stroke of what is now called fact, and then something obliterated, drowned, burned, lost. And then another stroke, until an entire structure of a life begins to rise, brilliant, with long reaches, venturesome, airy, full of risk, moving in a way that speaks to us in our century.

He is a rebel who appears to fail at every climax of his life. He can be seen to go deeper at these times.

The fact that his story has been lost is deep in our own history. In a very real way, he is the first explorer on this land of a way of thinking, a real and possible strength to our time. This book is built according to the nature of an interest in Hariot and the problems, not solved by him, but indicated by him.

An introduction raises the questions. The first part tells the story of the year in America. Then, as Hariot sails home with Drake, he goes into his own past and the English past since 1560, the year of his birth. His ancestors are claimed for him, and his "parents," although we know nothing of his biological parents. Then, as he (and Drake) reach England, we reach the time they landed, in 1586. From the season of Hariot's return, we follow his life chronologically. Through the Irish years with Spenser and Ralegh, Kilcolman and Molanna and Youghal; Marlowe's death in which Hariot was implicated deep; the fortunes of his two patrons in their pride and downfall; the Armada, the Gunpowder Plot, and the great structure of family-ing thought that makes Hariot a central figure for us; Bruno in England, in Germany and at last the acting-out of the stoppage as he comes home; Donne in the closeness of his life to the main persons of this story. Always, this is an account not of Hariot's life, but of his *traces*, as we know them now. How he reaches us.

These separate scenes flash on each other. They are linked, as Hariot's look at a river in Virginia shines a river in England to him; and then in a stream of sequential time. The scenes are most strongly connected through their reinforcement of each other. They are the way he and our recognizing of him move. But how did he move? In what web of lives?

He had as patrons two of the most magnetic, powerful and wealthy men at Court, Ralegh and Henry Percy, ninth Earl of Northumberland, the Wizard Earl. He moved with them from their life of power to their disgraces and imprisonments in the Tower of London — dungeon and center of life — working and teaching there, although he himself was never condemned and lived outside, in London and at Syon House where Northumberland had given him his house and his laboratory. Not condemned, except to be lost.

In his patrons' time of power, Hariot carried his meanings to the Indians of Virginia, reporting his regard for them, telling the clue anthropological stories of their lives of pride and skills; he lived, too, in the other Caliban country, Ireland of green grace and burning.

He came back from Ireland to the post-Armada world, when the war with Spain had become something else in caves and tunnels under the English spirit, when the killing of Indians and Irish and Spanish had changed phase, and the combat between Spain and Elizabeth was dying with the Armada and the Queen. Years of the accession of James, the immediate conviction of Ralegh — who to James was a curious deep enemy, that dark-bearded flashing man pouring smoke and arrogance; years of the Gunpowder Plot, which James prided himself he had caught, putting down the powers of night; and the imprisonment of the Wizard Earl — seventeen years in the Tower. Until the reach for the New World, Virginia or Guiana, seemed over and past with that one stab at triumph lost by Ralegh.

Then Hariot made the leap in his imagination, with all that defeat and imprisonment: from the new world to the moon.

He can be seen as a man who met the headlong force of every current of the time. He had with belief encountered Bruno's thought as the marvelous raging Italian streaked, learned, hairy, through two years in England, that comet leaving fury and passionate conviction behind him just before Hariot sailed for the New World, who heard the news of Bruno being burned, gagged, at the stake as the new century began.

He and his friends spoke to each other of "our diligent Galileus" and went still in the last miserable years of sickness and silence after Ralegh's beheading, when the Inquisition caught Galileo as it had caught Bruno.

Stroke after stroke, the evidence of his life, among enormous wreckage and destruction, is given in flashes to us, until we begin to see Thomas Hariot among the others whose names and lives we know. A structure different in kind from the life of Shakespeare, known only so in flashes but given in poetry, the many-voiced full speech of this mystery and its physical gestures of deep war and solvings, of desperate love. Or from the life of Marlowe, pioneering the mind going beyond the limits set for it, and himself driving on furiously to his own murder, and was it political? doubly political in a time like our own of secret errands and double agents, or was it sexual only? Can experience be separated, so that a murder is sexual only? But they could separate soul from body, as they shared head from body; the Queen's own mother, Anne Boleyn, ended so, and Essex, and Ralegh. Hariot, however, had in his life a different structure, which is more and more clearly visible even among our ignorance and loss.

Thomas Hariot was born in 1560 at Oxford, and went as a local scholar to St. Mary Hall, Oxford University during years of strong life and turmoil among the academies. In 1580, he went up to London, to the household of Ralegh as tutor to this courtier eight years older than he, marvelous proud, ascendant, dreaming power, the sea, and the great Queen his giver.

With Ralegh whose tutor he was, Hariot knew sea-captains, ships and the shipwrights, the docks and harbors of the west country from whose winds and blues and greens Ralegh as well as Ralegh's half-brothers, the Gilberts, came; he went to Plymouth and Portsmouth docks and harbors and among the ways and planks and hammer-noise of London waterside. He was teaching, making notes on the observations which would lead to his two handbooks, *Articon* and *The Regiment of the Sun.*

Three years later, he began to work on the needs and conditions for voyages into the sea. The Atlantic — or rather the one ocean that flows among the world — is the unknown of that age. On the title page of Bacon's *Novum Organum,* the picture of a ship sailing through the Pillars of Hercules into an endless ocean of newness, the bunt of whose sails shows the strength of a following wind, speaks for the opening-out of thought and reach. Bacon stayed home. Hariot, at twenty-five, went out with the Second Expedition to Virginia as geographer, planner, the link with the Indians. He sailed from Plymouth under Sir Richard Grenville on April 9, 1585. Grenville was captain of seven ships, with the *Tiger* as flagship; Simon Fernandez, the Portuguese Protestant who had piloted the first short expedition for Ralegh the year before, under Amadas and Barlow, was master. The 600 men who sailed included two tall Indians, like white Moors, Manteo and Wachese, who had lived in England, taught Hariot some of their speech, and who were returning to their country now.

It is a country of sandbars, shoal waters, low drifting dunes, blond long beaches, birds in their migrations. The inner island can be reached by a bridge now, and there are high bridges connecting some of the sandbars. Far within, North Carolina reaches, wooded, full of creeks and inlets.

Their voyage was to a wilderness of extreme fear, the limits of challenge, and the strong temptation promise of gold. Haunted by many kinds of doom — the fury of the Spaniards, ready to slaughter them as intruders who came to dispossess

men who had been there for eighty years and who worshipped,
not Elizabeth, but Mary . . . Spaniards who at the same time
proved vastly civilized, offering graces and learning that some of
the English found they craved, as well as provisions and water.
To the Spaniards, all English were pirates, Harriot too being
"pirata." Another doom that haunted the English was the fear
deep in the psyche, unspoken, of the consequence of assaulting
Eden. Wealth, profit being the prize, although planting and
colonization is the stated goal. The entry into what is, in one
aspect, a livable forest with people existing "as if in the golden
age" — these were on the other side after the endurance of the
Atlantic, the entry into the unmapped world.

Harriot was one of the leaders of this expedition. He went
through this first clash of the English Renaissance and the
Golden Age. What was the sign of this clash, and what do we in-
herit of this year?

The first surviving book in English out of the New World
is Hariot's *A Brief and True Report*. It is the short version of
what Hariot intended to publish. After the year on the Outer
Banks and Roanoke, when the relief ship that was expected
did not come, and when Drake with his ships sailed storming
up the coast (doing as his last errand on the Caribbean raids
what he was charged with, looking in on Ralegh's adventurers)
he offered them choice of a ship, fully provisioned, or the chance
to return at once with him. It was only when a violent storm
of four-day force tore at Hatteras and drove the offered ship
out to set that the decision went completely in favor of sailing
on the instant with Drake and his men. In a passion of finality,
sick of wilderness and abandonment — their relief ship months
late — the men threw themselves and their belongings, their
cards and weapons, the charts and mathematical instruments,
the pearls for the Queen, into sea-chests and loaded the small
pinnaces. The Sound behind the Outer Banks is shoal water,
one and two feet in places, hardly depth for a boat of any draft
at all. If you take a rowboat out, you go around again and again;
you can pole off with an oar; the ferry can back off by engine.
A chart helps, but not much, for the sands shift continually,

and the charts go out of date. In almost 400 years, the bottom of the Sound has shifted, the channels have moved; some have closed up entirely; the shapes of the islands have changed.

The pinnace stuck, as the *Tiger* had the year before. In frenzy, the sailors threw everything overboard to lighten ship. The writings of Hariot, and his instruments, were jettisoned. The pinnace, riding higher now, floated; they rowed out through the channel to deep water, the place of conflict where the northern and southern currents of the Atlantic meet at Hatteras and Diamond Shoals. Just north of that elbow, they came to Drake's fleet, riding diminished far enough offshore to be safe, in a sparkling day after hurricane. They boarded and made for England, where they arrived at Portsmouth on July 28, 1586. England was deep in preparations for a Spanish attack; recruiting in all the shires, warning parties set up on on the headlands.

Hariot's book was published in February of 1588. The Armada sailed three months later, and was sighted off the Scilly Islands late in July.

Of the expeditions Ralegh sent out, that of the Lost Colony had already died. The next was sent in 1590, the year in which editions of Hariot's book — an encouragement to investors — appeared in Frankfort in four languages: Latin, English, French, and German.

We have no record of the time that Hariot spent in Ireland as Ralegh's tenant and probably as his estate manager. In Hariot's will, he makes the request that two bags of "loose papers" be burned; one bag held the record of the Irish time. Perhaps in a great library in Ireland, or buried under a tree in County Cork, the writings will be disclosed. Curiously however, the writings will be disclosed. Curiously how-ever we can piece together, in poetry and in the other ways that meanings move, that time. Hariot was given as his home the little island with the Abbey of Molanna on it, at a bend of the river a few miles up from Youghal, where Ralegh was. Molanna will come back to us again, in a work of Spenser's carrying ideas of change that are familiar in Bruno and in Hariot: Spenser's great poem, *Mutabilitie*.

Known to us are the return from Ireland and the famous years at Court of Ralegh, clothed in silver and jewels, in the riches, the poems, the complicated adorations. Ralegh's haste of ambition, his talks at Durham House, his friendship with Northumberland, and Northumberland's intercession to keep young John Donne from being thrown into prison by his father-in-law — an intercession that failed. Ralegh at his post standing outside the Queen's council-chamber as captain of the guard; longing to go to sea and being prevented, until he found that he would be seasick every time he crossed the Thames in a ferry. The abrupt disgrace when it was discovered that Elizabeth Throckmorton, the queen's lady-in-waiting, was pregnant by Ralegh; his and her imprisonment; until the tall Spanish carrack, the *Madre de Dios*, was taken in all its wealth and brought into port. It was clear that only Ralegh — forever a hero to the west country, for all the hatred vented on him in London — was the only man who could stop the rioting and looting of the ship and save some share of the prize, the largest ever taken by England, for the Queen and the other investors in the raiding company. Then Ralegh, set free with his wife (the baby Damarie has vanished from history), goes to Sherborne in Dorset, the castle given him. Harriot goes with him, until Ralegh's friendship with Northumberland means that finally Harriot takes as his new patron the Wizard Earl, becoming one of the "three Magi," men of science living within Northumberland's generosity and work in learning.

He lived from then on chiefly at Syon House, outside of London at Isleworth. His researches gathered. In the confused, out-of-order papers in many hands, the structure declares itself, however partially and through loss and obliteration. The work is in laws of sight, the telescope, invention of symbols used to this day, algebra, observation of falling bodies, work in close-packing, clues to crystal structure, the clusters of the early atomists; studies of the comet that became known later as Halley's comet; eclipses and the moon (Harriot had seen an eclipse over the Atlantic as he sailed to America, he and the

Indians spoke of it together); the signs, the dot, the "larger than" and "smaller than" signs; the moons of Jupiter; the nature of the tropics; river-currents; the elixir; fortification and military tactics, the five-sided fort . . .

Was Hariot a great scientist? A great man?
What are the three sea marriages?
What article of clothing marks the dichotomy of body and soul?
Why did the Indians think the white men were gods?
What is the Cerne Giant?
Why was Ralegh in deep disgrace?
What death came to Northumberland's father in the Tower?
What marriage was arranged for Northumberland's daughter, and why did Northumberland refuse a pardon?
Were the metal soldiers cast as part of a child's game?
What castle is on Sleep Hill?
Is there really a connection between tobacco and cancer?
When was the tempest?
What is a dot?
How many infinities?
Is a shipload of men a homosexual culture?
Is the Bible an atheist book? If you rub yourself with it?
What did the Earl of Essex say at the block?
How do you get from a prison to the moon?
What is the true relation between To Be and Not To Be?
What is the horse half-leaping out of the world?
Why did Prospero break his staff?
Why is the statue of Ariel within the walls of the Bank of England?

These are some of the questions that rise. I will try to answer them.

The search for the traces of Thomas Hariot has led to answers, to questions, and to a further sight of his life so fine in its structure, in the language of what it says to our time, that I take it as far as I can among the obliterations, and let it go for others to take further.

The devastations continue, and a triumph accompanies. Ralegh was condemned and thrown into the Tower for years beginning in 1603, Northumberland in 1605. The highly-colored society of their great houses was destroyed; even young Dudley Carleton, who afterward rose very high, to an embassy, to friendship with Rubens, to great place at home, was suspect, as secretary to Northumberland, when it was plain that Carleton had rented the building whose cellar was used to store explosives and fuel intended to blow up King and Parliament in the Gunpowder Plot. Hariot was involved in those years of prison; they included help to Ralegh as he wrote his vast *History of the World;* friendship with Chapman, Jonson, and with Hues and Warner, the other Magi. They included long work, long illness.

He was a man tripped and beaten down; Quixote was another. But Hariot met his defeats in another way, and there are clues here.

When the first Indian village came to chastisement, Hariot's sense of these people clashed with a military rule dependent on property and property rights as the base of war. The telescope and what it implied carried enormous punishments dealt out by religion to defend writings that had to be considered sacred. Another penalty was carried because of casting the horoscope of King James.

Why did Hariot not publish? His will says plainly that he wanted it.

At the end, dying of a "nothing" as they said, mocking him because he too had said, "Ex nihilo nihil fit," Hariot was still making a great configuration, repeated in many ways throughout his life, repeated I would say each time he was beaten down. Beaten down, step by step, and at each step he opened his life beyond the beating.

At the end, staying with an old friend and his family—Thomas Buckner who had been on that voyage to the New World years ago—Hariot died with his patron still in the Tower. Northumberland emerged months later, and heard Donne preach to him, Donne now Dean, and Northumberland broken. He had a monument raised to Hariot, and began to see his books through. The *Ephemeris* was never published; the *Artis Analyticae Praxis* appeared in 1631. The monument went in the Great Fire; it stood in the graveyard of St. Christopher-le-Stock, land which is now the green grass of the inner, silent garden of the Bank of England : another face of the idea of the New World, a deep greenness surrounded by money.

The thick walls of the Tower of London carry Ralegh's Walk, where finally Ralegh was forbidden to go, the sailors cheered so as the ships sailed past. At the Tower, they will show you the place on the wall where Hariot built a sun-dial for the long slow time of blood; they will hazard at the site of Ralegh's smelting-room and laboratory; they know where the riding-ring was, and the lions; and here in an open pit they have uncovered digging the darkened yellowed bones of a little child and a woman, exposed and very moving, with the archaeologist's brushes beside her. And within, where the Guard meet, the plaque and memorial to the Gunpowder Plot, from which King James saved us all.

In the great libraries, the folios and account rolls. Up the river, at Syon Reach, the great house stands, that began as a nunnery. If you approach from the noisy road, down the brick lane, you stand suddenly in that other world of the fathers and sons, the chains of inherited power, opposite on the black-and-white of floor, the live memories, the statues, portraits, books; the maps; the kings and princesses. Outside, the long reaches, and the airy palace of the greenhouse; slow cattle; the mulberry tree given by King James; and the lost place, for now nobody can say where Hariot's house stood; and the lovely stretch of the Thames, with Kew across, this bank, the road of river to London, waterway to Essex Stairs, to Blackfriars, to

Traitor's Gate where Lady Jane Grey went from here, and Thomas Percy after coming here to dinner like a fool the night of the Gun-powder Plot whose bonfires still burn, Novembers.

Or Petworth with its Turners and its mulberry tree, its deer park and gardens, the glowing yellow walls of the paintings, the Molyneux globe and the locked white room upstairs with the toys of vanished children, the buffalo pictures of vanished America, and the books of the Ninth Earl, who broods out at you from a portrait with his complicated look.

Or far in the north, at Alnwick, that grey dragon of a castle whose library shimmers high vibrating gold, the books of these wild dreams and keenest observation and experiment, history and in the alchemical flask, the bird diving into a lake of stars called "Creation." Here is the huge keep that could hold 6000 men, near the border of Scotland, and the lead statues on the battlements, drinking, shouting, pouring molten oil, all in lead. At one corner the round tower, grey stone, with its Muniment Room, whose accounts carry life in the castles, men stripped of fortunes and building fortunes; the bravery of the recusants and the fierce loyalties of the Percies; the new life of England as a world-center, ramifying through oceans and centuries from these farms, these mines and rainy months, these people. Even the scroll summoning the widow of Hotspur to come to London and call for his head and the quarters of his body, butchered by edict and shown at the gates of four cities, and give them Christian burial. All this leads to Hariot.

It leads to him in the past. The past has to be here, whole in the present, to give him to us with exactness in history. Copernicus, Avicenna, Roger Bacon; Faust, Quixote, Prospero; they feed into his story; the watermen on the Thames, the science of calculating the masts and breadth of ships as the new ships were built, carrying cannon, and the fireboats sank forever; the instruments of navigation, astrolabe, cross-staff, ring, Lead and copper floating on mercury, and what the droplets are to us today.

Why is his name almost lost?

And what in the present leads to him?

And those women. All contradictions of life : universities full
of men forbidden to marry; ships full of men gone to the New
World without women. And those women central to this story,
sources of enormous perception and strength. Not only Queen
Elizabeth; let me remember Katherine Champernown, mother
of the three Gilberts and of Ralegh; Dorothy Devereux, sister
of Essex, wife of Perrot and Northumberland; Lucy Percy in
the Tower; and Lady Ralegh; their struggle, the loves, their
unrecorded lives.

Echoes in the lives of schoolboys even, who make a resonance
for Hariot as mathematician.
Live voices in the poems : Spenser, Chapman, Jonson, Shakespeare, Ralegh's

Knowing she can renew, and can create
Green from the ground, and flowers, even out of stone,
By virtue lasting over time and date —

And Hariot's "Three Sea Marriages" and the jingle that carries us cheerfully past an old tradition, "If more by more must
needs make more." It ends

So both are one, for both are true,
Of this enough and so adieu.

His work is part of the long work in history and the present
to expand the limits, to risk, to break bounds and establish
further imagining, that is, to change the world and the body of
man in its possibilities.

I think of what happens as one stands on Roanoke where
Hariot's house was, the fort and the village, where now there is
a Hariot Trail, edged with all the New World plants he
describes in his *Brief and True Report*, "Hariot?" they say.
"Nobody knows who he is. Well, one or two do."

The trail takes you down to the Sound, shallow and peaceful; just to the right was the weir the Indians made of reeds, trapping the fish which teemed in these waters.

Standing at the shore, you look out over the little waves, past the sea-birds moving between you and the Outer Banks. Sand at the sea-bottom shifts, the water moves, the sandbars are shifting slowly. It is the landscape of imagination. You are looking straight across from the site of the City of Raleigh to the short truncated wing of stainless steel and granite at Kitty Hawk which marks the first flight of the Wright Brothers. Actually, since the dunes shift, it does not mark the place; a big boulder pins down the spot. The wing is a monument to that kind of imagination.

Beyond it is the sea.

1
The Voyage

*T*hey sail out, through known waters, pass out of soundings where the continental shelf drops to floorless water, out into fighting seas; out into the waves that lead to the Spanish islands.

Then they would be out past those into unknown streams in the ocean, where the whales are. Where, they say, are to be found gold, and the other ocean.

Hariot, in the sun, is a young man watching a sailor coil a rope. He leans on the starboard side, where the master's men are. The sailor, seeing his interest, shows Hariot the coiling of ropes : you run it round, so, with the sun, one turn after another; a single turn is called a fake.

The sea glitters. The mists of England are days behind.

Five good ships, including the two pinnaces, and a good admiral : Grenville. Captain Ralph Lane, who will be in command when the admiral leaves them in Ralegh's Virginia. And Hariot's friend Thomas Cavendish, the same age as he; and John White with whom Hariot will be working, writing and making observations and accuracies while White makes his own accuracies, the pictures of the expedition.

They come to this beginning bearing guns, grain, dolls, musical instruments, nails, beer, raisins of the sun, the Bible, brass mathematical devices, books, and a hundred men.

Hallucinating gold and emeralds.

The two Indians, Manteo and Wachese, standing together at the prow, are going home. They have given Hariot many words of their own language, concrete words for this thing and that thing. The sea compels them; they stare all day; their only boats are dugout canoes.

The chief properties of a ship in the sea, Hariot writes : To go well; to steer well; and bear a good sail.

The cry comes : Roomer! Roomer! Give her room!

Veer! comes the cry. Veer! And the answer in the sun : All is out, to the bitter end!

It is the lookout watch, the first watch from 4 to 6 in the afternoon. The sailors are still talking about the leak. They had to bring her upon the careen, far over on her side, to caulk her. We drink more than we pump, says one.

It's been mended, says the other. She's as tight as a fish.

Aluff! comes the cry — And shake in the wind!

On the tenth day out from Plymouth, they were facing due west when the curious thing began to happen, Hariot had warned them, but no matter how the warnings have been given, that shiver of darkening and apprehension arrives as the sun begins to darken. It was a double darkening. As the sun went down, it deformed, deformed in full eclipse. At sunset in these latitudes (they were sailing at about N. 20°, W. 30°) this eclipse was seen only as a partial one, one side of the sun melting away as the light turned red and faded black.

Far behind them, hours behind them, in Denmark, Tycho Brahe at Uraniborg had built his new observatory, Star City. In the summer of 1585, his collection of instruments and his staff were at the height of their working powers. The path of this eclipse, however, began to the west of Brahe. Across the ocean the sun went sinking and changing. In the Americas, people met it with the fears that can be seen today, and have always been shown. Hariot on his deck brought out his instruments while the sailors watched in silence. The old stories told of the Persians banging their pans together to frighten it, to bring it to birth. Here was the true phoenix, burning and dying, and would it live again? Here was Jonah, they said in Asia, swallowed by the fish, and would he come forth? The Indians of America saw the total and full eclipse. They met it dancing; they danced and stamped all night in one long sustaining rhythm, carrying themselves through, carrying the sun through till it rose in the morning as they danced and shouted, reborn. Born again whole.

On the 11th or 12th of May (according to the map of John White or the report of Ralph Lane), the fleet of Grenville came to anchor at the Spanish colony of Puerto Rico, in Tallaboa Bay, on the southwestern coast — then called "the Bay of Moskito in the Iland of S. John." Within a falcon's shot from the shore, they anchored, and came ashore in the small boats.

They began to dig entrenchments at once. It was a good place to fortify. They had most of their company with them, although Master Cavendish was still separated from the fleet, and had been since the Bay of Portugal, and a few men stayed with the ships. The rest dug.

It was a naturally defended site : the sea with its narrow beach ahead of them, the river to their right. There was a pond to their left, at the rear corner of their fort, and woods within the fortifications, as well as off to the left. The sound of axes was very loud in the silence. The logs were being dragged toward the walls as they went up, with their angled embrasures for the men with guns. There was a house being built far in the rear, among the trees, for Ralph Lane, who was Governor.

As for Grenville, his dwelling was going up near the beach wall. He rode off on the captured horses that had been corralled within the fort across the shallow river with about thirty men to reconnoiter. John White piled up sand on the beach, and leaned against the mound, his back to the sea. He was drawing the fort : a bird's-eye view, the *Tiger* riding at anchor, horses in a corral, sea-birds standing in the bond, some men on a raft in the freshwater river; and, off in a corner of the fort, men at work on a new pinnace, very much needed according to

21

Simon Fernando, who knew the waters they were coming to. The timber near the beach was not much good for boat-building. The men went on expeditions into the island, far as three miles inland. They brought the timber back on trucks, "the Spaniard not daring to make me offer resistance."

It was a question, whether the Spaniard dared; or what he intended. After they had been there a few days, a party of Spaniards — eight horsemen — rode out of the woods a little distance from the fort, and reined their horses in, standing for about half an hour, watching this landing, building, digging, fortifying party, but making no move toward them. After a while the English sent ten men, "ten of our shot," marching toward them. The Spaniards did nothing; that is, they wheeled and "retired into the woods."

Then, to their uneasiness, a ship arrived at their little island of Cotesa. The men on the *Tiger* cried a warning to the fort. The ship looked like a Spaniard or a French man-of-war; but when the *Tiger* set sail and came within sharp vision of the ship, it was seen to be Cavendish, separated from them since April 14th, "for joy of whose coming our ships discharged their ordinance, and saluted him according to the manner of the Seas."

In the next days, they met Spaniards again, twenty horsemen this time, across the river to the right of the fort. Grenville sent out twenty of his men on foot, and two horsemen. A flag of truce was shown by the English, and a parley begun. The Spaniards, the report says, offered "very great salutations to our men, but began according to their Spanish proud humors, to expostulate" as well they might, about the arrival and fortifying of the English. But by our men's discreet answers "were so cooled" that, when they understood the English required only to furnish themselves with "water and victuales, and other necessaries, whereof we stood in neede," and that by fair and friendly means — or else by the sword — the Spaniards offered them what they needed, "with large promises of all curtesie, and great favour, and so our men and theirs departed."

But the next day, when the pinnace was finished and launched, they waited for the Spaniards at the place arranged, about four miles upriver, in a marsh. But there were no Spaniards, there was no food. The English did the thing that occurred to them : they set fire to the woods, marched back and set fire to the fort.

That night, they were all aboard their ships, covered with mosquito bites, and stinging. The smoke of the burning fort did not help, with the wind off the sea. They had built in such a way that the fire was delimited, and by dawn the smell was almost gone, even when the wind veered. They were ready to set sail, angry, frustrated, and without the provisions they had expected. All day they talked about perjury and breach of promise.

Toward evening they comforted themselves. Against the sunset, the tall masts and spars of a Spanish frigate. This time, her crew showed sense, and forsook their ship at the sight of the English, shouting "Piratas!" Next morning, very early, another frigate appeared, "with good and rich fraight." They took the ship and all on her; among these, there was "divers Spaniards of account" who brought ransoms of "good round sums" when the English landed them in St. Johns.

While they were taking their two frigates, Ralph Lane had gone off to Rojo Bay for salt, with a Spanish pilot. But when he had landed, he did not bargain for salt; he took twenty men with him on the beach, and entrenched himself around a salt hill, taking what he wanted under the eyes of two or three troops of horsemen and men on foot, "who gave him the looking, and gazing on, but durst not . . ." Lane and the rest of the fleet made rendezvous at St. German's Bay, and sailed for Hispaniola.

Within two days, the Governor came to meet them. The English report says that it was because he knew "that in our fleet were many brave and gallant Gentlemen."

The Spanish report says, however, that Diego Menendez de Valdes, Governor of Puerto Rico, had learned of the landing of the English, the building of the fort, the cutting of wood, building and launching a pinnace, and finally, the taking of two frigates carrying merchandise and what happened to these frigates. Among the inquiries now in the Museo Naval at Madrid is also the testimony concerning a fleet commanded by Richarte de Verde Campo, with its twenty men "qui parascia gente de respeto," carrying silver and gold-plate, carrying two Indians who are tall and fine-bodied and who speak English; carrying musical instruments, among them several organs, and saying that they know the Indians care about music; carrying the Bible translated into Castilian; they have taken maps and papers from the frigates, and they have a Portuguese, their Lutheran pilot.

Another piece of testimony refers to the pilot by name : Simon Fernando, a Portuguese from Tercera, and this set of answers speaks of gold, silver, and pearls, taken from the frigates, as well as their own "muchos artificios de fuego."

The Governor came accompanied by "a lusty Fryer, and twenty other Spaniards, with their servants, and Negros," to the sea side to see this "flota," these "navios que andaban robando en aquellas islas."

They sailed up the Atlantic, past the fires on the Florida beaches — Canaveral and the other northern, Spanish shores; past where the French had tried to plant a colony and met massacre; and to the flat islands of sand at Hatteras, the Outer Banks of North Carolina, called Virginia by the Elizabethans and in this account. At one of these, Wococon, they waited, trusting Simon Fernando to bring them in.

Three days they stayed at anchor at Wococon. On the 29th of June, they attempted to bring the *Tiger* through the inlet into the sound. These are shifting sand-bottoms, seeming to move as you sail. Today, with a well-marked chart showing the depths as varying from one to six feet, you are cautioned that all things shift, and the ferry that runs across will go aground again and again, and backwater off the shoals and bars. Ralph Lane, keeping the log of these days, writes that "through the unskillfulness of the Master whose name was Fernando, the Admirall strooke on ground, and sunk." This sinking was simply a running aground, the ship lying beating upon the shoal for two hours, but the salt water got into the grain in the hold of the *Tiger*; it was the first adversity. The great ship was of 140 tons.

There were fires up the islands of the Outer Banks. Better to send ahead to the Wingina, the chieftain, at Roanoak Island; four days later, the messengers were sent to say that the English were at Wococon. Then the men began to deploy. Master John Arundel was sent with Manteo to the mainland, across the shallow sound, the Indian returning to his people after the months over the ocean, with his news of England. Two of the other captains went to Croatoan, and found thirty-two men, two of their own, the others left by Captain Raymond three weeks before. These came back to the *Tiger* on the 10th of July.

On the next day, four of the small boats set out across the Sound. Hariot went, with Lane and Cavendish and twenty others in the new pinnace that they had built inside the fort at St. John, headed for the mainland with provisions for eight days. The General was in a tilt boat with Stukeley, Arundel, and others; Amadas — the Admiral — and Clarke with ten men in a shipboat, and the artist John White and Francis Brooke in a second shipboat went on the first sail of discovery. Across the Sound. When you go aground, you go over and into the water, and push the boat off the sand. From the sandbar where the others are, you seem to be walking on the water, pushing a boat riding high. The shore birds appear to be standing on the water, watching; they run, they run, and take off over you, flying along the bars. In this voyage, says Ralph Lane, "we first discovered the townes of Pomejok, Aquascogok and Secotan, and also the great lake called by the

Savages Paquipe, with divers other places, and so returned with that discovery to our Fleete." These are the swamps and salt creeks of the mainland, with the more southerly of the Indian towns. It was in one of these that the first confrontation between the two civilizations came.

It was in a form visible to the naked eye, a few Englishmen meeting a few Indians on the 13th of July, 1585, after they had passed by water to Aquascogok, on the broad Sound. In the four-oared boat, they rowed over the shoals, knowing a boat that drew even a foot or so more water could not be used here.

On the 15th they went to Secotan, of which Lane reports only that they were "well entertained there of the Savages."

But on the next day they came away. There was a flaring anger in some of them : a silver cup was missing. One of the boats with Grenville and some unnamed men went back to Aquascogok to "demaund" the cup. At first they believed that one of the Indians was going to return the cup. They believed this "according to his promise." But, whatever the facts were, the English did not get the cup back. The first frightfulness began. The threatening, and the lack of understanding of language on both sides. The guns, and the fire. White smoke beginning to curl up from the cornfields where the young corn planted last month showed, too young to burn fast; it was the corn of two months ago that was burning. The people of this village were planting now in the third field, which stood, prepared and fertile, red-brown; they straightened up and stared. The red flames were beginning to show under the smoke. The people first stood for a moment, beginning to understand. They ran for the woods. Out of the small houses, rounded at the top and made on poles over which stretched the mats, or strips of bark, the others ran. In a few minutes the village was emptied. "We burnt, and spoyled their corne, and Towne, all the people being fled."

The flames crackled among the corn. The little houses sucked up flame, and were gone in a minute. The little hut of the watchman flashed; one of its poles was of green wood and took a little longer. A child who had hidden in another kind of field came out from among the leaves. He was crying, but stopped when he reached the main path, and ran as fast as he could for the forest. He was the last.

So they burned their first village.

Two months after the settlers arrived, a great comet appeared in Pisces. It was seen by Hariot and the Indians, and they spoke of it night after night, from the 18th of October until the 20th of November. In Uraniborg, Tycho Brahe observed this comet too. His assistant, Olaus Cimber, made observations, and it is from him, through Giordano Bruno, that we have its description. For Bruno, in England in 1585, wrote of this years later, in the greatest of his poems, *De Immenso*, his last and finest work. In London, he was with Mauvissière, the French Ambassador, with Sir Philip Sidney, to whom he dedicated two of the books strangely placed, on their title-pages, in cities on the Continent, for prestige; but actually printed in London. This book carries in the long note after Book VI, Chapter xx, a description of the comet : "Ex quo possimus intellegere esse planetam, deque natura aquae speculariter splendentem, non autem de natura flammae principaliter. Tenebroso (ait Olaus), subpallido, et obscuro lumine praedita erat, adeo uo nebuloso gyro Cancri, ubi praesepe est, quam simillima stella fuerit. Fuit etiam undequaque rotunda compactior et lucidior aliquantulum in suo meditullio, sed circa extremitates rario et obscurior (ait ille)."

A few days after the comet appeared, the first signs of a sickness began among the Indians. "I want to mention," says Hariot, "one other rare and strange accident, which moved the whole country that either knew or heard of us, to have us in wonderful admiration."

In any town, he goes on, where schemes were practised against them, and the English left the inhabitants unpunished and the trickery unrevenged ("because we sought by all means possible to win them by gentleness"), within a few days after the English left the town, "the people began to die very fast, and many in short space; in some townes about twenty, in some forty, in some sixty, & in one six score."

These were large numbers. The English never heard of any place where the sickness struck that followed any pattern other than the one they noted : the arrival of the English, some stratagem used against them, and left unavenged; the leaving of the English; and then the terrible sequence of the disease, so strange to them that "they neither knew what it was, nor how to cure it."

According to the oldest men in the country, nothing like this ever happened before, says Hariot, "time out of mind."

The Indians then began to believe this about the white men, after they saw this sequence followed in four or five towns, that it was the work of the white men's God through their means, and further — "that we by him might kill and slay whom we would without weapons and not come near them."

The leaders of this first settling expedition knew that every man, "from the most to the least among us," wanted to discover the mine. "For that the discovery of a good mine, by the goodness of God, or of a passage to the South-sea, will make our nation settle in Virginia," Ralph Lane said. "And with the discovery of either of the two, it will bee the most sweete and healthfullesst climate, and therewithall the most fertile soyle (being manured) in the world . . ." provided a harbor can be found. And "this river of Moratico [the Roanoke] promises great things, and by the opinion of Master Hariot the head of it either rises from the bay of Mexico, or else from very near, and opens out into the South-sea."

The Indians told them continually that there were metals, there were precious stones, but the English did not find them.

Reports of riches in metals and jewels have always been given of this territory. Apart from bright leaf tobacco, cotton, and corn, settlers early and late have desired metals and a harbor. The back country promised gold . . . promised silver . . . promised copper. There are bronze-streaked sandstone in the Appalachians, copper and gold at Gold Hill, and in Sacred Town the Indians and whites have mined for gold and precious stones. There are great holes, with huge trees now growing in them; the holes are believed to be the old mine-shafts left by a Spanish expedition in 1560, following De Soto's trail.

Experts "believe that mineral resources of the region have hardly been touched. Both precious and semiprecious stones occur, including garnet, sapphire, beryl, aquamarine and fine rubies."

"They did not believe that these were the works of men. We showed them mathematical instruments" — the cross-staff had become popular during the last five years and Hariot himself had designed the back-staff — "and sea compasses" — Dr. Dee had lately designed a "New Sea Compass." He brought the Indians around a bowl of water, and floated the magnetic needle on a reed. It wavered on the water, and then was still. Hariot held a stone — a lodestone — at the bowl's edge; he caught the attention of the needle with this stone, and the faces of the Indians bent over the bowl as he began to move the stone. As he passed it around the bowl, the needle began to follow it, the point swinging around faster. He made swift O's around the bowl, and the needle spun. Suddenly, he pulled the stone away. The needle turned with its own momentum, and settled in the direction pointing past the fort toward Trinity Harbor, Chesapeake, and all the north. From now on the needle would point north, he told them. He took the bowl and moved it beyond the circle; put it down again. The wavering needle moved only slightly, and then held, pointing toward Trinity Harbor.

The Trinity harbors in England, Deptford Strand, and the three others.

He showed them perspective glasses, those combinations of lenses "wherein was shewed many strange sights," the sea upside down, a deer still standing in the forest as if time had stopped and then suddenly been brought near; a woman who thought nobody was watching. He held a burning glass near a little pile of twigs in a tent-shape, with crumbled dry leaves among them, and they waited with him. In a continued movement, without any point of beginning (like that imperceptible moment when snow falls off a branch in England), a sigh of grey smoke rose. It seemed to breathe as they watched, and then a pointed flame rose. The little tent was on fire.

There are fireworks too, set in shallow pits on the beach, with the Indians standing far off. A Weroance says "Ah!" It is a spout of fire, a tree, a fountain of fire. "They are wild-fire-works," he told them.

Fireworks on the Thames. On the Arno.

A box of flat white leaves that are very flat. The box is open on one side, it can open its mouth wide, and the small marks can be seen. Some have pictures. A book. There is one book which is sacred. He shows the Bible to them in every village he comes to, many times. They understand that it is powerful magic, and they take it, passing it over their chests, all over their bodies, kissing it, holding it to their breasts and heads. He tells them that it is not the book "materially and of itself" that has the virtue, but what is in it : the setting forth of "the true and only God, the true doctrine of salvation through Christ," stories of miracles and the "chief points of Religion." They seize the book, this young man, that sick woman, and draw it lovingly over their bodies.

He smoothes a chip of wood, using his knife to perfect a surface. He writes "Manteo" on it, and tells these friends, who have no written language, what the marks signify. He shows them the word "Manteo" and the man. One boy, very beautiful, understands; his face lights, and the muscles of his arms and chest quiver.

Ralegh had treasured the fine strong paper in England. He had had none as a boy.

"Spring-clocks that seem to go of themselves" he shows them, and talks about time, not only the moons by which they measured, and a day's journey, and ten sleeps, but small divisions, these little marks like straight twigs. He counts for them; they see the hand move on the clock. They marvel at the spring-drive, which could keep the clock going for a long time; he does not tell them that it does not — to his displeasure — move at a uniform rate.

They think that these are not the works of men, but of gods. Some of them think we are gods. Some think that the gods had given us these things. They talk among themselves about it, and look sideways at us.

We show them guns. It appears to them that we could harm from so great a distance, killing with great accuracy — although their arrows could bring down people, bear, deer, fish, these are limited wavering things compared with our weapons. They think we are loved of God.

They think that perhaps they do not have the truth of God and religion already, but it may be that it is to be learned from us. They think they are very simple compared with us. And they respect and credit us for speaking of these matters.

The soldiers are delighted that the Indians hold these beliefs.

It is not only because we had these inventions that the Indians think we were gods, or cannot tell whether we are gods or men.

The deepest reason are these two : that all the time we are there, while sickness runs through all their villages, not one man of ours is specially sick, or died. And there was another reason. The main reason was that we brought no women with us. How could living men have no women?

"Neither that we did care for any of theirs."

The command against the Indian women; was this a command not to attack them, a property proscription? Who were the grey-eyed people they told us about? A ship had been wrecked a lifetime before, they said.

Hariot saw the woman at the edge of the water. Strong, lovely, her breasts wide apart, her feet braced lightly on the ground like the feet of a dancer. She looked over her shoulder at him, and smiled, a subtle complex look that can be seen in certain Italian paintings. Her elbows were wide out, as if she were going to lift off the ground; it was because she was carrying a strong child, a boy, on her back. The child's grasp was on the rich muscles at the base of her neck; one of his legs hung down, but the woman held his other leg with her elbow, and held one hand before her, over her breast, as some lord might wear the paw of a fur-bearing animal; but this hand is held lovingly, this strong very young leg held strongly. That other leg hangs down over her skirt, fringed top and bottom; a short skirt, well over her knees. She looks at him; her hair is down over her forehead, a tress hangs before her ear on each side, the rest hangs freely to her shoulders. Her free hand is curled over her other bare persimmon-color breast. She has an extraordinarily beautiful long gaze; her smile has deepened; her full throat curved inward. Her breasts lift as she advances into the water, wearing the child, looking at him. The pale clear blue-green water spreads behind her in a transparent cloak. She looks at him with her whole body. The birds on the surface of the water near her rise into the sky.

They carry their children in an unusual fashion, quite different from ours in England.

Some of our men had only been in cities and towns, Hariot says. Some had never seen the world before. Or cared only about silver and gold, and were not finding those; not yet. Some had little or no care of anything but to pamper their bellies.

The houses are not fair, not like English houses, even though two have built in two storeys near the fort. Captain Lane has one such, I have one; and there is good timber for building houses and ships : walnut and oaks, and rakiock — a soft wood good for the making of canoes (which are burnt out or gouged out with hatchets or with shells), and has timber "great, tall, soft, light and yet tough enough I think to be fit also for masts of ships."

They complain because the food is not "their old accustomed dainty food" of England. They want soft featherbeds, or beds of down. They find this country miserable.

There are other woods : cedar, good for chests and boxes — we are making them for our bedding, our goods, my notes — and bedsteads and musical instruments; maple, witch hazel that the Indians use for bows, supple, six-foot bows, curved back at both tips. You see the men leaning lightly on them, the bow-string twirling loose and graceful. They stand naked, full-muscled, wearing as decoration and allegiance-mark on their backs the emblems of their chiefs : a long arrow, an X with serifs, four arrows diminishing in length, three arrows uniform. This man has feathers erect on his head, shaved or tweezed clean with oyster-shells except for his crest running from his forehead back to the nape of his neck, a soft leather loin cloth finishing over his buttocks with a tail like a lion's tail; this must come from far inland. There are none here, and I do not have enough language of theirs to ask, nor to tell all the strange trees here (although I have their names in the Virginian language), nor really to tell them enough of our religion, for they want to learn more than we have means in their language to express.

God has made these savages a wonderfully industrious people, although they are rough and simple. To speak truly, I cannot remember that I have ever seen a better or gentler folk than these.

They have a grain of marvellous great increase; they call it Pagatowr. This is what we knew in the West Indies as maize. We made very good bread of it; and malt.

Whereof was brewed as good ale as was to be desired. As good as English ale? The grain is about the size of English peas; and there are flat beans, in shape like beans in England. In taste they are altogether as good as our English peas : they are Okindgier. And there is Wickonzowr, called by us Peas, to distinguish them from the beans; they are far better than our English peas. They make good soup, and a kind of bread.

And gourds, pumpkins, and many herbs,

In the planting of this rich country, that needs no manuring, nor plowing nor digging, as we do in England.

The women of Secotan are of reasonable good proportion. They wear deer skins well dressed, and wreaths about their heads. Their foreheads, cheeks, chins, arms and legs are pounced. About their necks they wear a chain, either tattooed or painted. They have small eyes, plain and flat noses, narrow foreheads, and broad mouths. Earrings of long pearls. They are delighted with walking in the fields, and beside the rivers, to see the hunting of deer and catching of fish.

They have towns with fences; and open towns; with groves and corn fields and gardens where they grow Tobacco, which the natives call Uppowoc.

Dried and powdered, the smoke and fumes thereof are

taken, sucked through clay pipes into stomach and head. Tobacco opens all the pores and passages of the body, purging phlegm, preserving the body from obstructions. The people here, who suck tobacco, know not many grievous diseases . . .

Wherewithal we in England are often times afflicted.

Secotan is the southernmost place the colonists discovered — about eighty miles from Roanoke, across the shoal water, where only a four-oar boat, a wherry, could take fifteen men with their provisions for seven days. The pinnace draws too deep water, and will not stir for an oar. But winter is coming on, and we leave the south for later.

Chesapeake, the farthest north we visited; for a while part of the colony was there; and all the towns, with only about twenty or thirty in each. The country of the king, Okisco; with its river that as it straightens grows narrow.

As narrow as the Thames between Westminster and Lambeth.

There is one large town here, after the Woman's Town, and the Blind Town with its goodly cornfield. It is able to put 700 fighting men into the field.

The King beyond this place has pearl in great quantity; the Indian lords and gentlemen are adorned with great pearls, and the beds, and houses; great store of pearl white and round, from the deep water, and shallow-water black pearl.

He gave Captain Lane a rope of these pearls, but they were black. Yet many of them were very large, and a few orient and round. The rope is to take home to the Queen. About five thousand pearls there were, from which this fair chain was chosen.

And there is iron, one source eighty miles and the other one hundred twenty miles from our fort at Roanoke, where we have built a pentagon fort rather like the fort at St. Johns. The mineral man's assay show these to be rich deposits. This is a marketable commodity, considering the cheapness of labor here; the infinite store of wood, and the expense and scarcity of wood in England; and the need for ballast in our ships.

But copper. And silver. These are further inland, with white grains of metal in the rivers. I saw pieces of silver hanging in the ears of a chief Lord, or Weroans. And the copper was found by trial to contain silver.

Silver in his ears of the weight of a Testrone.

The mine is up the Moratoc River, a most notable river, with many creeks and turnings, and for the space of thirty miles rowing, or more, it is about as broad as the Thames between Greenwich and the Isle of Dogs.

The current runneth so strong, being entered so high into the River, as at London Bridge upon a vale water.

Where is the supply ship? Captain Lane would send men to the northward, to find a better harbor, if boats and men, and victuals would come, until the new corn were come in.

Now we have heard of Chaunis Temoatan. This is the country of Wassador (they call by that name every metal whatsoever). They have a bowl with a skin over part of it, leaving one part open for the mineral. They hold the bowl over the water, waiting for the current and the change of color in the stream, and then suddenly chop down, catching as much metal as the bowl will hold. And presently melt it in a fire, with a yield of two parts of metal to three of ore.

Of the two Indians brought back to Virginia, Manteo was friendly, and remained friendly forever; Wachese was with the other party. The missing of the cup and the burning of

36

the first village was the first; now, up country, at three at
night, we heard certain Savages call, we thought. They seemed
to call "Manteo!" He was in the boat with Captain Lane. We
were glad, and hoped for a friendly meeting. They sang. We
believed it to be a song of welcome, surely it sounded like one.
But Manteo, listening, took up his gun, and said "It is a war
song, they mean to fight with us."

Volleys of arrows. No hurt, God be thanked.

They landed their canoes at a high steep shore, and fled into
the forest. We stayed there. We ate dog-porridge. We rode
down with the current, fast, that day. That night we ate
pottage of Sassafras leaves. The next day we faced the Sound,
the wind blowing, and we fasting. This was Easter eve. On
Easter day we came to Chipanum, and found some fish in the
Indians' weirs. The next morning we reached Roanoke, our
home.

[The discovery of a good mine, or a passage to the South-sea
... nothing else can bring England to want to inhabit Virginia,
says Captain Lane.

The young man Hariot is making his record as one of the
resources of his New Found Land. He was gathering observations and notes for a chronicle of the entire voyage and colony;
the wholesomeness and dangers of the fresh, desperate, green,
rich country, with its people to whom he is drawn, with whose
help he is living, perception bright, appetites healthy. He cares
for them and throws his fortune in — as chronicler. He has
specimens, and seeds.

This he knows about the inhabitants : the English need not
fear them, and the settling and planting will not be troubled.
The Indians — he knows this too — will have cause both to
fear and to love the English.]

For the river of Marotico, says Captain Lane, promiseth
great things.

Chestnuts there are; walnuts, harder and thicker-shelled than our English walnuts; persimmons, not good till they be rotten; as red as cherries, and very sweet; but whereas the cherry is sharp sweet, they are luscious sweet.

Two kinds of grapes — Captain Amadas, or Captain Barlow, wrote last year, "The land sandie and low towards the water's side, but so full of grapes, as the very beating and surge of the sea overflowed them." One kind small and sour; the other far greater, and sweet. There will be wines here, when they are planted and husbanded.

Berries, mulberries, applecrabs, hurtleberries . . . such as we have in England.

Strawberries as good and great as those which we have in our English gardens.

And a fruit from which can be made a sort of cochineal, red dye.

And deer, the snags of whose horns look backwards; and grey conies; small beasts, Saquenuckot and Maquowoc; grey squirrels; black bears; a kind of lion; wolves or wolvish dogs; and twenty-eight beasts whose names I have been given.

They are at their hallowed fires, making a sacrifice. It is Uppowoc, tobacco, so precious that they know their gods are delighted. They burn it to quiet a storm, and if they are on the sea, they cast some up into the air, and into the water. When they build a new weir of reeds (they do this with great skill, using the strong reeds of the country and effective forms) they cast tobacco into the weir and into the air; when they have been saved from danger, they also make a ritual offering of tobacco.

They are doing this now, stamping and dancing, with their gestures that are strange and powerful; clapping, now, holding their hands up. They stare up into the heavens. They are speaking or singing, perhaps these are incantations. Uttering. Chattering strange words and noises.

We ourselves suck tobacco. It is rare and wonderful.

Ensenore died. He was a friend; and Granganimo the great chief, our friend. Menatonon, a very grave and wise man, but impotent in his limbs, our friend (says Captain Lane of all of these). Ensenore's son is Pemisapan; and he has heard, as they all have who are hostile to us, that we are more dangerous dead than alive.

Now we have Menatonon prisoner, and his son Skyco is at Roanoke. And a plot has begun against us; some of the Indians are saying that God and Jesus are not God, since he suffered us to sustain such hunger.

Many of them hold opinion, that we be dead men returned into the world again. Is it that we seem ashen to them, as their dead are? They say that we do not remain dead but for a certain time, and that then we return again.

Menatonon sent pearls for a present, or as a ransom for Skyco. Captain Lane refused them; but the chief wanted to yield himself in allegiance to the great Weroance of England, and after her to Sir Walter Ralegh, of whom we tell them. There is now an offer to set up weirs for us; they have shown willingness to help us in a way that says, "We admire your guns and your writing, your clothes (there is a story about that) and your ships. But we know you are lost and bewildered in our country, and we will show you how to live." They have sown enough ground to feed our whole company. But perhaps the weirs will fail us, says Captain Lane; perhaps they won't help us with Cassavi and the China root, and the other roots on which we now can live. We will be like the horse starving in the stable waiting for the grass to grow.

Now the fires are flaring on the sand islands. Now Ensenore our friend is dead. And Wachese, the one of the first two who always hated us, has gathered chiefs about him. The rattles can be heard far off. You can see the sorcerer dancing, with the black bird fastened over his ear, across the narrow sound; they are listening to him.

In the good days, we make friends with them : we offer them glasses and knives. We give the children dolls of English-women. When we gave them the puppets and dolls that we had brought from England, they were highly delighted.

There is silk-grass here; cloth can be made of it. And silk can be grown, flax, and hemp, if men come to cultivate this land. The friendship can still be made, perhaps. They are willing to acknowledge Her Majesty. Their kings are strong. And they have much tobacco; these roots are nourishing and sweet.

In the dead time of night they would have beset my house, says Captain Lane, and put fire in the reeds covering it, to smoke me out in my shirt without arms, amazed. And then knock out my brains.

Manteo, Wachese, from the beginning. Cain and Abel. But we are both Cain and Abel, they are both.

The same order was given for Master Hariot. All of us who had our own houses, says Captain Lane, were to have our houses set on fire. The fort as well as the town. And no food to be supplied us. And the weirs broken and robbed, and they would never help us with the weirs again.

They want to scatter us to the sand islands, Croatan, Hatteras, to live on shell-fish, and the great flocks of migratory birds. Captain Lane sends Master Prideau with the pinnace to Hat-teras and ten with him to live there; and sends a group to the mainland every week, to live off cassava — for spoonbread — and oysters.

Where is the relief ship?

Now they are gathering, and Skyco attempts to run away. Captain Lane threatens now to cut off his head, and Skyco is assured that he is our enemy to the death.

It is the last of May, 1586.

The big assembly of Indians is due to meet at Roanoke.

But the town takes the alarm before Lane meant it to. He sends an officer to gather up all the canoes in the setting of the sun. He meets a canoe going from the shore, and taking it, cuts off the heads of two Indians.

The cry is up. In the fighting, three or four of them are shot dead. Captain Lane goes to the Council, and among the weroances, he gives the battle-cry. Christ our victory! he calls and the Colonel shoots the king. There he lies, shot through, and Lane checking to see whether Manteo's friends, the friends of English policy, are sorted out and safe.

Suddenly the king starts up, and runs away as if he had never been touched. Captain Lane's Irish boy shoots him through the buttocks, as he runs; with two men after him into the woods, the Irish Nugent and the deputy provost. Captain Lane meets them a little while after, coming out of the woods with the Indian king's head in Nugent's hand.

A lookout on Hatteras shouts at daybreak. Sails! Six great ships, fifteen! More than any relief party. Then, with fear in his voice, Twenty-three sail! One of the men runs to Captain Stafford.

The Captain cannot tell what these ships are. He sends word to Lane, twenty miles up the Banks, at Roanoke. After a year of empty huge surf, the sails crowd up the coast. Friend? foe? Stafford's words say, "Stand upon as good guard as you can."

He waits on the beach as the ships anchor offshore, where the currents meet. English! flying the flag. The boats come closer, oars beating on the white crests; the sailors leap in and pull the boat to the sand covered with shells. It is the General — Sir Francis Drake, come up the coast from his West Indian voyage, to do his last errand before he returns to England. He has come up from Saint Augustine, past Saint

Helena, seeing watchfires all along the shallow-water coast. On sight of one special great fire, he knew he had found his countrymen, and sent his skiff to shore.

Writing a letter to Ralph Lane, Drake takes some settlers aboard to pilot him to the road at Roanoke. Stafford goes ahead with the letter, traveling all night and all the next day. That letter brings excellent news to Lane and his 103 men; Drake offers full supplies to them, food, clothing, munition; and also barks, pinnaces, and boats all to be furnished with all necessities. Their relief has come.

Drake himself reached "the road of our bad harborow" the next day; but some of his ships drew too much water to navigate that inlet, and being unable to enter the harbor, "anchored in a wild road at sea, about two miles from shore."

The following day, the 11th, Master Lane and some of his company went out through the inlet to Drake, and a conference among the captains was held. At the end of that meeting, the settlers were given their choice of two offers : A ship would be left, the *Francis,* of 70 tons, fully victualled for 100 men for four months, and a pinnace, and boats with masters and mariners. According to this plan, the sick and unfit of Lane's company would go home with Drake. In their place would be left oar-men, artificers, and others. This would make possible the work that had not yet been done "for lack of needful provision in time left with us" : it would be possible to search the coast for a better harbor. This was the longed-for finding that would make all things possible for Virginia. They would surely find the way in within two months; by August, according to this calendar, they would all be back in England. But staying here they would have what they needed : besides food and clothing, calivers, hand weapons, match and lead, and tools.

Or else, if they "thought they had made sufficient discovery already, he would give them passage."

They chose with great gladness, says Drake's report. They

chose to stay and accepted very thankfully that which was first offered.

Drake had the consent of two "as sufficient experimented Masters as were any in his fleet," with men who would employ themselves most earnestly in the action during this renewed time. The Masters were Abraham Kendall and Griffith Herne. The *Francis,* riding outside, was received into charge by some of Lane's men; but she was not yet provisioned. All of the stores would have to be redistributed among the twenty-two ships of the fleet.

But they were not going north to find a harbor.

Now the storm rose up.

All through the Caribbean and up the Atlantic, the inhabitants have worshipped the hurricane. He is a god, a demon; from the cross of the winds he rises, the life of the seas, from stars that whirl in the black sky, from the stars that turn with the Big Dipper. He is the spiral and the swastika; and the labyrinth of the intestines and the union of the sexes, and the sun running his course. He is Huracan, not only the ray and torment, but to the Carib, the god of torment. He is shown in nothingness, in a foot — the sole of a human foot with a spiral engraved on it, speaking of power and speed. He is the plumed serpent, who first means the winds; with his feathers worn sometimes on the head, almost always also on the tail, and often on the long body.

This monster is a mythic embodiment of all the concepts of air, with the attributes of birds — feathers, colors, beak — and the attributes of animals of earth, snake attributes, waves, jaws — and other animals, panthers, lizards. The spiral that stands on its toe is the sign joining sea and land.

The storm rises out of a still day.

A wind is felt, not strong, but steady, but ominous, sweeping from the south up toward Hatteras. All the currents seem to meet here, on these diamond shoals. The surf is now beginning to be lashed. Soon it is hard to think of it as surf.

The signs of this storm are complex and joined, as : the spiral, the cone, the triangle, the zigzag, the ladder and the opening.

It is rarely that these signs arrive separately; they are usually fused. The great wind comes pouring up the south, the whips of sand lash across the eyes, branches rip from the trees of the outer islands, the sea-birds go very low in the dents of the beaches on the Sound-side. Something is arriving from the mountains of the sky, and above those mountains are higher mountains. The masts of these ships, now trying to stand far offshore, simply point upward at this gale. A few ships are driven into the channel at Port Lane, but not many. Most of Lane's men are now on Currituck, or with Drake.

Perhaps it will only last one day, this storm.

"It is very strange," said Lane's men, "and extraordinary in June. There was no storm of this strength at any time last summer."

"The inhabitants told us storms break here late in autumn."

The wind rose higher. It put all Drake's fleet in great danger of being driven from their anchoring upon the coast. They broke many cables, and lost many anchors.

All day on the 13th the wind blew mighty; trees were up-rooted the next day, when the sky was black, and the water so blown and dissipated in the air that one might have been underwater. The whole sea was white with foam, and the wind blew the water up, so that the air was thick. On the ships, tremendous seas struck in the side, through the glassless ports and windows. They shipped so much water that they leaned far on the sea-side. Many of the ships were blown out to sea. The *Francis* was buffeted about in the treacherous harbor, but at last she was able to set forth. Many of the ships were already blown to sea.

The breakers were running masthead high. The arched houses of the Indians blew away, the mats of the roof first, then finally the poles themselves, and the pots rolled after them. The crying of the children, the yells of those with broken heads, did not come through the noise of the wind.

A kind of silence arrived. There was a woman with an open mouth, an O with a margin of face around it, but no yell came. A great crown of a cedar-tree came hurling through the air in complete silence. The noise had gone too far to let one hear anything.

The eye of the hurricane, that aperture that is blessed peace within destruction, appeared the morning of the 15th, early, before any sign of daybreak. In the night of night and the night of storm, there was a time when nothing happened. That was ease and luxury, feathers, soft music on gentle instruments.

It began again almost at once.

Seas of immense volume and force towered over the decks, over the sandbars. On these fragile islands, the sand shifted, swamps were filled in, channels closed. One new channel began to open, unseen. As day dawned, the billows rose as high as the highest dunes. It seemed as though all the sandbars would go under, there would be no more outer islands, only a few forested high mounds where the most prominent hills had been.

Birds were crushed in their thousands; and deer, and bears.

The Indians had been forewarned by the wild birds, and some of them had taken shelter. The white men were safe on the ships, except for those in the pinnaces and boats, for many of these were lost in this storm.

Drake had ridden out his storms. He had gone into the Straits of Magellan in 1580, changing the name of his *Pelican* to the *Golden Hind*, and brought her safely through and up California and back to be answerable to Elizabeth at Syon House, that legendary mansion of the Percies, up the Thames across from Kew. On this voyage, he had had contrary winds after the calm off Spain, and indeed lack of wind in the Caribbean.

Here the wind and swell kept high on the 16th, swept, battered, outleapt itself. Lo, Lord, Thou ridest! The screaming endured, the breakers folded land and sand in together. All the men renounced all things.

That night the wind, for the first time, began to be less. Late

45

in the night it was noticeably less, and toward morning it was over, with the wreckage of the islands and of their own minds strewn within their sight and in them.

Hariot and Lane and the chiefest of his company then with him met to consider what now to do. They met with Drake on the deck of the *Elizabeth Bonaventure*, battered and splintered now. Drake made a new offer.

They could have another ship, since Captain Moone and the *Francis* were disappeared at sea, and probably on their way to England. They could have the *Bonner*, a bark whose captain was George Fortescue, with him, a pilot, and sufficient provisions to last them until they could get back to England.

They spoke together among the gusts of wind. It seemed still after the four days of tempest. At any other time, however, it would be seen as blustery; savage wind. Hariot and Lane and the leaders pulled away to decide.

This was the condition: the *Bonner* was not to try to enter the Sound, but to keep riding offshore. No condition at all, and we were to make our requests in writing, says Lane, if I or my company wanted anything. Drake promised that he and his captains would do their utmost to help me.

We were all grateful for the General's offer. I looked at Hariot and the rest. We took stock of the situation. Our company was weak. There were only a small number of men left. Our ship and provisions and captains had blown out to sea. It was the Lord had held his holy hand over all of us. And the General, who had providently seen the worst himself. The *Bonner* was not the *Francis*. She was a bark of 170 tons. His second offer was rather different from the first; the ship could not even be brought in.

The hand of God seemed stretched out to take us away.

Grenville would never come, he should have been here around Easter; and England will be full of doings for Flanders, and sure new doings for America.

I would resolve myself with my company to go to England in that fleet.

The request was made to the General, and granted. Drake agreed readily.

Drake sent his pinnaces to Roanoke to take on the baggage and the few men who remained there. The chests were loaded into the pinnaces. There was the pearl necklace which one of the company, a man of skill in such matters (says Hariot), had gathered together from among the savage people about five thousand. Elizabeth's passion for pearls was famous; it was a passion mirrored by Ralegh, and the weroances wore their pearls in their ears, too. A number had been chosen for a fair chain, "which for their likeness and uniformity in roundness, orientness, and piedness of many excellent colors, with equality in size, were very fair and rare." This chain was going to be presented to Her Majesty.

There were also the charts, and books and writings, the mathematical instruments — including the perspective glass, the staff, the lodestone.

The sailors grunted when they felt the weight of the chests. The pinnaces might be needed to draw not more than a foot of water. Not even a man who knew the Sound and the channel could know it now after this hurricane.

The weather was boisterous.

They could see the masts of the three ships far outside. Three ships left, of Drake's entire fleet.

The pinnace struck bottom for the first time.

They poled her free, and went on for a bit.

She struck again.

The sailors stared at each other. They had had enough of the long and dangerous biding in this wild sea-place on the coast of wildness. After the spears and guns and fire, the hurricane.

The sailors were much aggrieved.

She struck another sandbar.

Now the sailors decided. Without more than a word, they threw everything over : chests, books, writings, instruments, all. Nothing was going to weigh down these boats.

On deck, the men and lightened pinnaces hoisted up, Drake weighed anchor. He prayed aloud. In this terrible storm, he has undergone more peril from shipwreck than in all his clashes with the Spaniards.

Drake's report says, "We had thunder and rain with hailstones as big as hen's eggs.

". . . great spouts at the seas as though heaven and earth would have met."

They sailed for England; Hariot in the stern, watching the last of the New World. He had only a few notes and roots with him.

2

The Patteran

PART ONE

*H*ariot sailing home to England with Drake was sailing back into the past. East to England meant London and the ships; it meant also Oxford of his childhood and himself as student. The waves, cresting behind them here, colored strong blue, turn green and bright with the Gulf Stream; weeks later, they reach the coast. The Thames is farther, among its miles of marshes, spits where the tideway flows between sands for fifty miles to London and the pulling cascades at the Bridge; past Westminster, past Mortlake and Syon, Hampton Court, Old Windsor, eighty miles up river to the gravel ridge where the Thames meets a last meander of the Cherwell, in flat meadows, under low hills.

Born here in 1560, young Tom Hariot knew Oxford as a lively town whose center was physically the four forks, Carfax, where the streets meet : High, Cornmarket, Queen and St. Aldate's. The streets and the river make a town, but the towers, the colleges and residences are the life that pulls the world here. The friars had been here for three hundred fifty years, the chancellor since 1214; and the town had soon after been required to take oaths of peace which subordinated it to the university. Five years before Hariot's birth, Ridley and Latimer were martyred here, on Broad Street; one year later, Cranmer went to the stake. But two hundred years before, the violence in the town was already expressed in the riot that began on St. Scholastica's Day and lasted through the next. "Its immediate cause was trivial, but the townsmen gave rein to their long-standing animosity, severely handling the scholars, killing many, and paying the penalty," for the king now gave the university its new charter with more privileges.

When Ralegh went to Oriel College, Tom Hariot was a young boy watching the river and the stars, doing his first errands. In the year of the boy's birth, rebellion and protest was flaring high at the University, where three colleges "have demurred to acknowledge the Queen's supremacy." The challenge persisted that Elizabeth was a bastard, not entitled to rule the realm or the colleges. In May, there were serious disturbances at the inauguration of Doctor Thomas Francis as Provost of Queen's College. In August, the complaint is that "some heads of the Colleges of Oxford have taken wives and occasioned much irregularity." The cry went up that there was "much obliterated."

When Hariot was five years old, the quarrel was about the scholar's clothing, and protests were made that their apparel was Popish and should be muted and revised.

The two Universities were approaching each other. The chancellors appointed by Queen Elizabeth were the Earl of Leicester for Oxford and Sir William Cecil for Cambridge. On September 2, 1566, there was a great reception made at Oxford, and for the arrival of the two chancellors, George Coryat wrote the congratulatory verse. The boy may have watched from the highway or from Bagley Hill as the processions entered the town. In these years, among the proposals to incorporate Oxford and Cambridge, there were continual frictions for various reasons. There were complaints to Cecil of the state of insubordinations into which some members of All Souls' had lapsed; when the boy was fourteen, there was the muster of all able men from the County of Oxford for fighting in Ireland and on the Continent; there were nine months of town and gown strife during this time, and the next year five preachers were expelled. A week later the University of Oxford sent a petition to Leicester for the five, and for six Masters of Arts who were also involved. The following day, Father Walsingham, secretary to the Bishop of Winchester, stood up for the expelled. Bishop Horn wrote to Walsingham, promising to do all that lay in him "to quench the fiery coals."

Fires in the mind of man; fire in the sky. After the water of Hariot's birth-year, for 1560 was a time "of strange portents. There was such incessant rain that it might have been asked : 'How many Oceans of Water would be necessary to compose this great Ocean, rowling in the air without bounds or banks?' and answered: 'Some great violence had been offered to Nature, such as we suppose to have been in the General Deluge when the frame of the Earth was broken.'

"The rain had faded with the fading of the last year, and now it seemed as if the weather had been set on fire."

In the blood-red heat of France, with a sea "that seemed of the element of fire, not water," the doom fell, killing at first its 60 men a day, then 500, and at the end of June, 2000 men out of a garrison. At the end of July, the remnant came home to England, by proclamation of Elizabeth, who had wanted to risk infection by going to thank her soldiers. But her council would not allow this. Through August, the death spread, spotted, racing through 2000 lives a week by the fourth week. Until they ran on horses, the bells ringing, the multiple graves dug, London almost deserted, and the bells "ringing all about London as if the Coronation day had beene halfe a yeare long."

In Oxford, the plague was used to stop the assemblages of students. The two forces to be prevented were marriage and epidemic, according to this thinking. In 1561, the following marriages were prohibited : those of masters, provosts, heads of houses, fellows, that they might "prove more learned and fit to be advanced to ecclesiastical dignities."

Marriage, the judgment went, impoverished the houses. And it was "unfit for women to be in so great a society of young men."

Four years later, the two Universities set rules for a tract of 5 miles in compass about themselves, as a means to keep themselves free from "unlawful assemblies tending to riots and routs, and all other light actions that might draw the students from their learning, or bring infections of popular diseases

53

to the same." The regulations were also aimed against "attempts of light persons, for filthy lucre, to set up places of shows for unlawful games." The authorities, were, with whatever motives, setting up their laws against "beholders and practicers of lewdness and unlawful acts" and protecting their community from "so general an infection of the plague."

The young boy was in the water-meadows; he looked into the glassy river; the rains fell; the sky, when it opened, was endless. The nights were rained over often, but often full of stars.

The record of Hariot's birth has not been found. There is no word written of his boyhood and youth, except by Antony à Wood, who says that he "tumbled out of his mother's womb into the lap of the Oxonian muses in 1560."

Our knowledge of Hariot's boyhood does not yet come from records, although these may yet be found. We have only the line of Wood's.

But very much may be deduced, projected backwards from the loose papers that have come down to us, part of the traces in his own hand, in many hands, in notes and fragments, signals for which the best term perhaps is that word used by the travelling people for the signs which tell where they have been and in what direction they are moving — "patterans." By these inscriptions and objects, the diagrams covering this folio, the writing this-side-up on half the sheet, that-side-up on the other, that lets us know that here the master sat and there the students, by deaths and forgettings, tortures and instruments, the little pit where the foot of a compass was planted long ago, silk-grass waving near Hatteras — by these we guess, and ourselves move leaving our patterans.

At this date, we know nothing of Hariot's birth, parentage, upbringing, how he left home, whom he loved in these years, how he went to London.

But we know from the later work what was gathering here.

And we know — from his will, drawn a few days short of his death — that he had a sister. She is unnamed, she married a man named Yates and had a son. No name, no attribute, no university, no trace but this.

It was as a "bateler" or "commoner" that young Tom Hariot went to St. Mary's Hall, Oxford. The hall had been the manse of St. Mary's church, and is among the oldest of the colleges, with Oriel, Merton, Balliol, Lincoln, and Magdalen. In this period, many of the colleges are newly founded and built: Brasenose, early in the century; Christ Church, in 1546; Corpus Christi, in 1516, with its mathematician, Charles Turnbull, coming in in 1573; Exeter extended in 1565; Jesus College given its charter by Elizabeth in 1571, its chapel not built until the year of Hariot's death; Trinity, sixteen years before Jesus.

These colleges were then new; the tradition, in this century, was that of the medieval universities broken open before the expansive concerns of the Renaissance, the traditions of Aristotle and St. Thomas; history in the terms of the Bible; language as Latin, Greek and Hebrew; the brilliant experimental tradition in science at its moment of birth, but seen as the line of Simon Bredon, the Oxford astronomer, whose observations were handed down as material to the young Hariot; and above all, Roger Bacon in his greatness and mystery, a huge unfinished figure, seen rather as we see Coleridge, challenging, beaten down by the schoolmen who will slander the innovator as a magician who confounds alchemy with all other things, poetry, prophecy, science, the leap of the founder who thrives on what other people call intuition, but which is apparent as a most subtle and representative human power — attention, or noticing, or trust in experience.

The water-meadows of Oxford overrun by flood; the snow and ice of winter; the castle with its secret, a mound whose meaning no one knows with a well enclosed in it.

The end of the 1570's. Two hundred Oxfordshire men mustered. Secret information given as to recusants in the University and in the town. The description given by Richard Stanclyff to Mr. Tomson : He speaks of disorderly government and dealing in the University, where he finds injustice, "colourable dealing, malicious seeking of advantage, and cruel subtlety." Many accuse Tomson, says his informant, of desiring the ruin of the colleges; but as for himself, he desires that impartial judges be appointed to decide the controversies respecting the statutes in question.

In July, 1580, the Mayor of Oxford takes musters for military service in the city and the suburbs, and there is now talk of the difficulties that may arise from this task, since the number of private persons is increasing.

Violence and the fields and river; the stars to infinity.

Hariot goes to London at this time, and during this period begins his lifelong friendship and work with Walter Ralegh.

Drake brought the *Golden Hind* into Plymouth in September, 1580 — the little *Pelican*, 120 tons, renamed in the Straits of Magellan, working back from the South Pacific to Cape Horn, and then setting north against the undefended western ports, plundering and persevering north to California, to that inlet now known as Drake's Bay, and searching in all those bays for the western mouth of a northwest passage. There must be a way through, from Norumbega. There was nothing found but the natives of California, who accepted allegiance to England.

The second year of his voyage he sailed the Pacific, and after almost three years rounded the Cape and came home.

It was at Syon House that Elizabeth received this commander, who had brought both the riches and the word of the possible world to her.

Syon Reach is one of the most beautiful stretches of the river. By road it is only 7 miles from London — by water, as the waterman would bring you, past Westminster, past Richmond, and Mortlake, where Dr. Dee lives, who said what day was best, astrologically speaking, for the coronation — and among the ducks and swans, with Kew on the other back, to Syon House.

This was a nunnery of St. Bridget, with monks as well here,

a place hated by Henry VIII, who confiscated it for the Crown. Catherine Howard left from Syon, going down by the river to be beheaded. The Protector followed, beheaded too; and Lord Guilford Dudley — Northumberland — and his wife, Lady Jane Grey, Queen for a few days at the age of seventeen and then down by the river too, to Traitors Gate to be beheaded.

Elizabeth looked down at Drake who knelt before her, with his loot spread out in words — silver filling the hold, one and a half million ducats, and jewels that England had never seen, taken on the Pacific which until then had been an open field to Spain. He had bars of gold, gold plate; the return on Elizabeth's investment three years before would be fourteen hundred per cent, unless she did the unthinkable thing of returning it to Spain. Henry VIII would have kept the money and spent it. Her father was very close to her at Syon House, a closeness of shudder fact.

The storm of learning and appetite in him, storm of power, destroying, making music, killing whatever was in his bed, his queens, his young son the king with his own weakness, pouring out his learning and his wish for learning on his children, even this princess he called his "little bastard," and turning finally into the enormous monster who had to be set on a frame and helped by two or three through the wide doors only of the palace. He was here as Elizabeth talked to Drake, praised him, spoke of his coming knighthood, on the *Golden Hind,* at Deptford, among the banners and pennons and the crowd. Drake had commissioned from the London jewelers a gift for the queen : a crown for her head, made of five emeralds and "a quantity of diamonds, of which two were round and three long-shaped and nearly the length of a little finger, she would wear it next New Year's Day."

But now behind her head was something else. On the last journey on earth of Henry VIII, on his last night above-ground, dead in his huge coffin, the funeral procession had stopped on the way from London to Windsor at Syon House, and here the coffin "burst in the night at Syon."

Some young mathematician was brought to Drake shortly after his return from the voyage round the world. He needed a man of maps and mathematics to instruct the coming navigators. It was the strong historian of all these voyages, now and to come, young Richard Hakluyt, who brought the possible lecturer to Drake. But terms were never agreed upon, and no arrangement was made. The most probable candidate for this, says the biographer of Hakluyt, was Hariot. He did then find a patron, or perhaps it was also Hakluyt who introduced Tom Hariot to Walter Ralegh.

On New Year's Eve, the last hours of 1585, during the raid which ended by taking Hariot home, Drake commanded all his men to take to the boats, pinnaces, other small barks. He passed the night in the *Francis,* and they all lay on the sea, bearing small sail "until our arrival to the landing place, which was about the breaking of the day."

They came in their best strength on New Year's Day, 1586, to the great island of Hispaniola, allured thereunto by the glorious fame of the city of Santo Domingo, being the ancientest and chief inhabited place in the Caribbean.

The harbor of Santo Domingo is small and rather poor. Drake landed about ten miles from the city, and at about 8 in the morning, they began their march. At noon, or 1, they came to the city, and the "Gentlemen or those of the better sort" (about 150 horsemen) came out to defend it. Drake's small shot, backed up by pikes began the attack, and the Spaniards opened the way to the gates of the town.

Drake had 1000 or 1200 men. He now divided them into two forces, and planned the entrance, arranging a meeting between his forces and Captain Powell's forces in the market place. "Notwithstanding their Ambuscados, we marched or rather ran so roundly in to them, as pell mell we entered the gates."

They came to the market place, of very fair spacious ground.

This is the center of the 90-year-old city, founded by Columbus' brother in 1496. The two brothers were imprisoned in the fortress here by order of Bobadilla, and here Columbus is buried. It is the great Spanish city : massive stone houses with colored walls with confident huge doors, windows, surrounded by its walls and bastions.

The English fortified the market place with barricades, and the next day entrenched "and planted all the ordinance, that each part was correspondent to other." They held the town for a month. All during this January, events marked the beginning of perceptions: a black boy with a white flag of truce was met by some of the Santo Domingo men who "had been belonging as officers for the King in the Spanish Galley, who without all order or reason, and contrary to that good usage wherewith we had entertained their messengers, furiously strooke the poor boy through the body with one of the horse-men's staves." This boy returned to Drake, and died before him. The General at once hanged two prisoner friars, and threatened to hang two prisoners each day until the murderers of the boy were given up to him.

The Virginia Indians saw the English as "fearful about every-thing." The group was about the same in numbers as their own; they did not seem to know how to do anything, and they clearly needed a lot of help, although they had curiously and finely-made clothing, adornments and weapons. These Algon-quins were extremely hospitable, and they were a sovereign nation; there would have to be treaties.

They did not want to have their people taken back as showpieces, although Manteo and Wachese had been permitted to go in 1584. Farther south, the Spaniards with Columbus had taken Indians back to Europe ninety years before; by now, the West Indies were being used as an area for planned deculturation, until soon there were no Indians in the islands, and never to our time would be. In Mexico and the Southwest, the policy was one of enslavement. But the English had begun differently, although the policy — if it could be called that — vacillated, and friendliness turned into wars of panic and contempt, love and sex wavered into untouchability.

In the beginning, there was help again and again, not only in the finding, and hunting, and planting, of foods, but in all things. This was broken by a stuttering of violence that became the Starving Time, the massacres.

Sailing to the European coast with Drake, Hariot sailed to England boiling in hope, plunder, casting far out for the reaches of power. The edge of land here, Finisterre fallen astern and Plymouth before them, Drake wrote a letter to Lord Burghley, from his flagship, the *Elizabeth Bonaventure*. It is dated 26 July 1586 :

> Right honorable, having yeat in remembrance your honours wyshe in your last letter that the receat of my Letter which I had written unto your honour a Lyttell before had bynn dated rather from Cap Venester than from Plymouthe, I cannot omit to give your honor how to understand that as we then slaked no possyble travell or dyllygence which myghte anyway belong to the handlying of so great a dyspatch : so lett me assure your good Lordship

This is the assurance : that only 12 out of the whole treasure fleet which the King of Spain had out of the Indies had escaped Drake, "the cause best known to God and we had at that instant very fowel weather."

He is sending the bearers as actors and eyewitnesses of all.

> My very good Lord ther is now *a very* great *gappe* opened very *Littell to the lyking* of the Kyng of Spayne, god work it all to his glorye.

Hariot, with these ships, was coming home in loss and failure, his notes gone. Did he have tobacco with him? Did he have
those tubers? any notes at all? or only himself, his experience,
what he carried in his body and head, that is, in his body, in
himself?

It was this voyage on which Drake brought Hariot home that
can be seen as the crucial act in the drama with Spain. Before
this summer of 1586, there were competing piracies. This was
the long streak around the Atlantic that led Philip to cry out,
How can God allow this to go further! After that we come
to another part of the unfolding : the raid on Cadiz, the Spanish
towering attempt at revenge, another raid at Ralegh's after-
math, with Hariot always behind him, planning with him,
mapping, his strong support.

The idea of history as memory was mapped by Francis Bacon,
who divided the country of knowledge into poetry, history,
and philosophy, these being ruled by three powers, three fac-
ulties which are imagination, memory, and understanding.
In the words of Collingwood, "To say that memory presides
over history is to say that the essential work of history is to
recall and record the past in its actual facts as they actually
happened. What Bacon is doing here is to insist that history
should be, above all, an interest in the past for its own sake. . . .
His interest is in the facts themselves.

"Actually, Bacon's definition of history as the realm of
memory was wrong, because the past only requires historical
investigation so far as it is not and cannot be remembered."

Hariot was thrown into history because he was relying on
memory. He was telling the story of another culture thrown
into the moment of confrontation with his own : the anthropological moment.

He had walked into the paradox which arises when we know that history is experience. "What really happened" is only "what the evidence obliges us to believe." He, Hariot, is the evidence. And Virginia, with the English gone — is Virginia history, with a culture of small villages, agricultural and hunting communities with no literate means of communication and preservation of human materials? The facts of history are the facts of the present, with the past acknowledged and alive. "The historical past is the world of ideas which the present evidence creates in the present. In historical inference we do not move from our present world to a past world; the movement in experience is always a movement within a present world of ideas."

Hariot is sailing away from a world — a world of ideas — with the task of summoning up that world in himself and making it coherent.

But his worldly task is to write a brochure for possible future stockholders.

Two reigns later, life in the Universities is briefly made plain in a letter from the king. This time, in three commandments : of women, of "scandalizing" and "contemning" :

"Whereas we have been informed, that of late years many Students of that our University, not regarding their own birth, degree, and quality, have made divers contracts of marriage with women of mean estate, and of no good fame, in that Town, to their great disparagement, the discontent of their parents and friends, and the dishonour of the Government of that our University, we will, and command you, that at all times hereafter, if any Taverner, Inholder, or Victualer, or any other inhabitant of the Town, or within the Jurisdiction of the University, shall keep any daughter, or other woman in his house, to whom there shall resort any Scholar of that University, of what condition so ever, to mispend their time, or otherwise to mis-behave themselves in marriage, without the consent of those that have the Gardiance and tuition of them, that upon notice thereof, you do presently convent the said Scholar or Scholars, and the said woman or women thus suspected, before you, and upon due examination, if you find cause therefore, that you command the said woman or women, according to the form of your Charter against women, *de malo suspectas,* to remove out of the University, and foure miles of the same : And if any refuse presently to obey your commands, and be ordered by you herein, then you bind them over with sureties to appear before the Lords of our Privy Council. . . . And if any refuse presently do obey, to imprison them. . . .

"If they resort to such houses and places . . . to eat, drink, play, or take Tobacco, to the mispending of their time, and corrupting of others by their ill example, and to the scandalizing of the government of our said University . . ." and the punishments.

"That you do severely punish all such of your body, of what degree of condition soever, as shall contemn their superiors, or mis-behave themselves, either in word or deed, towards the Vice-Chancellor or Proctors, or any other Officers of our University, particularly in the executing of their office."

The clashes are the same, with the notable addition of tobacco. As in our time, they will be seen by some as issues that are small. They are not small issues, however, but indices of those extensive movements under the life of the young who see the demands of rigid authority for what they truly are : demands of structure — whether it be in the life of parents, the court, or of institutions playing to endure by strictness — since there is always one further demand that cannot be satisfied, since that would lead to the self-government, the "contemning," the "scandalizing" which can never be brooked.

One of the true ancestors of Thomas Hariot was Roger Bacon, in his central concerns and at Oxford. Bacon is a landmark in this history of the buried life of the imagination. His life-work rises out of the country, the sea and flow of these lives; in a way lost, for the books have not yet been published and the legend goes under among the tags of alchemy, Friar Bacon of the plays and stories.

This is the middle of the thirteenth century. As a boy, as soon as he was old enough, he joined the Franciscan order; went to Paris and studied mathematics and medicine, and returned to Oxford where he worked until his death in 1292.

"He was of that superior and penetrating genius that acquires a science, and fathoms it to the bottom, until its main principles are demonstrated." Famous in alchemical philosophy, "he was acquainted with theology in its depth, and nothing was strange to him, not only in such necessary sciences as medicine and physic, but even of those which being only of curiosity were almost unknown in his time. Mathematics, geometry, mechanics, perspective, and optics, were his occupation and delight. He penetrated into chemistry almost as far as any have done after him."

Roger Bacon writes on perspective; on optics in all its branches, of the reflection and refraction of light, and describes the camera obscura and lenses used to augment or diminish. He worked on the properties of gunpowder, on a flying machine to draw a chariot through air; on the method of drawing speech from a head of brass; on an optic tube; on the calendar reform not adopted until Pope Gregory's time three centuries later.

In 1278, his works banned from the friars' library, he was imprisoned until he made the statement of repentance of his work in arts and sciences. We have his *Opus Maius,* but his great planned study, the *Book of the Six Sciences,* has not come down except in fragments of logic, language, philosophy, alchemy, science.

Hariot may have known the works in manuscript, at Oxford. He had some of the books, of which the following were extant during his lifetime in Latin or in English : *Speculum Alchimiae* (1541); *The Cure of Old Age,* then in Latin (1590); *De Arte Chimiae Scripta* (Frankfort, 1603) containing both the *Secretum*

Secretorum and the *Speculum Secretorum; Perspectiva,* the fifth part of the *Opus Maius* (1614); and *Specula Mathematica.*

Whether he was a great original thinker, persecuted and recanting, or a systematic worker who organized the materials of an age whose best minds were being drawn into formal religious thought, this is the English master of the tradition into which Hariot entered as he grew, and into which arrived Bruno, the fiery, rough, piercing man who lived in London in the early 1580's, and whose story interpenetrates that of Hariot's in many ways — the thought itself, the heresy, the life tangential to Sidney's, Mauvissière's, the Court's, up to *De Immenso* and all the "heresies" and marvels.

Humphrey Gilbert undoubtedly had a strong influence on Ralegh's development. In the beginning of the 1560's, he had wanted to form a new type of man; the technically trained man — and not throwing away the humanist and scholarly tradition, but fusing literary and scientific education. He wrote of the possibility of reorienting English training and English society through men in whose lives rank and the status of birth would not carry everything. The men whom this would benefit would archetypally be the younger sons of noblemen. In *Queen Elizabeth's Academy,* Humphrey Gilbert writes:

"Whereas in the universities men study only school learnings, in this Academy they shall study matters of action meet for present practice, both of peace and war. And if they will not dispose themselves to *letters,* yet they may learn languages or martial activities for the service of their country. If neither the one nor the other, then may they exercise themselves in qualities meet for a gentleman. And also the other universities shall then better suffice to relieve poor scholars, where now the youth of nobility and gentlemen taking up their scholarships and fellowships do disappoint the poor of their livings and advancements."

Here, in this academy, political philosophy includes government and history and law; astronomy and geography are concentrated on navigation; fortification is studied to the exclusion of many problems of mathematics; English is the language of instruction. An "experimental garden" and a warship are part of the campus; and these applications of study are thrown in balance by the other disciplines of modern languages, law, music, and fencing and dancing.

She stands before him, above him. The Queen, Elizabeth, stands over the young man Ralegh, in the moment of their recognition of each other. Elizabeth the child lost among the crowns and power fucking, in rags and with the secret of her mother's execution half-kept from her, the head falling, the small neck, the accusation of incest; a young princess declared a bastard and that word having nothing to do with birth and love, but a yellow star of disgrace to be worn not by adults but by their young children. Elizabeth learning, feeding on the world, helped by her governess Kat Ashley and by her tutor Roger Ascham, learning the tall script which she wrote in wit and grace and instinctive defensive assumed power, even when her black dress was cut off her in the sunlit garden by the Admiral, in his laughing sexual power, before his queen-wife who held down Elizabeth. Elizabeth taken to the water-gate of the Tower of London, climbing the rainy steps, and becoming her next self at that moment when she comforted the weeping soldier as if he were England.

Elizabeth assuming all of her time's history in herself, assaulted in the fevers and delicacies of a stormy red-headed woman, inflated forever with the power of her roaring father whose howling need was for a boy, a son; Elizabeth an accretion of histories and powers, transcending griefs, these accretions worn glistering, so many pearls sewn to robes, borne as jewels, worn on the fingers, in the hair, everywhere. Taller and taller in her stories, her towering inventions of England. Tall above Ralegh.

He is the young captain who wants the sea. He is of

common "blood," sea-blood and strength of Devon, a Champer-nowne and a Ralegh, half-brother to that Kat Champernowne who became Kat Ashley, Elizabeth's other mother. It was at her death that Elizabeth withdrew, struck down by loss and the reverberation that went back to her mother's being axed. It was through Kat Ashley that Ralegh (and the Gilberts) doubtless came to court, and then these six-foot strong men rose. Ralegh rose. He had been briefly at the university, briefly at the Temple, fought with his cousins in the "religious wars" in France, and is here bending before Elizabeth, all his fortune on his body — clothes, jewels, his pearls, his cloak.

Did he fling down his cloak before her? The Spanish followed this as custom. The story of the cloak thrown down in the plashy place has accreted to Ralegh; it is true to his nature. Let us accept these accretions; they are worn as pearls. It is in character for Ralegh; beside that, it comes as an answer to another family story of the Champernownes, for it was Sir Richard Champernowne's company of musicians who were asked to the court of Henry VIII. Sir Richard dressed them in costly new liveries and took them to Windsor, where they waited and waited while Sir Richard paid all charges, and were in the end dismissed. When Elizabeth heard of the musicians, she summoned them to Court. Richard said the last visit had crippled him; the Queen retorted, "I shall cripple you indeed!" and took his manors.

It is in that line that Ralegh opens his arm, opens his gifts. With that gesture he creates, not making theatre as Shakespeare, Marlowe, but in himself being theatre. The theatre of the new world, of which he and Elizabeth are god-parents, or father and mother, and of which, since Ralegh himself was not allowed to go there, Hariot is the emblem and man and son.

Ralegh found Hariot at Oxford or just after Oxford, in 1580, and Hariot was then for life his friend and arm. It may have been Hakluyt who brought Hariot to Ralegh. He tried to get a scientific lectureship for a young man who sounds very like this young scientist; someone, who may have been Ralegh, decided the fee that was offered was not enough. And as Ralegh then went off to Ireland in his war-captaincy of blood, Hariot's life was bound up with the "primitive lands" of America and Ireland, with the policies of Elizabeth and Ralegh, and with his own imagining, not in blood, but in reaching — part of that gesture of the reaching arm making the next imagined phase.

Nicholas of Cusa, sitting in Germany, thought of Constantinople and of infinity. Trained to the law, a hundred years before Bruno, he lost his first case and turned to other things : Catholic unity, the check of abuses, man's wisdom being to recognize his ignorance, and God the maximum, God the minimum; and always infinity.

Forerunner of Bruno, who calls him "divine Cusanus," he is loved by Hariot, who goes on with his work on infinity.

And he is related to The Cloud of Unknowing, and to many other darknesses. Nicholas of Cusa wrote :

"In all faces is shown the Face of faces, veiled and in a riddle. Howbeit, unveiled it is not seen, until above all faces a man enter into a certain secret and mystic silence, where there is no knowing or concept of a face. This mist, cloud, darkness or ignorance, into which he that seeketh thy Face entereth, when he goes beyond all knowledge or concept, is the state below which thy Face cannot be found, except veiled; but that very darkness revealeth the Face to be there beyond all veils. Hence I observe how needful it is for me to enter into the darkness and to admit the coincidence to opposites, beyond all the grasp of reason, and there to seek the truth, where impossibility meeteth us."

He as bishop was imprisoned by his archbishop who then was excommunicated by Pope Pius II, his friend. His mathematics, his work in natural science, was what they call "ahead of his age," meaning deep in his age, but they had not yet arrived to their own moment. Nicholas died in Umbria in 1464; his complete works were published in Basel in 1565, when Hariot was a child.

Bruno arrived in London, a fiery, hairy Italian, a poet, playwright, teacher on a mission from the King of France to the French Ambassador, Mauvissière, a patron very welcome at the court of Elizabeth. Giordano Bruno of Nola had been a monk and had left the monastery; had taught in the French universities, and had written his books on and first play called *Il Candelaio,* The Candle-Man. He was a candle-man; this is a philosopher-poet of the most extreme bravery, laughter, bitterness, and unifying force. The play foreshadows the six brilliant dialogues done in London.

He came into England early in 1583, bearing letters from Henri III. In April, May, and June, he was in Oxford. Immediately, he was debating the Aristotelianism of the universities. He had been a boy debating — he had seen the mountain of his boyhood home appear barren, and climbing it, had come to the green mountain-top; he learned what greenness unperceived could be. From then on, he questioned the appearances, the seemings; he laughed at those who drank from the unquestionable fountains; as he moved, he went further into everything that makes our life bound into universals everywhere, and that makes the universe infinite. That lets the universe be infinite.

Everything in the times went against him. At Oxford, that June, he ran foul of Prince Laski, and was forced to leave Christ Church (Sir Philip Sidney's college, although Sidney was long gone and indeed had been in Frankfurt in 1573, visiting the brilliant and civilized printer Andrew Wechsel there; and meeting Languet, and going then to Italy). Bruno went back to London, to the French embassy, a house on Butcher's Row, between Wych Street and the Strand, recognizable by the fleur-de-lys on the walls, and otherwise a rich merchant's house.

In the two years that he stayed in London, Bruno published his Italian dialogues, using title-pages that showed the names of European cities. These names were false; the books were printed in London; and there is internal evidence that here Bruno began that great waterfall of a poem, *De Immenso,* which speaks of the Virginia expedition.

There has been a theory that Shakespeare knew Bruno, had met Bruno when Shakespeare was a printer's devil working for the London printer, Vautrollier, in whose shop Bruno might very well have corrected the proofs of his own books. This is the way the story goes : a young man came down from Stratford-on-Avon in 1579, and was apprenticed to Vautrollier. This was Richard Field, who worked in the print-shop for six years, and then, after the death of Vautrollier, married his widow. Field printed *Venus and Adonis* in 1593 and *The Rape of Lucrece* in 1594. There is a hole in the story here. Some writers have speculated on the link between Shakespeare and Bruno, guessing that Shakespeare worked as a printer's devil for Field when he first came to London. But that was not until 1586, when Bruno had left for the Continent with Mauvissière. And we do not know who printed the Italian works of Bruno. The only assumption that would link Vautrolliers to Bruno is a letter of his referring to some "troubles" in 1584. The theory, originating with the German writers, has been carried in books about the Tudor bookman.

Bruno, the Nolan, is linked with "trouble"; it runs past this, into far philosophy and far tragedy. As for the London printing of his books with the places of publication given as Venice and Paris, Bruno spoke of this at his trial in Venice, still years away. He said it had been done

> That they might sell more easily, and have the greater success, for if they had been marked as printed in England, they would have sold with greater difficulty in these parts.

Henry III had become Bruno's patron because of his reputation for memory; and Bruno's book on mnemonics had been his second book, with the very Nolan title, *The Shadow of Ideas.* He had lived on a salary for a lectureship, after dedicating this book to the King of France. In England, he clashed with the provincial ideas of the island, bursting with nationalism, with peasant fury, with snickering, laughing boors, who jeer at you and call you dog and foreigner and have proverbs that say an Italianate Englishman's a devil incarnate.

But he found well-wishers and friends to his vitality, his focused persistence and the sharp, sensual perceptions that he gave them in talk and writing : Sidney, Greville, Florio, the translator of Montaigne who said that he should apologize for translation, "Yes, but my old fellow Nolano told me, and taught it publicly, that from translation all science had its spring."

He had taken excerpts from other books of his, naming the selection *A Modern and Complete Art of Remembering.* He added to it an Introductory Epistle to the Oxford authorities. It is one glimpse of Bruno in the early days in England. He speaks of himself as

> Doctor of a more scientific theology, professor of a purer and less harmful learning . . . a philosopher approved and honorably received, a stranger with none but the uncivilized and ignoble, a wakener of sleeping minds, tamer of presumptuous and obstinate ignorance, who in all respects professes a general love of man, and cares not for the Italian more than for the Briton, male more than female . . .

Leicester ruled Oxford as Chancellor; he was high in favor, and hoped still higher. The Vice-Chancellor had been Sidney's tutor. These were his enemies. Bruno said that the three fountains at Oxford were named for Aristotle, Pythagoras and Plato; from these all the water for making beer and cider were drawn.

The friends of Bruno have been called a society — Copernican, metaphysical, philosophical, seizing the hook, says one writer, that is baited with descriptions of the society of which Ralegh, Hariot, and Marlowe were members. We are close here; and close to Sidney's society, the "Areopagus," which uses the rules of verse as its index of life and conversation. Bruno, later, at his trial conducted by the Inquisition, spoke of a matter he debated "in England at an Ash Wednesday supper with certain doctors of medicine at the house of the French ambassador at which I dwelt."

Bruno, like Hariot, was ignored in England. Everything he said swam against the main current. Fulke Greville, Sidney, Florio — little enough is found in them; or in Gabriel Harvey, but there is a stroke for each, Bruno and Hariot, here. Bruno as seen by his friends lives in his own description, as does London, seen here as Bruno goes with Florio and Matthew Gwynne down Dorset Stairs to the Thames. Suddenly we are at the river of passage, among the watermen :

"There we shouted and called oars, that is gondoliers"; and after a long time, in which they could have gone to their destination by land, "from afar off, two boatmen answered and right slowly came shoreward as though to put in; then, after much question and answer about whence, and where, and why, and how, and when, they brought their bows to the lowest step of the stairs . . . One of them, who looked like the ancient mariner of Tartarus, put out his hand to the Nolan; the other received the rest of us."

The watermen go only to Temple Stairs; they live near there. So the travellers make their way through the mud of low-tide, and reach the Strand near Temple Bar, twenty steps from Bruno's house. They go forward and are mobbed at Charing Cross, Bruno saying "Tanchi maester," thank you, master, for not being cut down; and so reach the banqueting chamber, where the company has given them up and has sat down to table in despair.

We see with Bruno the Oxford doctors, the servants, and Bruno sitting beside Florio at the foot of the table, and the others. The dispute turns to temper and shouting and a broken parting. What is the argument? what diagrams are on the table? It is the motion of the earth that is at the center of the journey, the banquet, the silences and refutations.

At the end Greville and the cavalier (is it Sidney, to whom so many of these dialogues are dedicated?) and the doctors beg Bruno to pity the land, which is "widowed of all good literature so far as touches philosophy and mathematics." The return is in the dark, without "coming on any of those butting and kicking beasts" whom they had met on the way.

Bruno mocked the love of Sidney, in acid friendship. It was the famous love of Astrophel for Stella, the star-lover for the star; and the star was Penelope Devereux, the beautiful Lady Rich, whose brother was Essex and whose sister was Dorothy Devereux, briefly married to Sir Thomas Perrott in a rather secret and rather mysterious brief marriage, and then for the rest of her life married to Henry Percy, ninth Earl of Northumberland.

Sidney had arranged to marry Penelope Devereux when she was a very young girl of no particular interest to him. They did not go ahead with the plans, largely because of his lack of interest; but when she married Lord Rich, Sidney's love constellated, and its power lasted through his poems and deep into his life, even married, like Dante and so many others, to another woman.

Bruno came to London, as Frances Yates suggests, on a French political mission, after having been active in French politics. His vigor would not let anything be driven apart from the rest of life. In his Italian dialogues, *The Ash-Wednesday Supper; On Cause, Principle and Unity; On the Infinite Universe and Worlds; The Expulsion of the Triumphant Beast; The Cabala of the Pegasean Horse;* and *The Heroic Ecstatics* (all printed by J. Charlewood in London), we have the confrontations of everything that were popularly seen as contradictions that could not live in the same room, the same air.

His self-contempt came through solely as contempt for the Jews. In this society, this basic emotion was translated into contempt for the Indians, for the Irish, for the base-born, and — catch-all — for women. Bruno, contrasting earthly and divine love, writes a sonnet to the "nymphs of England." *The Ash-Wednesday Supper* gives them to us in blond, white, pink, their lips' enticement, breasts of ivory . . . hearts adamant. But Elizabeth is accepted and allowed the heights, even at Bruno's trial.

He adored the contraries. He acknowledged them fully, he was the contraries. In *On the Infinite Universe,* he writes :

> On this diversity and opposition depend order, symmetry, complexion, peace, concord, composition and life. So that the worlds are composed of contraries, of which some, such as earth and water, live and grow by help of their contraries, the fiery suns. This I think is the meaning of the sage who declared that God creates harmony out of sublime contraries; and of that other who believed the whole universe to owe existence to the strife of the concordant and the love of the opposed.

The center of these opposites can also be questioned. The center is farther; the center of worlds, that is, not the earth and "why the sun? A candle flame grows smaller as we recede; why may not suns do likewise?" It is the power to hold the contraries together that is the actual power, that will give us *magisterium,* as Hariot says with the alchemists; will give us what Bruno calls magic. His concern is with the theory of change and transformation, and the function of opposites in making a new unity. Magic is the relation of science with the unknown, as Lindsay says, with such matters as action and re-action at a distance.

"Bruno's magic is concerned with objective causes; it is concerned with the link between the world-soul and the individuals. The link, *vincolo,* is an element of action." *Magia,* in *The Heroic Ecstatics,* is the supreme wisdom by which the thinker reaches consciousness of the changes of things and so can direct action with prevision. In Chinese terms, the basis of the

I Ching. It is the perception, the knowledge of, the comprehensive behavior of things (and people), through which the individual (or the thing) can be seen in the light of the normal behavior of nature. He is in the line of Plotinus and Ibn Gabirol, Maimonides, Avicenna. Things in their tending toward each other, let us see nature as an ocean, whose inner energy begets, whose various shapes form according to a forming force; these movements, however, can be seen and foreseen by man. This is magic, in Bruno's sense : the grasping of the point where unified opposites meet.

He flattens process, however. The flaws in Bruno can be seen by us in the light of our own ideas of development, particularly in our ideas of the identity of things as not excluding other parts of the range of possibility — ideas which have been formative in our concept of children and childhood, of individuality and matter.

He was present when the hopes for Mary Queen of Scots were being sifted in London; the French embassy was a storm-center. Although there is hardly a favorable word about him in England for a hundred years, his influences have begun to be traced : on Donne perhaps most of all; on Spenser, on Hariot, on Gilbert and Bacon; on the scientist Bruce and on Burton; on Thomas Carew, who based a masque on *The Expulsion*.

In Europe, Kepler valued Bruno, and reproached Galileo for not paying tribute to him.

Why did Spinoza not speak of him? Was it his own excommunication? How far can we realize the penalties?

Bruno's mathematics — particularly his treatment of the vortices — finds resonance in Leibnitz, who traces Descartes' dependence on Bruno here.

Coleridge comes to him as his trail-finder, and there are monuments to Bruno in all of his thinking; in page after page of the *Omniana*.

Warner, Hariot's friend, and Bruno, in his greatest work, the poem *De Immenso,* begun in London in this period, speaks of the circulation of the blood, and the story goes that Pro-

theroe — that keen-eyed young man who loved Hariot so
well — was seen by Warner talking in the hall of the Earl of
Leicester to Harvey, and that is undoubtedly, Warner says, how
Harvey came to his idea, which is stated in the Sixth Book,
Chapter 8, of Bruno's poem.

And he influenced the young Goethe.

And the idea of the moon-journey in Godwin, who has the
ship of travel drawn by swans, was taken from Bruno. But
long before Bruno were Lucian and the ancients, and the old
dreams of the moon, the unknown and nearly loved, the white
goddess, and the flights to the moon.

Bruno and the French ambassador, Mauvissière, left together,
in 1585, while Hariot was in Virginia. For a year Bruno found
"boarding and lodging there . . . the greater part of the time
at my own expense." The students protested his teaching. In
July, 1586, he went to Germany. There was no opening at
Mainz; that same month, he was refused the right to teach, at
Marburg; at the liberal university of Wittenberg, he found a
place for himself for a while.

All the narratives of voyages, and all the support for voyages
to North America were not gathered in the hands of a few
English venturers, or ever into English hands; and not for a
moment should it be possible to ignore the fact that the English
followed by a hundred years the first discoverers, by ninety
years the city-builders; they never came to the gold they craved;
they did not come to the great populations, the Caribs who were
killed during this period, or were killed and enslaved and died;
the Mayans and Incas; they never came to the jungle fertilities.

But Gilbert and Sir George Peckham and Richard Hakluyt,
who gathered the narratives and raised money and moved men,
and the women with them in England, to support these ven-
tures and fantasies and enterprises and piracies; and Carleill
and Walsingham, and Eden and Willis with their books, were

instigators at a moment when this casting-out became possible.

In March, 1583, Hakluyt went to Bristol, and two weeks later, seven hundred pounds had been raised and two ships could be fitted out.

Sir Philip Sidney was a subpatentee of Gilbert's colony, and wrote, "We are half persuaded to enter the journey of Sir Humfrey Gilbert very eagerly, whereunto your Mr. Hakluyt hath served for a very good trumpet."

Both Sidney and Carleill tried to join Drake's raiding voyage of 1585, which ended with his looking in on the Virginia colonists. But Sidney, like Donne, never reached the New World; the knight went to the land wars in Flanders instead, to Zutphen and a legendary death. Hakluyt too planned to sail to America; but he went to France in autumn of 1583 with the embassy of Sir Edward Stafford. Back in England in summer 1584, he wrote for Ralegh his discourse on western planting, calling for royal aid. This he offered, at court, to the queen. "Hariot took up the American mission . . . to explore America, to audit the knowledge of America already achieved elsewhere."

Thomas Cavendish was the same age as Hariot, and his life to this point ran parallel. Born at Grimston Hall, Trimley, he went to Corpus Christi, Cambridge, and possibly lived for a while at the Inns of Court. In 1580 he assumed his family estates, and at the age of twenty-four, he went to Parliament for Shaftesbury.

Associated at this time with Ralegh and young Hakluyt, with Drake and Grenville and the Gilberts as well as with Wingfield and Cumberland, he was close to the projected enterprise of Ralegh. In January, 1585, Cavendish was given the work of consulting with the experts in regard to laws, military organization, the fort to be built. There are three and a half pages at the Essex Record Office "For Mr Rawleys viage." They are headed "Notes given to Mr. Candishe," and list these concerns : the nature of the country, the fact that they would be dealing with naked men who must not be unnecessarily alarmed. A word of caution here that they may expect clashes with the Spaniards, and speak of a fort to be built in the shape of a pentangle, with the large horseshoe-shaped bulwark which is to include a market place provisioned for a month. The technical staff is to include a geographer, an alchemist, an engineer.

The punishable offenses against the Indians are to include rape, theft, enforced slavery, fraud and ill usage.

Cavendish was responsible for the supplies for the *Elizabeth* of 50 tons, a ship of Grenville's fleet.

In the account rolls of Henry Percy, ninth Earl of Northumberland, for the period from September 1, 1585 to November 27, 1586 is the entry "to Mr. Hylyearde for your Lordship's pycture, ix s." There are four other such entries.

Northumberland was about twenty-two. He was a friend of Ralegh's (the same account roll lists the payment of twenty shillings to "Sir Walter Rawley his man, that brought your Lordship a shirt of maile"). He succeeded to the earldom in July, 1585, after being brought up as a Protestant, and sent on his travels in France, with every precaution being taken "to prevent his falling into the hands of the exiled English Catholics." He was watched over by the Ambassador in Paris, Sir Henry Cobham, who reported that young Lord Percy was in "dangerous intimacy" with Sir Charles Paget, a Catholic — in contemporary terms "a notorious Recusant." However, Paget wrote, and Percy wrote to Walsingham and to his father, protesting "how loth I would be to doe anie thinge that might anie way shake me in the Fauor of her Maieste, I prayed Mr. Pagett to forbear my Companie."

But the eighth Earl, his father, sent a servant to Paris to watch over his heir. He himself was living under suspicion of sympathy with the Catholic party. The young Lord was men-

tioned, in the following year, as a possible match for Lady
Arabella Stuart, who was still a child of eight or nine standing
close in the line of inheritance to the throne.

His father was close to his end, a death which is still in doubt,
in all its implications. Condemned for treason, he admitted
that he had plotted and worked for the liberation of Mary
Queen of Scots and for tolerance of all Catholics; but he had
not "conspired against the crown, far less against the life of his
sovereign." Committed to the Tower, he lay there for six
months without any move to bring him to trial. On the 20th
of June, the lieutenant of the Tower was ordered to substitute
another warder for the one who was guarding the prisoner.
Late that night he was found dead, shot through the heart and
still in his bed.

The jury of inquest found that the three bullets from "a dag"
(a pistol) had been fired by the Earl into his own chest, "not
having the Almightie God or his feare before his eies, but being
moued and seduced by the instigation of the devil." His
"wretched carcase" was buried in St. Peter's Church within the
said Tower of London.

Hints, outcries, then began. The Catholics and the Protestants
both in England raised all the questions about this killing, for
which the official pretense was that the Earl did it so that his
son might succeed to the land, title, and property which would
have been confiscated had the Earl stood trial and been con-
victed as a traitor. In 1585, a pamphlet was published at
Cologne; it openly accused Elizabeth and Leicester of employ-
ing an assassin, and of covering up the murder by charging it
as suicide.

Walter Ralegh wrote years later about this death to Cecil,
saying, "For after-revenges, fear them not. Humors of men
succeed not, but grow by occasions . . . Northumberland that
now is thinks not of Hatton's issue." It was Hatton who sent
the order to the Tower.

The young man, Henry Percy, who became with Ralegh the
patron of Thomas Hariot, sat for his portrait in this time to the

great limner, the miniature-painter Nicholas Hilliard. Furious, brilliant, deeply attached to his father, impetuous, generous, kind, bitter, without control; we know Percy through his own works, through Hariot's traces, and through two portraits made by Hilliard.

With all the other pieces of evidence in this story, these pieces shine, quiver, move. They are ambiguous only in this : that the pieces are very often not identifiable. They are live, but cannot be measured. They are traces.

One portrait is a medallion from which the broad-cheeked face of a young man looks out, strong, contemplative-eyed, judging narrowly, with a stamp of sadness and something of controlled disgust on his mouth. He is lying among trees and flowers, with his head propped on his right hand. Behind his elbow, with a black edge of cloth past his black sleeve, is a book, open, the ribbons of its ties flying, as decorative as the deep red, yellow and white flowers over his other shoulder, in the grass where a glove lies as if it were a hand raised in greeting. He wears lace at his wrists and at his open collar, so different from the stiff ruffs that, for the aristocracy, split body from head. His hair is brushed back plainly, and hangs down at the sides. He looks out in a musing, part-closed look.

This portrait is called by the Fitzwilliam Museum at Cambridge, where it is, *An Unknown Poet*. It is more recently identified as Henry Percy, ninth Earl of Northumberland (?).

A remarkable full-length miniature of the same subject has been called *The Young Man,* and is now named Henry Percy, ninth Earl of Northumberland (?). The young Earl lies across this strange landscape, right across the foreground. The book is in the same position, but is shut; the gloves are strewn across the other side; they are hands about to clasp, or just having left a clasp forever. The head is propped up on the right hand. He lies in a small walled garden. Within this is another wall making a mid-line in the picture; four trees grow, spaced, out of this wall.

From the lowest branch of the foremost tree hangs — in a space of open pale-blue sky and distant trees — an object in balance, an object now called a mobile. Suspended from a ring, a bar carries a sphere, heavy and very close to the fulcrum; far off to the right, far enough away to allow the bar to hang even, is a feather.

In the air under the feather rides the word TANTI.

"The meaning of this emblem is not quite clear," says Erna Auerbach, "but has been interpreted as showing that the written word is as important as the world, with an allusion to the sitter who may have been a poet or man of letters. The romantic and poetic atmosphere of this lovely limning is closely linked with that of the *Unknown Youth Among Roses*" (another marvelous work of Hilliard's).

The emblem appears to carry more than that; it shifts between the balance of the world against a feather, which is like the feather of Maat, the ancient Egyptian goddess of Truth and Justice, against which the soul is weighed. It seems to be a cannon-ball hung even with a feather-pen. It seems to be the world hung even with a word. It is the true attribute of the ninth Earl.

In Hariot's ancestry at Oxford was the astronomer Simon Bredon. We know only the date of his death, 1372, and one gift, probably his, an equatorium given to Merton College. This was a most important instrument of great economy and ease of use, serving for computing the position of a planet at any given time for such applied arts as casting a horoscope.

Chaucer loved the equatorium, and as he wrote of the astrolable for his son, he wrote — or, again, it was probably Chaucer who wrote *The Equatorie of the Planetis,* in 1392, twenty years after the death of Bredon and one year after the *Astrolabe.* The instrument was of a beautiful simplicity, being built of only two inscribed circles.

Hariot records an observation made by Simon Bredon at Oxford on Christmas night of 1345. He lists this Christmas together with his own observations and those of Tycho Brahe, for a group of nights in March of 1584, 1585, 1586, 1587, and 1588. He is charting the movement of the fixed stars, and calculating movements in the sidereal year.

It was Mauvissière who acted as the drop for letters for Mary Queen of Scots. There were only two embassies in London, the Spanish and the French, and it was through Walsingham's skill in planting a returned Catholic exile that he finally was able to read the correspondence that uncovered the Babington Plot to kill Elizabeth and put Mary on the throne.

The plan to get letters safely to Mary was splendid. The exile, Gifford, told Mauvissière that a brewer could be used as letter-carrier; he would stop the bung-hole of his barrels with an inner container in which the letters could be concealed. The letters were, of course, in cipher. Walsingham's cipher expert was stationed near the place where Mary now was kept, since Bess of Hardwick had complained of her husband's relations with his royal prisoner; she said that Sadler had made Mary pregnant. Now the first letter was allowed to go through. Soon Mary called for all the letters which Mauvissière had kept for her since the Throckmorton Plot. The two years of correspondence began travelling in beer barrels, to be deciphered and read by Walsingham's man.

Bruno was staying with Mauvissière all during this time. It was not until June of 1586 that Mary wrote to Babington, agreeing to the plan but ordering the murder of Elizabeth as a first step, not to be delayed until Mary was free. The letter meant the death of Mary; it also meant the end of time in England for Mauvissière and Bruno.

Ralegh was with the Queen in the privy chamber two days after she had signed Mary's death warrant. Signing had opened horrors for her, some that she knew and some of that knowledge that swims slowly into shape — of hysterical laughter? of sexual ease? of a very small neck?

She could have had the warrant cancelled. But she had not; and she and Ralegh were telling dreams when her secretary, Davison, came to them. The Queen spoke in a pleasant way, smiling at Davison as she told her dream : that Mary had been executed. She added that she had been so troubled by her dream that she could have run Davison through, if she had a sword. They bantered together.

Mary was executed a few days later; her head was struck off at Fotheringhay on February 8th. It was not grief nor remorse that battered Elizabeth then, but towering anger, a storm that turned to Hatton and Burghley. Davison was sent to the Tower, and finally fined ten thousand marks and imprisoned without term, at the Queen's pleasure. He emerged after the Armada, but never held office again. None of the council, who felt that they had saved Elizabeth's life, ever admitted that they had sworn not to tell the Queen of the execution they had hastened, until it was over.

Spain watched. Philip II, in his new city of Madrid, made of will at the geographical center of Spain, read his dispatches and found the acts of "Isabel Tudor" abominable. The English pirates were infesting the seas and the coasts. They had sent out many raiders; the most dreaded being the "famoso Corsario Francisco Draque." Against Drake, then, the King of Spain called the Duke of Medina Sidonia, from his palace at San Lucar, at the western end of the Bay of Cadiz, among the salt beaches and the wine country, where the green Guadalquivir opens into the ocean.

In the spring of 1586, the correspondence between the King and the Duke — sardonic, rational, of enormous influence — began to reflect what Spain considered the direct effect of a contract between Elizabeth of England and Francis Drake. The letters from the court spoke of the pirate Drake and his "Armada" which was marauding on the Spanish Main. By the 28th of April, thirteen nobles were summoned up, and Medina Sidonia was ordered to call the men of Andalusia, and prepare for embarkation. The main purpose now was to stop the raids on the Indies, and to protect the fleet which sailed from the harbor of Cadiz, those galleys under the Captain General, Alvaro Flores de Quinones.

It seemed impossible to the King of Spain that God would let these depredations of the English continue.

It was not only that she had had the dream; it was that she had done nothing about it. That dream was a turning-point. It left Mary's son, James, as the sure heir of Elizabeth, longing to be acknowledged as that by her, but never having that word. The sword that was not at hand was there, to be turned against Spain, with the country united for Elizabeth and for the Protestant cause, in a boldness that she herself had shrunk from, but had assumed by silence — by not speaking to her councillors or her courtiers during the crucial week. She came through that week of the dream with enormous seeming of strength. The pope now said of her, "It is a pity that Elizabeth and I cannot marry : our children would have ruled the whole world."

Peru and New Spain, and Honduras, and the rest, were all at stake. Mary Stuart, the rightful Queen of England according to Spain, had had the sword of Damocles poised over her head, and now she had been killed. She had not been crowned or even rescued. A heretical and regicidal queen was still enthroned; there were allies of Spain in Ireland, but nothing was possible until the rightful heir, the son of the rightful queen, could take the crown.

Medina Sidonia prepared for war. Against his will and under threat from the King. He was a land commander, who had never led a fleet. He knew wars against the Moors, land battles, and carefully he offered arguments against this new command. They were not accepted. The Invincible Armada was being gathered, galleys, galleons. Drake, now in a lightning raid on Cadiz, and Juan Aquines (John Hawkins) waiting for the fleet from New Spain, were only two of their chief enemies.

The entry of Drake and his twenty-five ships was the peak of arrogance of any pirates ever. They came bannerless, and with the help of the tide and a fresh wind.

The Duke came overland from San Lucar, and fighting men arrived, nobles, cavalry, townpeople. But the raid was over, the English gone. The Spaniards would go out after them.

In a letter Don Sancho de Arce wrote to King Philip (Cartagena, 15 February 1587) he reports that Medina Sidonia has asked him to go from Gibraltar to Isla Espanola, after Drake. Gibraltar, Cadiz, San Lucar were enormously active ports at this time, and Draco, The Dragon, was the enemy together with the She-Wolf, Elizabeth, who according to the Spaniards was the anti-Mary in whose idolatry the English pirated and made war and stood for Antichrist; and it would be the Virgin Mary who would give Spain the victory.

The crescent of great ships, seen off the Lizard. Why did they not enter Plymouth Bay? What was this tall hierarchy, under Medina Sidonia?

A hierarchy of tall camels advancing in a crescent across the desert. They were not in sand; they were ships, and this was

water. The nearest land was a coast pricked out with fiery dots :
the watch-fires, cressets, many iron baskets of fire stationed
along the coast at ten-mile intervals to give the alarm : the
Great Armada come to invade England.

The great ships came : galleons, galleases, carracks, sailing
into the trap of the English Channel. But it was the wind that
trapped them. The water. These camels were fighting in another element. When the English had the weather gauge; when
the men, Howard, Ralegh, Drake, took the initiative in their
fast and maneuverable ships; when the fireships were set, the
hay burning, the crews leaving for safety, and the flames coming
on the wind close to the Spanish fleet, and there was no safety
in the lowland ports. The flakes of fire broke and drifted toward them. They burned, and ran for the north; and then the
storms broke, up the North Sea, around Scotland, around Ireland, where perhaps their allies were. But these galleys sank,
they lay on their sides in the surf, they rolled and sank.

The English scarlet and gold of the ship that Ralegh had
built and then given as the *Ark Royal* to Elizabeth, flung it
before her in his old gesture, the one we feel to be true, the
gesture of an arrogant man spreading the cloak down before this
woman. Accretion of history like a seeding of pearls. The great
ships; the legends flung like sandbars before a virgin coast.

Medina Sidonia, back in Spain, where the people believed
that the storms had defeated them. But he always thereafter
traveled in his carriage with the leather curtains down, so that
he not be seen.

The Armada was defeated, and the galleons swept around the
north of Britain, burned, swept by storm; around to Ireland,
where one after another, they sank, or went aground, as far
south and west as Dingle Bay and Smerwick, where Ralegh
had fought years ago, as a young captain.

Ralegh went back to Ireland the next year, in 1589. Leicester was dead, and the grief of Elizabeth carried power to one or the other of Essex or Ralegh. Essex went off, against orders, to Lisbon with Drake and Norris, but he returned still in favor. Ralegh was no longer in the prime place, he was in an uneasy disgraced place of grief. He denied it, but Bacon's brother Anthony had a letter from Sir Francis Allen saying that Essex had driven Ralegh from Court and into Ireland.

The Irish friendship of Ralegh and Edmund Spenser is famous to us because of the great revealing writings of both poets at the height of their powers. The poems we know belong to this period are the first three cantos of *The Faerie Queene,* which Spenser brought back to London when he went with Ralegh on the voyage told in the beginning of *Colin Clout's Come Home Again.* But a part of the manuscript of *The Faerie Queene* had been circulated in London two years before this. These years are the time of work and friendship, going on into Spenser's long poem and into the lost poem of Ralegh's, *The Ocean's Love for Cynthia,* of which we have only the eleventh book and a fragment of the twelfth — two marvelous poems called "fine and sweet inventions" then, and speaking to us now in the subtle complex music which gives full power to Ralegh, declares the bonds between the Queen's power and his own — or, more truly, between archetypal power and his own self — and makes Ralegh intelligible to us as none of the arguments of scholars, looking for prose logic, can.

But there is another part of life in Ireland, poetry and science, and the buried life, which now becomes visible.

The clues are in that most great fragment of Spenser's, called *Cantos of Mutabilitie.* Spenser's printer, Matthew Lownes, set the two cantos and two stanzas of a third along with *The Faerie Queene* when he printed the 1609 edition, after Spenser's death.

"Lownes apparently knew no more about them than we do, for he introduced them merely with this brief note : 'Two Cantos of Mutability which, both for form and matter, appear to be parcel of some following book of *The Faerie Queene*

under the Legend of Constancy. Never before imprinted.'"
There is internal evidence that this "fragment" was written
after *Colin Clout's Come Home Again* — in or after 1595, says
this writer.

Mutabilitie of the sports of change, the wheel of change.

> Proud *Change* (not pleasd in mortall things
> beneath the Moone to raigne)

and the story of how she reared herself against all the gods.
This challenge for the empire of the gods is the contest of a
daughter of the Titans against all law; against nature, and
justice, and policy. It has the immense scene that is only followed in English poetry by Milton, and by Keats in *Hyperion,*
with the huge resonance of deep forces facing each other in
the circle of the world, where death becomes the milk we suck,
and the "bad seed" is the kernel.

The form here is not that of *The Faerie Queene.* There is
only the Spenserian stanza, but the mode is different, the
confrontations are different. What is kept is the Irish landscape. Here are change, time, nature, and the great line of the
poets who have moved toward the acknowledgment of the
world of nature in its unity. In generation after generation, this
movement of the spirit has been denied, and the attempt has
been made to split the quick life up. The line of poets in
English goes from Chaucer, to whom the work on the astrolabe
is native as spring and her birds are native — to Keats with his
hospital groans, and all the means of identification, taken and
given up, with the bird of identification let go last so that we
can arrive at our sole self. The Western line goes through
Heraclitus, Empedocles, Lucretius, Bruno.

This is the country where science meets dream, the archetype.
The landscape starts high in the Irish mountains, and goes
down through the rivers.

What mountains? What rivers? And who was there?

The Spenser scholars have quarreled about all of this. The
evidence that I offer here has never been offered, and is only a

stroke, as so much of this story consists of a silvery stroke in a place, and a great gap then of ignorance or destruction, another stroke, and a greater gap. But soon, with all the gaps, a large structure begins to be evident, a structure before which surmise strikes deep into one's life.

Ralegh rode up from Lismore through Buttevant to see Spenser at Kilcolman, the castle of which one stump is left, where Spenser and his wife, Elizabeth Boyle, lived. Higher he rode, for the Galtee Mountains begin here.

> Eftsoones the time and place appointed were,
> Where all, both heavenly Powers, and earthly wights,
> Before great Natures presence should appeare,
> For triall of their Titles and best Rights :
> That was, to weet, upon the highest heights
> Of *Arlo-hill* (Who knows not *Arlo-hill?*)
> That is the highest head (in all men's sights)
> Of my old father *Mole* . . .

The river Mole has flowed in *Colin Clout,* and Mulla, a river who is here, soon after Cynthia enters, and among the nymphs, Molanna.

> that is sovereign Queen profest
> Of woods and forests . . .
> . . . She chose this Arlo; where she did resort
> With all her Nymphs . . .

Let us find Arlo first, and then see what Molanna signifies.

Arlo is on no map, not in that spelling, but Spenser himself, in his *A View of the State of Ireland,* gives us the information we need. Of course Arlo, used in *Mutabilitie* as the setting for the trial of the gods, is also a real place, and a place-name that has come down to us. Here is the passage : In this book, which is a dialogue between Eudoxius and Irenaeus, Eudoxius asks,

"Where will you have your thousand men garrisoned?" And within Irenaeus' answer these words arrive, after the proposal to defend from Bantry (on the west coast, south of Dingle), to plant a good town there, to put men at Castlemaine "which should keep all Desmond and Kerry"; to break the nest of thieves around Kilmore in country Cork; a hundred at Cork, and two hundred at Waterford.

> . . . Moreover on this side of Arlo, near to Muskery Quirke [which is Blarney, and had to do with Sir George Carew — M.R.] . . . I would have two hundred more to be garrisoned, which should skoure both the White Knights country, and Arlo, and Muskery Quirke . . .

Not spelled this way, but spoken this way : "Tipperary lies in the 'Golden Vein' . . . Immediately to the S. is the outlying ridge of Slievenamuck (1215 ft.) between which and the main group of mountains is the Glen of Aherlow."

The arguments among authorities on Spenser begin with the convictions in this poem, and proceed at once to the name Molanna. The doctrine Spenser seems to combat is Bruno's, says Sebastian Evans, and the problem is more intelligible in this form than it would have been in any scientific language known to the sixteenth century. He moves to the concept that matter cannot be in motion without change, and asks, "Is Change, then, the ultimate fact of the universe, or is there a generalization beyond, wide enough to embrace all the phenomena of change?"

In the poem, Nature answers, in the brief climactic words of the end. For here Spenser swings all change about. All gods, all alteration, all evidence turns as seasons and months and day and night. Now Nature gives her "doom." All things are not changed,

> But by their change their being do dilate,
> And turning to themselves at length again,

they work their own perfection. Over them Change does not rule,

> But they reign over Change, and do their
> states maintain.

The assembly is dismissed, and Nature vanishes. We are at the last words of the poem, which is called "unperfite," incomplete. The scene is cleared bare. The "I" of the poem thinks "on that which Nature said,"

> Of that same time when no more Change shall be"

He brings us to it, to the pillars of eternity, beyond movement,

> For all that moveth doth in Change delight :
> But thenceforth all shall rest eternally
> With Him that is the God of Sabaoth hight :

Now, in one movement of intense energy, we reach a given tension between change and rest, in the throw of a word which plays lightnings on the meanings of Sabaoth — hosts — and the Saboath idea of renewal in rest. *Mutability* ends :

> But thenceforth all shall rest eternally
> With Him that is the God of Sabaoth hight :
> O thou great Sabaoth God, grant me that Sabbath sight!*

Away from the trial, persevere through the arguing : that there is more Bruno here than is accounted for by direct knowledge of Bruno, since Spenser was in Ireland during all of Bruno's time in England; that it was too soon for Bruno's influence to be felt; that Bruno declares for a goal of perfection at the end of change in his *Spaccio*; that proof of the Spenser-Bruno connection is lacking.

The scholars go on to the name of Molanna, which appears just here in the poem. Roland M. Smith writes, "The name of Molanna may have been formed by Spenser" from two river-names, Mole and Behanna, ". . . but it should be pointed out that if Spenser made the fifty-mile journey by road from Kilcolman (via Lismore) to Youghal, where Ralegh's house still stands, he would doubtless have been familiar with the name of the abbey Molana (Irish Molanfhaidh).

And at the abbey of Molanna?

---

* The deep pun is familiar in Hebrew. A variant text is used.

On the Blackwater, the river of Spenser and Ralegh, the "Irish Rhine" (says Muirhead), four miles from Youghal, Ralegh's town, there is Templemichael, with a keep of the Fitzgeralds facing "the now ruined Molana Abbey, on an island joined to the mainland by a causeway."

The Irish State Papers for the 1580's tell the story.

On January 9, 1587, the widow Anne Thickpenny petitioned Burghley. She was one of Her Majesty's farmers in Ireland, and she asked for despatch of her suits touching "certain small parcels of land called the abbey of Mollanna, *alias* Molanassa, and the house of Observant Friars, near Youghal . . ."

But on May 12, 1589, there is a listing among all the lands and people of Ralegh's :

> Upon the Abbeyhouse of Mollanna
> Thomas Harriot, gent. and his family
> inhabiting upon the lands & possessions of
> Sir Walter Ralegh Knight, Lord Warden of
> the stanneries of Cornwall and Devon
> County of Waterford

After Hariot settled at Molanna, the Queen granted the land to Ralegh and his heirs. The record is to be found in the Patent and Close Rolls, among the Chancery lists for Ireland. On the 2nd of July, in the twenty-ninth year of her reign, "the abbey or monastery of Molanassa, otherwise Molana, and the priori called the Observant Friars, otherwise the Black Friars of Youghal, go to him.

"And as Sir Walter made humble suit to enable him the better to perform the enterprize for the habitation and repeopling of the lands, to grant him and his heirs, in feefarm for ever, the possessions of the late dissolved abbey or monastery called Molanassa, otherwise Molana . . ." the roll, in Dublin, goes, "now, in consequence of the wars in Munster, waste and ruined, and as they lie adjoining the lands already granted to him, her

Majesty is pleased to comply with his request, and by her letters, dated at Greenwich the 2nd of July, 1587, directed to the Lord Deputy, expressed her intention to that effect. Rent, for the possessions of the monastery last mentioned, £ 12 19x 6d."

But this was the year of James' accession. In January, with the Queen dying, Ralegh made a deed between himself and these three: Nicholas Throckmorton, Alexander Brett and Hariot. The deed was to guard the safekeeping of Sherborne forever by conveying it to young Wat Ralegh, and reserve a life interest only to his father. Unfortunately, says Rowse, the clerk who copied the deed left out the key phrase which would make it legally operative. Neither Ralegh nor Hariot caught this error.

To Hariot, Ralegh now gave a long lease of Pinford, "and an outright gift of an abbey in Waterford, which he had had from the Queen, and of which Hariot had made £200. Rowse does not identify the abbey. But it was Molanna that played a notable part in the history of Ralegh, Hariot, and Spenser.

Hariot did not keep this land for long. On April 2, 1606, according to the Patent Roll of 2° James I in the Hall of Public Records, an inquisition taken at Tallagh, in Waterford, finds that Ralegh was on his attainder seized of ". . . Also, that the priory and convent of Molanan, *alias* Molanassa, were seized, in fee, at the time of the dissolution thereof, of the site, etc. of said priory, containing 1½A. on the river Awemore, near the castle of Tamplemighell and Ballinetra and 7A arable land, country measure."

So did Hariot lose Molanna.

Two plays speak for the archetypal figure of the magician — and Hariot is an ever-growing magician of his time — more than any others of this period. The popular plays and comedies and jigs were of course the plays that were seen most often by the large audiences. *Pickle Herring Dill Dill Dill,* a farce with a great many doors, was the most-performed play, in Europe and in England, of the age. These plays, of learning and magic, of the powers seen as dangerous, have come down to us : *The Alchemist,* the quack and slapstick version; Marlowe's *Doctor Faustus,* and Shakespeare's *The Tempest.*

What are the powers? What are the dangers? What mastery is here?

Marlowe, coming from Canterbury, the cathedral dominating one's head, the river, the dungeon at the gate, went to Cambridge and from there straight into government service as an agent. But his poems and plays in their grace of fulness, tense wild rich, come to us pure and fiery, sexual in music, variable in thought held to all kinds of conquest in pride.

After the epic powers of Tamburlaine, Marlowe wrote *Faustus,* probably in the winter of 1588-89, although there are signs that it was begun earlier. There is a ballad of the life and death of Doctor Faustus, licensed on February 28, 1589, which probably followed the success of the play. It was performed by the Lord Admiral's Company until a complaint by the Master of the Revels caused the Lord Mayor to "silence the company."

These two far-reaching plays may not be reduced to statement, nor to a philosophical core; their universe is that of poetry with its correspondences; its resonance sounds against a physical reality in which the splinters of mind and plot are fused, absorbed; body is absorbed in soul, but not negated, for it is the instrument.

What happens to the instruments in *Faustus* and *The Tempest?* The man each time is the learned man, the magus, the necromancer. He has earned his intellectual powers, Faustus in his 30 years as student, of which his books and his power to evoke are the signs. Prospero has a past of his powers, and he has already lived in his Tower, his island, his punishment is exile.

Faust summons up Mephistophilis, and his prizes are answers, on the condition, not as we are told, of selling his soul, but on the exchange of both, a deed of gift of body and of soul; after which he can ask what he will. First hell; then a wife; then

the three books of magic, of the stars, and of all plants. The
signing of the deed has been in blood; that makes the first
event, in which Faustus' blood refuses to flow, and then flows
again. His soul is his own, and Faustus signs. The second event
is his sight of the heavens :

When I behold the heavens, then I repent . . . and Mephistophilis says

> Why Faustus,
> Thinkst thou heaven is such a glorious thing?
> I tel thee tis not halfe so fair as thou,
> Or any man that breathes on earth.
Faustus : How proouest thou that?
Meph :   It was made for man, therefore is man more excellent.
Faustus : If it were made for man, twas made for me :
> I will renounce this magicke, and repent.

He assures himself that God will pity him if he repents. But
he has already lost that power. He cannot name salvation, faith,
or heaven; he is face to face with suicide. Pleasure still conquers
suicide, despair. He asks his questions. They are of astronomy
(still called Astrology here); not the elementary ones: the
"poles of the world," the double motion of the planets. These
are slender trifles that his servant can decide.

He asks the larger questions : has ever sphere a dominion?
And, in the 1616 text : But is there not *Coelum igneum* and
Christalinum? And gets the answer : No Faustus they be but
Fables.

And asks : Ist not too late?

And gets the answer, as he has before, doubled, from Good
Angel and Evil Angel :

> Too late.
> Never too late, if Faustus can repent.

Here Faustus calls on Christ and here Lucifer appears. He is
with Beelzebub, the other Prince of Hell. He tells Faustus

> Christ cannot save thy soul, for he is just.

And Faustus asks pardon for talking of Christ. He will never
name God again.

Now the rewards arrive. The seven deadly sins appear, and when Lucifer asks Faustus "How dost thou like this?" he answers according to his own need, which has struggled for its fulfillment from the beginning :

> O this feedes my soule.

The journeys follow: not to hell as Faustus asks. That will come later. But to Rome, where he sees the Pope, and boxes his ears; where he beats the friars singing malediction, and flings fireworks among them. And to the palace of the Emperor Charles the Fifth, where the servants Robin and Ralph steal a silver goblet from the vintner.

> Vintner. Soft sir, a word with you, I must yet have a goblet
> paid from you ere you go.
> Robin. I a goblet, Rafe, I a goblet? I scorn you : and you
> are but a & c. I a goblet? Search me.

But the goblet — Mephistophilis forces its return, and the stolen book, which would have given the servants those same powers that Faustus has, is handed back too.

The raising of the dead follows : that famous raising of Alexander the Great and his paramour, and after many magics, the return to Wittenberg, grapes in January, there is the first sight of Helen of Troy. One further chance to choose comes to Faustus with the appearance of the Old Man, the actual sage of this history, who offers choice. But Mephistophilis presents a dagger, and despair and repentance struggle in Faustus.

This last movement of repentance is the trigger of the arrest of Faustus' soul for treason to his vow to Mephistophilis. But Marlowe has this devil say even now that he cannot touch the soul. He can torment the body, he can answer a last wish. This last wish uses him as pander, as he was used in producing a wife for a curiously passive Faust, whose one way of achieving anything is to require it, to buy it of Mephistophilis. This is the last wish :

> To glut the longing of my hearts desire,
> That I might have unto my paramour

> That heavenly Helen whom I saw of late
> Whose sweet imbracings may extinguish clean
> These thoughts that do dissuade me from my vow,
> And keep mine oath I made to Lucifer.

The appearance of Helen is immediate, in the "twinkling of an eye," with a great sweep of promise pointing to her and to all else Faustus shall desire. But she is the last.

She is actual woman at the height of her female powers, the beauty of the world in the lines that open the speech to her. She is silent throughout, but her powers unfold past imagining, past Mephistophilis. In three lines :

> Faust. Was this the face that launched a thousand ships?
>   And burnt the topless towers of Ilium
>   Sweet Helen, make me immortal with a kiss : (Kisses her.)

we are given the war-making power, traditionally attached to Helen; and beyond that, beyond the 24 years which Faustus has bought, he is given what he has wanted from the beginning, "to make man to live eternally," and still, for the kiss, his soul is given, this time, for this kind of gold,

> Her lips suck forth my soul, see where it flies;
> Come Helen, come give me my soul again.
> Here will I dwell, for heaven be in these lips,
> And all is dross that is not Helena.

The echo is here of

> All places shall be hell that is not heaven.

In this absolute of woman, of requirement, the end has come. If Marlowe was exclusive in his homosexuality — and we do not know this — we have here, in this tribute to female power, all that he can attribute to woman, as in the praise of Elizabeth, Cynthia, we have the praise and power-drawn seeking of Elizabethan man. But Helen, at the peak of beauty, silent, the giver of immortality, is the last gift. After her come devils and the doom that had been guaranteed long ago.

It comes in a renunciation. Faustus knows that, though the serpent that tempted Eve may be saved, he cannot be saved.

Would that I had never seen Wittenberg, he shouts, never read books.

It is in the last hour of his life that the doom is realized, in the 60 lines for the minutes. The stars move still, time runs, he comes to the naming of God. And at that naming, forbidden but never forbidden, the other desperate movement starts. The pulling-down of Faustus, and as he plunges down, the breaking open and flowing of all things across his eye that has turned into the breadth of the sky:

See see where Christ's blood streams in the firmament. The blood streams over all of life; now it is gone, and God's arm is stretched out. He longs for his stars to draw him up, he longs to be a beast whose soul is soon dissolved. He curses his parents.

> No, Faustus curse thyself, curse Lucifer.
> Now body turn to air.
> *Thunder and lightning.*
> O soul, be changed into little water drops,
> And fall into the ocean, ne'er be found.
> My God, my God, look not so fierce on me.

It is the last moment. In that last moment, Faustus says, in final act and promise :

> I'll burn my books.

And recognizes :

> Ah Mephistophilis.

The Chorus takes it up, as Faustus is carried to hell :

> Cut is the branch that might have grown full straight,

And the burning is seen —

> And burned is Apollo's laurel bough,
> That sometime grew within this learned man :

And the exhoration to us,

> Faustus is gone regard his hellish fall
> Whose fiendful fortune may exhort the wits

Only to wonder at unlawful things,
Whose deepness doth entice such forward wits
To practice more than heavenly power permits.
Terminat hora diem, Terminat Author opus.

God and hell, burning, renunciation.

Roger Bacon stands as an ancestor of all those who come to
imagination with faith in experiment; his attitudes also include
the following : affirmations of "the existence of flying dragons,"
his belief that magic "contained something of truth," his position in regard to astrology, until the end of the seventeenth
century the most important of the occult sciences, and his attempt to draw a boundary line between science and magic.

In this line are also Agrippa, Paracelsus, and Gian Battista
della Porta, born of a famous Neapolitan family in 1545. The
first edition of his *Natural Magic* was published when he was
fifteen, and the second in 1589. During these years of enlarge-
ment, Della Porta became the center of a group of young
scholars called the "Circle of the Secret Ones." Hariot knew
this work, with its fine suggestive passages. This is the beginning of the Seventeenth Book, "Wherein are propounded
Burning-glasses, and the wonderful signes to be seen by them.

"The Proem. Now I am come to Mathematical Sciences, and
this place requires that I shew some experiments concerning
Catoptrick glasses. For these shine among Geometrical instruments, for Ingenuity, Wonder, and Profit : For what could
be invented more ingeniously, than that certain experiments
should follow the imaginary conceits of the mind, and the truth
of Mathematical Demonstrations should be made good by
Ocular experiments? what could seem more wonderful, than
that by reciprocal strokes of reflexion, Images should appear
outwardly, hanging in the Air, and yet neither the visible Object
nor the Glass be seen? that they may seem not to be the repercus-
sion of the Glasses, but Spirits of Vain Phantasms? to see burn-

ing Glasses, not to burn alone where the beams unite, but at a great distance to cast forth terrible fires, and flames, that are most profitable in warlike expeditions . . . I shall adde also those Spectacles whereby poor blinde people can at great distance perfectly see all things. And though venerable Antiquity seem to have invented many and great things," (including the setting of a fleet on fire through a huge burning-glass) "yet I shall set down greater, more Noble, and more Famous things, and that will not a little help to the Optick Science, that more sublime wits may increase it infinitely." Chapter Four speaks of the operations of concave glasses. Find the point of inversion (the focal point) says Della Porta; he heads the passage *That all things shall seem greater*. At first, he gives us magnifications and curiosities : "Set your head below that point, and you shall behold a huge Face like a monstrous Bacchus, and your finger as great as your arm : So women pull hairs off their eyebrows, for they will shew as great as fingers. Seneca reports that Hostius made such Concave-Glasses, that they might make things shew greater : He was a great provoker to lust; so ordering his Glasses, that when he was abused by Sodomy, he might see all the motions of the Sodomite behind him, and delight himself with a false representation of his privy parts that shewed so great."

In Chapter Six, *To see all things in the dark, that are outwardly done in the Sun, with the colours of them,* he describes the camera obscura, that pleasant and admirable chamber darkened and sealed, except for its small round hole, through which will enter, brightly colored and reversed, all that goes brightly on outside. "You shall see them with so much pleasure" he says, "that those that see it can never enough admire it. But if you will

See all things greater and clearer,

Over against it set the Glass, not that which dissipates by dispersing, but which congregates by uniting, both by coming to it, and going from it, till you know the true quantity of the Image . . . and so shall the beholder see more fitly Birds flying, the cloudy skies, or clear and blew, Mountains that are afar off; and in a small circle of paper (that is put over the hole) you shall see as it were an Epitomy of the whole world, and you will much rejoyce to see it . . .

"And walking about, you shall behold the Image everywhere. But is such a thing fit to be discovered to the people? Shall I do such an unworthy Act? Ah! my pen falls out of my hand. Yet my desire to help posterity overcomes; for perhaps from this gleaning as it were, greater and more admirable inventions may be produced . . . I could open the matter no plainer, I have done what I could; I know he that can understand it, will rejoyce very much."

Della Porta's work marked a threshold in the history of science, where bombast and speculation gave way to discernment among new orientations and new concepts. Simple, without the formulas of mysticism, deep in suggestive knowledge, he opened to the investigators of nature who were finding their own climate, their own country — and of whom Hariot was one of the foremost — a country which until now had been hermetically sealed, by usage and by Trismegistus.

To Spanish poetry Donne came, perhaps at Cadiz where the English seized the library that became the core of the Bodleian, nourishing English writing; perhaps sooner, he came to that poet who was closer to his marvelous knotted music than anyone living, Góngora, born in 1561 as Hariot was.

Poet of the *Sonetos* and *Soledades,* allusive, world-creating, Góngora opens the possibility of making more than a landscape in poetry, of the god-robbing gift of making a universe which is both *there,* however artificial, and personal. There are two poets in Góngora, says Brenan : one satirical, scatological, a wit-writer; and the other "a lyrical poet with a nostalgic sense for the fugitive and intangible." But this is not two poets, this is one man. This is the balance named TANTI in the portrait of young Northumberland, the exquisite stretch in even counter-existence that is the stamp of the dazzling men and women of this age —

of every age, once the buried history is lit and brought to the surface.

Góngora is an Andalusian; Arab poetry is in his background, Cordova, movement and glitter, sun-baked, arid — contrast of water and aridity; and in this poet as in Donne, of an edge that is whole, but that is split by critics into mordant gaiety and an entire range from melancholy to the most ferocious despair.

And the silver, roses, crystal; the foam and sand and breasts and blond waves; the torture, the white lilies, the gold harpoons of death. Flickering among air and water, he is the poet of the butterfly in cinders, the rivers of pride and memory, the poet of

> Let liquid diamond
> muffle my bones, and the high crests
> seal, yes, but not oppress
> these few brief ashes with which I'll entrust them,
> if there are silent waves and earth be light.

> The ocean is not deaf; learning deceives.
> Even if raging it will not hear
> the pilot, or answers him in tempest.
> Serene, more likenesses of ears are shown
> than soft complaints are by the stranger sown
> a singing field-hand
> on his wavy plains.

In praise of Garcilaso de le Vega, in honoring the Guzmans:

> Esta, pues, pompa de la Andalucia,
> Gloria de los clarisimos Sidones,
> De los Guzmanes, digo, de Medina,
> Solicito suave tu capelo.

He honors Medina Sidonia while writing about the creation of the cardinal, Don Enrique, with the holy spirit, and purple of Tyre, the pure religion, the true dogma, divine politics. His praise is Roman; and his hatred is Roman, too. It foams out of the tradition in which the poems against the Caesars, the huge satires, were written; and the enemy is here Isabel Tudor, Queen Elizabeth — adulterous, in bed with everyone, tainted, queen : not queen, but she-wolf :

1589

Oh ya isla catolica, y potente
Templo de fe, ya templo de herejia,
Campo de Marte, escuela de Minerva,

—the idea of a school enters into this attack on the island
formerly of faith and now of heresy, field of Mars, school of
Minerva,

Digna de que las sienes que algun dia
Orno corona real de oro luciente
Cina guirnalda vil de esteril hierba,
Madre dichosa y obediente sierva
De Artures, de Eduardo y de Enrico,
Ricos de fortaleza, y de fe ricos;

Among these sterile grasses, this island that had been rich in
faith,

Ahora condenada a infamía eterna
Por la que te gobierna
Con la mano ocupada
Del huso en vez de cetro y de la espada;
Mujer de muchos, y de muchos nuera,
¡Oh reina torpe, reina no, mas loba
Libidinosa y fiera,
Fiamma dal ciel se le tue trezze piova!

This is the poet too of

Fixed — in the face of the cold mists —
On the burning diamond of the magnetic north

and the poet of the temple of the sun

Great America you are, gold in your veins,
Your bones silver —

the discovery of April, and tormented May.

He is alive to us in his own poems, which have come down
related through a line of poets colored by Gongorism, from
Donne to Wallace Stevens. Fury poured out after him, abuse
and a school of enemies. Did he give poetry a power of expression never dreamed of before? Did he lead poetry away from
its fertilizing sources in life? Or can these powers balance? Are

we in a landscape, a world, in which man does both these things, or his powers are so used, picked up by the secondary men, that both are carried on with or without discrimination?

Tanti.

"And this is all the fruits of our labors," Hariot writes to end his book, " that I have thought necessary to advertise you of at this present : what else concerneth the nature and manners of the inhabitants of Virginia" and of the voyages and of those by Ralegh "imployed, many worthy to be remembered; as of the first discoverers of the Countrey" and all the rest, "I have ready in a discourse by itself in manner of a Chronicle . . . and when time shall be thought convenient shall be published."

He commends the books to "your favourable constructions, expecting good success of the action, from him which is to be acknowledged the author and governor not only of this but of all things else" and takes his leave of us, this month of February, 1588, in London.

On the title-page, with its beautiful statement of *A briefe and true report,* he speaks of Virginia, of Grenville and of Ralegh, "favoured and authorised by her Maiestie."

The book is directed to the Adventurers, Favorers and Welwillers of the action, for the inhabiting and planting there; and these go down in time, from those men and women of the year when the beacons were ready all along the coast, when they were prepared for the Spanish Armada, not the new world.

"By Thomas Hariot," he writes, speaking of serving Ralegh, "a member of the Colony, and there imployed in discovering."

At the end of the *Brief and True Report,* Hariot writes about the next step. He begins by saying that here is all that he has thought necessary to "advertise" us of at the present. But of the other aspects, what else concerns the nature and manners of the inhabitants of Virginia;

The number "with the particularities of the voyages thither made;

"And of the actions of such that have been by Sir Water Raleigh [sic] therein and there imployed, many worthy to be remembred; as of the first discoverers of the Country";

And Grenville; and Lane; and many others;

Of the captains and masters of the voyages since;

"Of many persons, accidents, and things else," Hariot says, "I have ready in a discourse by itself in manner of a Chronicle," and when time shall be thought convenient shall be also published.

He said the chronicle "according to the course of times" was ready. Did he give it to Robert Robinson, the London printer of the Quarto Hariot?

Or did he give it, after the great events of the summer of 1588, to the Frankfurt printer to whom the *Brief and True Report* went, to appear in a large folio edition, with Hariot's text, to which are added the Hariot-White map and the white watercolors of people and scenes of Virginia, Europeanized and engraved by Theodore De Bry, and printed in Latin, German, French and English versions, with Hariot's captions — written at his freest, best, most vivid — and with De Bry's letter of dedication to Ralegh?

The chronicle was inexplicably lost, has never been mentioned in writing, and has not yet been found. That is one of the first steps of the hunting still to be done by those who go on where this work leaves off.

In 1589, George Clifford, the Earl of Cumberland, "built the greatest Fleet of shipping that ever any subject did," according to Aubrey. "The Armada of the Argonauts was but a trifle to this," and sailed to America.

Known for his interest in geography and mathematics, Cumberland was also known as a navigator, "the greatest," this is Aubrey again, "and did the most prodigious things at sea that ever any subject did at his own cost." He sold his inheritance of over sixteen thousands pounds yearly to outfit his own fleet.

On the famous expedition, he pirated from the Spaniards to the value of seven or eight hundred thousand pounds, all of which, with the fleet, was confiscated by the Queen and the Council, concluding that it was too much for a subject to have. This time, restoration was made "to the Spaniard."

Aubrey adds this unconfirmed and tantalizing note : "As I take it, Sir Walter Ralegh went this brave Voyage with his Lordship; and Mr. Edmund Wright, the excellent Navigator; and, not unlikely, Mr. Hariot too."

But in this year, the Irish State Papers list Hariot as a tenant of Ralegh's at Molanna. Eight years later, Hariot was collecting rents in Brampton, Cumberland.

Let us believe that it was Hariot who saw and knew all these delights while he was among the Indians of Virginia; that it was Hariot who worked with John White while the drawings were being made, and the maps; that it was Hariot who wrote or instigated the captions used in the four editions printed at Frankfurt by Wechel and Fischer, for which De Bry engraved the plates.

These then would be the occurrence of delight known in the New World during that full year : The people, void of all covetousness, live cheerfully and at their hearts' ease. But they solemnize their feasts in the night, and therefore they keep very great fires to avoid darkness, and to testify their joy.

The women of Secotan . . . are also delighted with walking in the fields, and beside the rivers, to see the hunting of deer and catching of fish.

The young daughters of Pomeioc are greatly delighted with puppets and babes which were brought out of England. (Puppets are dolls; the phrase may mean doll-children.) We offered them of our wares, as glasses, knives, dolls, and other trifles, which we thought they delighted in.

Virgins of good parentage wear hanging about their necks instead of a chain certain thick and round pearls, with little beads of copper or polished bone between them. They pounce their foreheads, cheeks, arms and legs. Their hair is cut with two ridges above their foreheads, the rest is trussed up in a knot behind; they have broad mouths, reasonable fair black eyes; they lay their hands often upon their shoulders, and cover their breasts in token of maidenlike modesty. The rest of their bodies are naked, as in the picture to be seen. They delight also in seeing fish taken in the rivers.

A great and solemn feast at which they dance singing, and use the strangest gestures that they can possibly devise. Three of the fairest virgins of the company are in the midst, who embracing one another do as it were turn about in their dancing. All this is done after the sun is set for avoiding of heat. When they are weary of dancing they go out of the circle, and come in until their dances be ended, and they go to make merry.

And he speaks again of their singing, when they have escaped any great danger by sea or land, or be returned from the war, in token of joy they make a great fire, rattle their rattles, sing after their manner, men and women together, and they make merry : as myself observed and noted down at my being among them.

They take much pleasure in hunting of deer.

Their devils; their Flying Men, or conjurors; their identifying marks; their goodly woods, store of rivers full of fish; their princes or Weroances. "And to confess a truth I cannot remember that ever I saw a better or quieter people than they."

Theodore de Bry dedicated the book to Ralegh : "I have

thought that the figures were of greater commendation, if some history which treating of the commodities and fertility of the said country were joined with the same, therefore have I served myself of the report which Thomas Hariot has lately set forth, and have caused them both together to be printed and dedicated unto you, as a thing which by right doth already appertain unto you. Therefore do I crave that you will accept this little book . . .

"And so I commit you unto the almighty, from Frankfort the first of April 1590.

"Your most humble servant,

"Theodorus de Bry"

Adrian Gilbert, the other half-brother of Walter Ralegh's through his mother's first marriage, is a man of shadowy fascination. We know him as the scientist of the family, involved in Humphrey Gilbert's expeditions, and a friend of Dr. Dee, who visited him at Mortlake, very possibly with Hariot, who presented a book to Dr. Dee which is still preserved.

From Adrian Gilbert's mine Hariot was given a "loadstone"; he records an experiment in which this was used, and another with Sir Walter's "Toure ashes." Of a later time.

In the years he passed in England and France, Bruno had written his plays — for the dialogues must be called drama — of the arguments for the bonds of men and of infinity, of the integrated universe, of creatures that live on other planets. Failed plays, Bacon was to call them; and modern writers speak of their ideas as finding form in Campanella's poems.

They live in Bruno's poems, too, in his greatest work, the poem known as *De Immenso,* which he had begun in London and finished over the years. It was ready for the printer when he arrived in Frankfurt.

The printer to whom Bruno came was John Wechel, a center of civilization in this city of importance and tolerance and productive work. The printing-houses were meeting-places, like the aisle of St. Paul's in London; the firm of Wechel and Fischer was the chief of these. John was the third in line; his father had entertained Sidney in 1573 — and, although Sidney has never mentioned Bruno even in correspondence, he was close to Bruno in London, accepted Bruno's dedication and loving mockery in the dialogues, and may have sent Bruno to Wechel. Bruno applied for permission to live in Wechel's house — the printers lodged, not only those scholars whose books were in press, but travelling nobles like Sidney. The refusal of Bruno's request is recorded in the Book of the Burgomaster for July 2, 1590 : "Resolved that his petition be refused and that he be told to take his penny elsewhere." (Echoed in the words of a twentieth-century passport official when a brilliant young scientist of comparable reputation applied for permission to go legally to Denmark to accept a fellowship : "Let him swim.")

John Wechel was able to get lodgings for Bruno at the Carmelite monastery. A bookseller, Brietanus, a Fleming living in Venice, told the Inquisition at Bruno's trial that he had talked with Bruno in Frankfurt — not about Christianity or Catholicism — and that the prior of the monastery had said that Bruno was "a universal man" who "could, if he wished, make the whole world of one religion." Brietanus could not mention any intimate friends of Bruno's.

Bruno left Frankfurt abruptly, in January, 1591, or at least before the last leaf of the initial book which Wechel was printing for him was ready, but he was back for his second stay in March, and lived in Frankfurt for six months. *De Triplici Minimo* was printed then, and permission was obtained. It was officially published, in the terms of the period.

Now *De Immenso,* the marvelous addition to *De Monade,* was set in type, by the partners John Wechel and Peter Fischer. It was ready for the Michaelmas Frankfurt Fair. It has lines that are found in *On the Infinite Universe,* after its beginning, "Est mens," which declares the subject — not heroics but the mind,

> . . . you let me hold death in disdain;
> You open the secret doors, you break the chains
> Which few can pass, which few come through free.
> Centuries, the years, months, light of days, the many
> Children and weapons of time, steel cannot stand against,
> Have made my keep against that raging foe.
> Fearless, spreading wings upon vast space
> I rise among the globes . . .

Reddor Dux, Lex, Lux, Vates, Pater, Author, Iterque . . .

The poem was started in England. It pays tribute to the courage of Drake and Howard, says its Italian editor. Actually, the tribute it pays is to Grenville and Hariot, and to Drake, to the Atlantic voyage (says the editor, not knowing of the existence of Hariot) "which is a clear allusion to the foundation of Virginia";

Solvit ut Americam premeret violentus Iberus

Bruno began the poem, according to this editor, in 1584 or 1585. But something was happening at Wechel's that was related to this aspect of Bruno's poem.

For John Wechel is the printer also of the De Bry edition of Hariot, in four languages — Latin, French, German and English — with De Bry's engravings based on White's watercolors and drawings. This new edition is called *America.* It has a further and extraordinarily vivid contribution of Hariot's : a set of captions for the pictures. This new writing extends the *Report* not only in material, but in language. The writing here is not a description for the purpose of getting support. The further disappointments have been lived through; Hariot is writing in a mood of the next phase of his life. He has gone deeper. Here the terms are those of true description indeed. There are no promises. The terms are, as we have seen, those of reality and delight.

Bruno's writing includes these terms, those of

The knowing spirit is not afraid of death

and the great miracle that is man, like god :

Hinc miraculum magnum a Trismegisto appellabitur homo, qui in deum transeat quasi ipse sit deus, qui conatur omnia fieri, sicut deus est omnia; ad objectum sine fine (ubique tamen finiendo) contendit, sicut infinitus est deus, immensus, ubique totus.

A dialogue is here, of course, between poetry and prose, science and poetry, the universe and man. More. A dialogue "between" all things, one speaking with everything, one speaking with the unknown and the world :

Est animal sanctum, sacrum, et venerabile, mundus:
Quoque animante animans est at quidquid vivit in ipso :

all the way to the last line of the poem:

Mens, Deus, Ens, Unum, Verum, Fatum, Ratio, Ordo.

The last except for the lyric ending, whose rough faun is himself among nymphs, so that after the infinitudes the flesh returns at last in full humanity :

Sic non succifluis occurro poeta labellis,
Non Ganymedeo cultus blandusque lepore,
Mellitus, scitus, tersus, graphiceque venustus;
At vero durus, villosus, rusticus, asper,
Callosus, rigidus . . .
Ergo ego setosum quia me natura creavit,
Non discam rudibus digitis aptare smaragdos,
Cincinnare comam, roseumque per ora ruborem
Fundere odoratis caput instrophiare hyacinthis,
Promere flexibiles gestus, mollemque choream,
Gutturis et de me vocem exentrare tenelli;
Ne vit agam puerum, ne de mare foemina fiam.
Quod si ut sum factus, divum pro munere, memet

III

Ingerero rigidum, membrisque viriliter acrem,
Infrenem, invictum, sementoseque sonantem;
Narcissis referam : peramarunt me quoque Nymphae.

From the house of Mocenigo in Venice, with its frescoed
dome, its family that had given three doges in these two centuries, a letter came to Bruno. Signor Giovanni Mocenigo had
been at a bookseller's buying one of Bruno's books, and had
asked whether the bookseller knew Bruno, and where he was;
Mocenigo wanted to learn the secrets of memory from Bruno.
(Even Mocenigo's name is tied to Memory, Mnemosyne.)

Bruno later testified : "Being in Frankfurt last year, I received two letters from Sig. Giovanni Mocenigo, inviting me to
Venice to teach him the art of memory and discovery, with
promises to treat me well; he said I should be satisfied with
him."

Venice was marvelous, and a center of trade; a center of
printing, many of whose books were condemned by Rome;
the only Italian state that had preserved independence and
resisted the narrowing of civil liberties. The method of mnemonics which Bruno taught was in fashion — a "craze among
the rich young dilettanti of Venice"; and his new patron was
powerful, he could provide protection.

Bruno always thought of himself as a Roman Catholic.

He said of himself that he was a "citizen and servant of the
world, child of the sun and mother earth." It was not as a
broken and wandering refugee that he went back to Italy.
Hoping for the South, he belonged anywhere.

He thought he could go back and live in the Campagna,
to be received by the Church, outside his order, to be sure.

He may have known that Mocenigo had been an assessor
with the three-man panel of judges that sat as the tribunal of
the Inquisition.

Bruno reprints Copernicus in *On Immensity*; he cites his fathers
Parmenides, Empedocles, Lucretius, and foreshadows Hegel.

Things that Humboldt, in his *Cosmos,* attributed to Kepler, were really Bruno's; before Galileo, he knew that the worlds move through space, secure in their own energy, heavier than earth. There is no difference between the heavens and the earth, not essentially; there are invisible planets revolving about the stars, and undiscovered planets of our sun. The sun is burning, liquid. He rejoices : the universe is eternal, its worlds decay, we die, the parts of all things enter into new arrangements.

On May 29, 1592, after having been in a cell for three days, Bruno said to his three judges and the assessor : "I shall tell the truth."

The father-in-law of the Countess of Northumberland is in the Tower, Sir John Perrot, who three years ago was Lord Deputy in Ireland. She has her brother, the Earl of Essex, on his side, with the Vice-Chamberlain; but the Court is split, some with the Lord Treasurer for him, and does not leave his chamber now; or with the Chancellor against him on the evidence of one priest. They speak of his "insolent government in Ireland" and his "irreverent speeches against the Queen."

The Queen has her own factions, keeping Essex and Ralegh through sex is it? power is it? It is that great shining female power where sex and rule and the world's potential are all held out together as at the end of a woman's arm, or is it body, or is it royal power, or is it golden life?

"The Earl of Essex and Sir Walter Ralegh are still rivals, but Essex is like enough, if he have a few more years, to carry Leicester's credit and sway."

Two extraordinary women enter this story.

One is Elizabeth Throckmorton. In her late twenties, tall, blue-eyed, fair, she is the daughter of the rebel Throckmorton, and she is a lady-in-waiting to the queen; one of that hedge of maidens who must be more virgin than virgin, that is, not virgin receptive, but guarded from any love because that belongs to the queen who belongs to England. We know nothing at all about Elizabeth Throckmorton until she is — what? seduced? stood scandalously against a tree by Ralegh, as the story goes in Aubrey? secretly married? At any rate pregnant, according to the Throckmorton diaries read by Rowse.

From then on, she is Lady Ralegh. She is fierce in her loyalty, graceful as the lady of Sherborne, the lovely castle-land in Dorset. But first she is thrown in prison; and much later, she is on her knees at Court with her young son, begging for justice for Ralegh, begging for mercy, begging for his land — his Sherborne — to be restored to him. Begging and proud.

The other woman is Dorothy, the second daughter of Walter Devereux, who married Queen Elizabeth's cousin Lettice Knollys — that Lettice who when the young Dorothy was fourteen married Leicester. Dorothy's brother was Essex; her sister, one year younger, was that Penelope Devereux who became known to all of Europe as the Stella of Sir Philip Sidney's sonnets. Known to Bruno, who jeered at love like that, which moved nowhere. But her father had hoped that Penelope would marry Philip Sidney; it was Lord Rich she married, and the puns on "rich" stand savage and coy in those lines of Astrophel and Stella.

Dorothy was less beautiful, but flaming, as Essex was. Her brief mysterious marriage to Sir Thomas Perrot (she was seventeen) came only one year before Essex was presented to Elizabeth by Leicester.

He was shown to Elizabeth — to supplant Ralegh? — beautiful, flaming, inflamed at once. At nineteen, he was accusing Elizabeth of disgracing him and his sister, of grieving his love, and the long dance of Essex and his two sisters was full begun; with its disgraces, its reconciliations, and dining and wars; Elizabeth finally received both sisters, years later.

And after Perrot, Northumberland, a wild procession of torments. Dorothy going to Essex House, running from her husband after a "muttering of unkindness" between them. This was only one of several separations that had all the gossips oscillating.

And later, the alliances : the Queen would help; all would be restored; the Prince would surely help. Dorothy is a great Countess; at her audience with the King, she thinks he is gracious, she hopes the great part of what she asks for will be given her.

But this is years away. Now she is proud and free; it is Elizabeth Throckmorton, Lady Ralegh, who is in icy disgrace. We know nothing of what passed between Ralegh and his wife until much later, in her attempts to act among the penalties. We have a portrait of her, stiff, a faithful face.

Recurrent forms : Hariot with Elizabeth Ralegh, in London, at Sherborne, in the narrow stone of the Tower.

Hariot with Dorothy Percy, in London, at Syon House, in the narrow stone of the Tower. Over long time.

The Twelve Gates by George Ripley is a text in alchemy written in the time of Edward IV, and dedicated to the King. Hariot had a manuscript text of this treatise in verse, a basic piece of description of the process with those by Avicenna, Roger Bacon, John Dee.

Sir George Ripley, canon of Bridlington in York, had studied in Italy, France, and Germany, and "had the happiness to see a transmutation performed in Rome." He was dignified by the Pope, and at Rhodes gave £100,000 to the Knights of St. John of Jerusalem. Drawing "the jealousy of his brethren" in Bridlington, he entered the order of Carmelites, and received an indulgence from Innocent VIII that allowed him to live in solitude, exempt from claustral observance, at Butolph. He wrote *The Twelve Gates of Alchemy* in 1471.

It was printed for the first time in London on May 12, 1591, set forth by Mr. Ralph Rabbards, student and expert in alchemical arts. "Wishing by all means possible to profit the Kingdom and State, Mr. Rabbards hath dedicated this work to her Majesty."

The poem begins,

> O hygh yncomprehensyble and gloryous Mageste,
> Whose luminous bemes obtundyth our speculation :
> One-hode in substance, O Tryne hode in Deite . . .

> O deviaunt fro danger, O drawer most deboner;
> Fro thys enyos valey of vanyte, O our Exalter,
> O power, O wysdom, O goodness inexplycable,
> Support me, tech me, and be my Governour . . .

The gates are the process : Of Calcination, Of Solution, Of Separation, Of Conjunction, Of Putrefaction, Of Congelation, Of Cibation, Of Sublimation :

> The fyrst cause ys to make the body spirituall
> The second that the spryt may corporall be,
> And become fyx wyth hyt and substantyall;

Of Fermentation, Of Exaltation, Of Multiplication, Of Projection.

Here, in Ripley, and in Roger Bacon's *Root of the World,* in all these texts, we meet sulphur and mercury in their processes, the matter, the menstruum, the eclipses, green dragon, white woman and red man in embrace, the scum of the sea, the burning of the flowers, the filth, the heaven upon the earth reiterated, the fatal eclipse of the sun and of the moon, when no light shall shine upon the earth, and the sea shall vanish; then is made our chaos, out of which, at the command of God, shall proceed all the miracles of the world in their orders — so Eirenaeus Philalethes writes.

This is what Hariot was doing : "Let not thy heat be over strong, and yet strong enough, and between Scylla and Charybdis sail like unto a skillful pilot, so shalt thou attain the wealth of either India; sometimes thou shalt see as it were little Island floating, and shooting out as it were little sprigs and buds, which will be changeable in colors, which soon will be melted and others arrive; for the earth as inclining to a vegetation, is always sending forth some new thing or other; — sometimes thy fance will be that thou seest in thy glass birds or beasts, or creeping things, and thou shalt each day behold colors most beautiful to sight . . ."

This is what Hariot was doing : Attend then to my doctrine : take the body which I have shewed you, and put it into the water of our sea, and decoct it continually with a due heat of fire, that both dews and clouds may ascend, and day, without intermission . . .

"And the drops which are continually running down to perforate the mass marvelously, and by continual circulation the water is made more subtle, and doth sweetly extract the soul of the Sun; so by the mediation of the soul the spirit is reconciled within the body . . ."

The regimen of Saturn.
The regimen of Mercury.
The regimen of Luna.
The regimen of Venus.
The regimen of Sol.

Most pure gold or silver, art, blessing, and adept may transmute imperfect metals into perfect, make precious stones and gems, make a medicine universal for prolonging life and curing diseases . . . Whosoever enjoyeth this talent, let him be sure to employ it to the glory of God, and the good of his neighbors.

> And soon it will enter and spread him full wide,
> But many for ignorance doth mar that they made.

Hariot marked out a triangle on the ground, and on it laid down the line of his round bullets. The second line, the third; and within them shorter and shorter lines of the spheres, until the triangle was filled flat. Then, carefully, he began to set up the second line, one bullet shorter than the base, and, carefully, on up to the peak of the pyramid. Then, that finished, he lined the bullets up in a second figure, and then a third. He made the notes on this occupation, so like a boy's game in its act, but with a far different reach, that gives it its meaning to our own time.

It was a hard day in December; the cold air, cold ground, cold metal of the bullets.

He wrote : "12 December 1591. There are three groundplates upon the which may be orderly piled bullets : the triangle : the square : and the oblonge. Concerning piling there are two questions . . ." and he asks about the number of bullets relative to the progression of the triangles and the progression of the oblongs,

As 10 is 30 · 40 · 50 · etc.
or 15 is 55 · 70 · 85 · etc.

The element of mature play, as found in these pilings — for there are several among Hariot's loose papers — and as revealed in such a paper as Kepler's *Essay on the Snowflake,* is part of the scientific life, revealed daily, says Cyril S. Smith, "in informal conversations in the laboratory but rarely in published papers."

What we need here is Hariot's talk as he piled the bullets.

Of this mature play, Smith says that something like it probably precedes all major advances in science. It is meagerly documented, he adds, making the task of the person who "seeks human reasons behind the advancing structure of science extremely difficult."

These studies are central to the problem of the crystal, which is the key to atomic theory, which might be seen to rest on this idea of composition of atoms "stacked in continuous array. One cannot help but wonder what simple generalizations similarly lie unseen behind the problems of present-day science.

"The greatest elegance of crystallography is undoubtedly in its mathematics, yet its richest intellectual value lies in the relationship of this to the organization of real matter and to the interplay between order and necessary disorder."

Smith goes on to speak of the emphasis on purity in these

studies as misplaced. "Crystallography would be as lifeless as a crystal if its established order did not lead to a study of imperfections and disorder."

The array does have a symmetry that does not necessarily belong to the units. Hariot shows this in his drawings of round bullets which touch each other in various points, determining various hexagonal or quadrilateral cells in space lattices. There are, in stacked spheres, spaces between the cells, of appropriate shapes.

The way of looking at these units and spaces is brought over into other modes in art — in Japanese painting, for example, where the shapes of the spaces is considered as carefully and in as fine relations as the shapes of the objects which fill space.

To the early atomists, the piling of cannonballs provided the image of unitary aggregates; and they had, in our war-history, cannonballs. They also had bricks and building stones. Cyril Smith goes back into the mud brick structures of Mesopotamia, the superstructures formed by stacking in the Ziggurats, and the close packing of circles at Uruk, where in the 4th century B.C. the decorative properties were used; the Mycenean and Etruscan goldworkers give us piled spheres, though perhaps this was "experimentally realized in millet seed before any of these," says Smith. The word *pyramid* may be related to the Greek word for heap of wheat.

There are applications to metals through this history, and the interest in metals is a quickening influence throughout the life of Hariot and Ralegh. The seminal book by Agricola, *De Re Metallica,* appeared four years before Hariot was born.

The relation of these interests to man's ideas of symmetry and chaos has a great deal to do with the development of these perceptions. "Man has been extraordinarily unwilling to see crystallographic symmetry in matter, perhaps because symmetry, if perfect, is not much more interesting than uniform chaos and bears no more relationship to the real world."

Kepler did not realize that, in working with snowflakes and answering the question about the sides of a snowflake, "Why 6?" he was dealing with crystals. "Though he was the first to publish speculations of this kind, he was not the first to do them," and he was not an atomist. "Thomas Hariot . . . was an imaginative and accomplished mathematician whose fragmentary notes show that he was a most advanced thinker. He was an atomist long before this was popular, and it was probably his atomic view which led him to think and to experiment on the manner in which uniform parts could be packed together. . . . He saw the relationship between the decorators patterns and the corpuscular theory of matter. He studied two- and three-dimensional arrays of circles and spheres apparently using tiny copper balls floating on mercury — a model which will delight twentieth-century metallurgists with its analogy with the bubble-raft model of a crystal, first described by E. E. Thum in 1926 and beautifully exploited by W. H. Bragg and Nye and others. He was the first to postulate that the closest packing was achieved when one ball was surrounded by 12 neighbors; he saw the difference between hexagonal and cubic close-packing, and in general had all of the insights into crystalline order which have been attributed to Kepler . . . It is certain that he contributed to that background of atomistic discussion in England which crystallized in the public revival of Greek atomism early in the seventeenth century."

From these early optical noticings — or optical intuitions, as Smith calls them — the discovery of diffraction through the use of X-rays in the twentieth century is one step. "The discovery of diffracation was of as much importance in establishing the nature of X-rays as in giving the structure of crystals."

The patterns were verified. They were of extreme use to metallurgists in studying alloys, and led to the quantum mechanical theory of alloys through the relation of electron-atom ratio and the crystal structure of alloys of copper.

Analyses and refinements of method followed, with the organic chemists' vision of what this meant to the analysis of vitamins, and to Crick and Watson's deduction, after Linus Pauling's work, of the structure of the nucleic acid molecule on the basis of chemical and X-ray studies, "probably the most significant structural determination ever made," says Smith, "but its background stretches far into the past."

That past is Hariot's.

Our time of high-speed computers exploits this method.

Cyril Smith now opens the human terms. "Though a crystal lattice is based upon the intimate relationship between an atom and its neighbors, the crystallographer's method of analysis has made him think of symmetry rather than of local clustering . . . Once one knows the structure, the uniform interior of a crystal is extraordinarily dull and uninteresting. It is the boundaries and imperfections that take on interest."

With an impulse to the study of imperfections, Bethe and Peierls "saw in them manageable examples of cooperative phenomena in general." These phenomena are all of practical importance in metallurgy.

The growth of a crystal proceeds in response to changes in pressure and temperature, by steps, around nodes, by shearing and twist. These deformations and dislocations give us the keys not only to steel, to glass, to the organic polymers with which we surround ourselves in the twentieth century, but they provide the structural basis for the "hereditary information transfer" which is the basis of all life.

Here we are not dealing with symmetry or asymmetry, but with the shape of the crystal boundaries themselves, a broader aspect of space filling. The youth of this noticing is in the piling of bullets that Hariot did on a cold day in 1591, in the watching of honeycomb and pomegranate structure by Kepler twenty years later and in all we know of froth of soap bubbles and all the foams — from bread to the surf of the sea.

Watching, we see the similarity of form in these meetings, in the diverse. Do we see the unit's effect on the structure or the structure's effect on the unit, or the dance of energy between them? Do we see the hierarchy of degrees of order and disorder? Do we see principles of structure in the molecule, in the metal sphere, crystal, human tissue, the organism? In the boundaries, the relation of the traces?

Ralegh complained: "I am not able to live to row up and down with every tide from Gravesend to London." On the 6th of May, he was on board the ship he had contributed, the *Roebuck;* there was the *Galleon Ralegh*, provided by his brother Carew; Cumberland joined with six ships. They sailed out to challenge what they called the slavery and tyranny of Spain. "What have they done in Sicily, Naples, Milan, and the Low Countries? In one island, called Hispaniola, they have wasted three millions of the natural people, beside many millions else in other places of the Indies; a poor and harmless people, created of God, and might have been won to his knowledge, as many of them were."

On May 7th, the fleet was overtaken with Frobisher. Ralegh, the General of the Fleet, was ordered back, leaving Sir John Burroughs (it is Hariot's spelling that is used here) and Frobisher in command. Ralegh did not at once go back, but sailed as far as Finisterre. Ralegh worked out his plan to challenge Spain by capture and raid, stationing half the fleet off the coast of Spain, under Frobisher, as decoy. The others under Burroughs were sent to make rendezvous with the treasure fleet as it came to the Azores.

Ralegh returned to the explosion that he might have foreseen if he had truly known Elizabeth, or if he could have listened to everything his aunt, Cat Ashley, knew.

They had always made rumors about the doings and speakings at Durham House. Now that Ralegh was in the Tower, sending every few days his laments to the Queen, to Cecil (about his castle in Ireland, now given by the Queen to a ward, his castle in the "most dangerous place in all Munster"), anything could be said against him.

And not only against Ralegh. The rumors were now in print;

not very sharp-edged against him, although if it were developed it might be worth his neck. Father Parsons, the Jesuit, writing under the name of Andreas Philopater, has published a book to answer the proclamation made against the seminary priests and Jesuits last October. A summary in English is printed with it. Sir Christopher Hatton, Cecil, both are attacked, and when he comes to Ralegh, Father Parsons says that "he keeps a school of Atheism much frequented, with a certain necromatic astronomer as schoolmaster, where no small number of young men of noble birth learn to deride the Old Law of Moses as well as the New Law of Christ with ingenious quips and jests, and among other things to spell the name of God backwards."

He compares the seminaries with the two Universities of England, for the young men of England, he says, are coming to the Continent. The English Universities are loose, the seminaries depend on order and studies. Cecil and Leicester are "cancellers of virtue" rather than Chancellors of Universities, and they have overthrown all. There is confusion, immodesty in clothing, harlots as baits for young men, "headships given to light and wanton companions, fencing and dancing scholls crowded, tavens filled with scholars, statues of founders contemned and broken . . ."

Ralegh, under the care of his cousin, the Keeper of the Tower, George Carew, learned early in September what had happened to the half of his fleet under Sir John Burroughs. Before this a Basque vessel had been captured and sent to England. These ships were taken in as the knights of Arthur brought in their victim kings and champion. But next sailed in the greatest prize of all, the great Crown of Portugal carrack, the *Madre de Dios,* tallest of galleons, a seven-deck tower with a cargo from Asia of pearls, a great offering of crosses and diamonds, amber, precious stones, and a fortune in musk; 537 tons of spices, with pepper worth £102,000 of that time; and 15 tons of ebony; and the finest of cloths, satins, silks, tapestries.

The *Madre de Dios* reached Dartmouth on September 8th.

Looting had begun on the seas; where Burroughs accused Cumberland's men of plundering. In port, the ship was open to the whole west country, where raiders and jewellers from London, buyers from the cities, fell on the ship with such shaking excitement that their candles set fire to her four separate times. The fires were put out, and the one man who was hero enough to the west country, however he was hated and in disgrace in London, was sent for and released.

Ralegh came out of the Tower at a moment when Dartmouth looked like Bartholomew Fair. He was in London for two days, and then travelled westward, with a keeper and possibly with Hariot. He writes, on September 17th, of the jewellers: "If I meet any of them coming up, if it be on the wildest heath in all the way, I mean to strip them as naked as ever they were born. For it is infinite that her Majesty hath been robbed, and that of the most rare things."

Cecil was ahead of him, turning back all he met on the road from Dartmouth or Plymouth; he said you could almost smell the amber and musk on them — my Lord, there never was such spoil! — an armlet of gold, and a fork and spoon of crystal with rubies.

Ralegh was in Dartmouth, trying to save some of this pirated treasure for the Queen. He was the only man who could hold the looting, contain it, and quiet these men. He did it through joy and love. That is what Ralegh meant to the west country, and it is Cecil himself who tells it :

"Within one half hour Sir Walter Ralegh arrived with his keeper, Mr. Blount. I assure you, Sir, his poor servants, to the number of 140 godly men, and all the mariners, came to him with shouts of joy; I never saw a man more troubled to quiet them. But his heart is broken, as he is extremely pensive, unless he is busied, in which he can toil terribly. The meeting between him and Sir John Gilbert was with tears on Sir John's part. But he, finding it is known that he has a keeper, whenever he is saluted with congratulations for liberty, doth answer, 'No, I am still the Queen of England's poor captive.' "

Hariot wrote, in his working papers, comparing this ship with a great English ship of the next reign:

The carracke taken by Sr John Burroughs 1592 voyages.

Late in May, the charges and harryings against Christopher Marlowe reached a narrow place. On the 18th, a warrant was sworn out for Marlowe's arrest. He was summoned to appear before the Star Chamber which, with the Privy Council, a subset of this court, was the most dread, unlimited, punitive of bars.

Marlowe was released on bail, but from now on his daily attendance was required, the days of meeting being Wednesday and Friday mornings.

This court "operated on the theory that once a man was arrested, regardless of the reason, any other wrongs that he had committed might be dealt with by them; this inquisitorial process was called 'scraping the conscience.' It even became an accepted procedure to arrest a defendant to answer a fictitious trespass in order to draw out unrelated subjects.

"Although they stopped short of prescribing the death penalty, cruel and inhuman punishments were ordered by the august peers of the Star Chamber: cutting off of ears, amputation of hands and plunging the stumps into hot pitch, branding, whipping, 'peine forte et dure' (a method of torture by loading increasingly heavy weights on a supine man's chest until he either agreed to confess or his rib cage was crushed). Unlucky the man, no matter how innocent, who was called before such a court. His chances of eluding their tentacles and escaping scot-free were extremely slim."

Marlowe, at 29, was living at Scadbury in Kent, the home of Sir Thomas Walsingham. He was working on *Hero and Leander,* and went to London — twelve miles — on the days prescribed. The last of these was Wednesday, May 30, 1593.

On the day before, an indictment had been delivered to the Privy Council by the informer set by the government to trail

Marlowe. The informer, Richard Baines, listed all of the opinions of Marlowe's which he considered "dangerous and horrible
blasphemies," and he added a rider which implicated other
men. Baines had gathered these as Marlowe's "Common
Speeches," and testifies that not only does Marlowe hold these
beliefs, but "almost into euery Company he Cometh he per-
swades men to Atheism willing them not to be afeard of bug-
beares and hobgoblins . . ." Baines ends the indictment :

> . . . And as I think all men in Christianity ought to indevor that
> the mouth of so dangerous a member may be stopped, he saith
> likewise that he hath quoted a number of Contrarities oute of
> the Scripture wch he hath given to some great men who in
> Convenient time shalbe named. When these thinges shalbe
> Called in question the witness shalbe produced.

There are sixteen charges submitted by Baines. They came as
Kyd, the playwright who had known Marlowe well and shared
chambers with him, was being tortured. Kyd in his informing
letter on Marlowe had spoken of Hariot as one of Marlowe's
closest associates. He implicates the School of Night: "such as
he convers'd withall, that is, as I am geven to understand, with
Harriott, Warner, Royden." (This could be Walter Warner the
scientist, or William, the poet; and Matthew Royden the poet,
or Edmund Royden, whose copy of Ralegh's *History of the
World* has come down to us.) Kyd had been cracked by torture
in the Bridewell, and on the rack, after he had said he was a
playwright, not an inciter to rebellion, after he had been shown
three pages seized in his room, he hangs and stares and says
the pages belong to Marlowe, not to him.

Kyd's accusation and Baines' have been received and the trap
is closing on Marlowe. What is the nature of this trap?

The espionage service is deep in the entire story; Sir Thomas
Walsingham was high in the service, and Marlowe had probably
been working in the service under Walsingham as far back as
1587, when Sir Philip Sidney died, and Marlowe very likely
went as a secret service man to Utrecht. His patron, Walsingham, was at the top of a pyramid engaged in espionage in the

Low Countries and elsewhere in the Continent; it was he who broke the Babington Plot that year, and Marlowe had worked for him ever since.

The School of Night is the other group most deeply concerned with the developments that would surely follow in the days to come. For these are the charges that Baines was making :

That the Indians and many Authors of antiquity haue assuredly written aboue 16 thousand yeares agone wher as Adam is proued to haue lived w'hin 6 thousand yeares.

He affirmeth that Moyses was but a Jugler, & that one Heriots being Sir W Raleighs' man can do more than he.

That Moyses made the Jewes to travell xl yeares in the wildernes, (wch Jorney might haue bin Done in lesse then one yeare) ere they Came to the promised land to thintent that those who were privy to most of his subtilties might perish and so an everlasting superstition Remain in the hartes of the people.

That the first beginning of Religioun was only to keep men in awe.

That it was an easy matter for Moyses being brought up in all the artes of the Egiptians to abuse the Jewes being a rude & grosse people.

That Christ was a bastard and his mother dishonest.

That he was the sonne of a Carpenter, and that if the Jewes among whome he was borne did Crucify him theie best knew him and whence he Came.

That Christ deserved better to die than Barrabas and that the Jewes made a good Choise, though Barrabas were both a thief and murtherer.

That if there be an god or any good Religion, then it is in the papistes because the service of god is performed wth more Cerimonies, as Elevation of the mass, organs, singing men, Shaven Crownes & cta. that all protestantes are Hypocriticall asses.

That if he were put to write a new Religion, he would undertake both a more Exxellent and Admirable methode and that all the new testament is filthily written.

That the woman of Samaria & her sister were whores & that Christ knew them dishonestly.

That St John the Evangelist was bed-fellow to C(hrist) and leaned alwaies in his bosome, that he used him as the sinners of Sodoma.

That all they that loue not Tobacco & Boies were fooles . . .

That if Christ would have instituted the sacrament wth more Ceremoniall Reverence it would haue bin had in more admiration, that it would haue bin much better being administred in a Tobacco pipe. . . .

A bit about coining; a bit about the Angel Gabriel; and the clincher that we know in our own day — as we know the exact tone of the informer on table talk, telephone talk, the light easy mocking talk collected and colored, used for shock purposes not as it is used in art, in writing, on the stage, but as it is used in the courts in conspiracy cases. This clincher, in an atheism case, is that one Rich Cholmley has confessed that he was persuaded "by Marloe's Reasons to become an Atheist."

Now we have Hariot mentioned for the third time (in the meantime Kyd had spoken of "Harriot, Warner, Royden and some stationers in Paules churchyard"); the School of Night and Walsingham have most to suffer here.

At ten in the morning, four men meet in a room at Deptford, across from London and a few miles east, about a third of the way to Scadbury. It was plague year, with its fevers, fear, rages against strangers; spy year again, murder year, poem year, mystery.

The docks are outside, the way to Europe. Ships come in regularly from Flushing. Did Poley, one of the four and an important government agent, implicated in the Babington Plot in a questionable way and in the Tower during 1588, arrive then from the Low Countries and meet Ingram Frizer, Nicholas Skeres, and Marlowe? The ships are docked at Deptford Strand, where also rides the *Golden Hind,* forever there since the knighting of Francis Drake until she rots and falls apart. Frizer and Skeres are Walsingham's men, also; Hotson has established them, as part of his extraordinary hunting and finding, spies and conny-catchers. Poley was a courier between

Denmark and England, the Low Countries and England, and in government employ during this period. Both Royden and Marlowe had planned to go to Scotland in the early months of the year, on the Queen's business, and Poley had in fact gone to the court of King James.

This morning they were in the house of Eleanor Bull — not a listed tavern, all we see of it is a room and a garden, where these four men meet, have dinner during the day and after dinner talk, walk in the garden until six in the evening. Then they have supper.

It is after supper that the thing happens. It is reported fully, but very curiously in the coroner's statement made on June 1. The story is of a quarrel about the bill, *le recknynge*. Christopher Marlowe is lying on a bed in the room where they supped; Ingram Frizer and Marlowe "uttered one to the other divers malicious words."

Ingram Frizer, in this telling, is sitting at the table with his back to Marlowe, quarreling. The other two men are sitting on either side of Frizer. According to the coroner's statement, Marlowe suddenly drew the dagger "of the said Ingram which was at his back," and "then & there maliciously gave the aforesaid Ingram two wounds on his head of the length of two inches and of the depth of a quarter of an inch."

Then Frizer struggled with Marlowe for the 12-penny dagger; he was not able to get away, but got the dagger, and stabbed Marlowe over the eye, "a mortal wound over the right eye of the depth of two inches & of the width of one inch; of which mortal wound the aforesaid Christopher Morley then & there instantly died."

Was his blood, streaming down over his sight, the last thing seen by Christopher Marlowe?

How could he do so little damage as was done to Frizer's head, if he was behind Frizer and in a position of advantage?

Why did Poley and Skeres not help? Why were they not asked what they were doing during the fight?

Was Marlowe knifed from behind as he lay in bed?

Why was the charge against Frizer reduced? Why was he freed at once and back in Sir Thomas Walsingham's employ the day after his release from prison? Why was Kyd refused employment and left masterless after his torture and release?

It has been suggested that this was a political murder, covered with a net of lies; that it was a homosexual murder; it has been suggested that Ralegh considered that the School of Night was threatened, and commanded this killing. It has been suggested that Walsingham, not Ralegh, had Marlowe killed; it has been suggested that Walsingham, used the help of Frizer, Poley and Skeres to get some sailor drunk at Deptford Strand, kill him, dress him in Marlowe's clothes, and see that Marlowe took ship for the continent, where he is alive and well and writing plays.

There are only three possible choices, says A. D. Wraight. "The first is to assume that Frizer's story is absolutely true," and this has been doubted since Leslie Hotson's discovery in 1925. "The second is to hold that Thomas Walsingham murdered Marlowe. The third will make all Shakespearian scholars quake. Namely the suggestion put forth by Mr. Calvin Hoffman that Walsingham, who was more personally and deeply concerned for Kit's safety, and probably also for the repercussions that might eventually ensue for the members of the School of Night, engineered not his murder but his escape by means of his 'death' and substituted another corpse."

Another theory has Marlowe filled with wine and killed in Eleanor Bull's house, by men of Ralegh's; A. D. Wraight says of this, "In order to do so" it is necessary to represent Ralegh "as an unscrupulous arch-Machiavellian ready to resort to murder for fear that Marlowe will blab under torture and implicate himself and others of the School of Night in the charges of atheism levelled against Marlowe, as Kyd had done before him.

"This, however, is not the picture of Ralegh which the full testimony of his life affords. Ralegh's true nobility of character and singularly fearless attitude of mind do not admit of such a ready assumption; indeed, they make such an assumption preposterous. Ralegh, we know, was arrogant and careless of public opinion as was Marlowe . . .

"That Ralegh, Northumberland, and many others of this circle would have been in sympathy with Kit in his troubles is self-evident, for they were constantly harried with similar accusations. That they would have stooped to have him murdered as some kind of sacrificial lamb is scarcely credible."

There is a sacrifice here. Is it to the School of Night? Is it to Shakespeare? Is it to truth, since the story is covered-over, "apparently by deliberate fabrication in the 'wonderfull yeare' 1593"?

Marlowe's poetry, and above all this story of the murder of Marlowe, evokes the angers and passions of the hearers according to their own wounds. Do they hate spies? poets? drinkers? homosexuals? mockers? Kyd's letter defending himself against atheism, says to clear himself:

"For more assurance that I was not of that vile opinion, Lett it but please your Lordship to enquire of such as he conversed with, that is (as I am given to understand) with Hariot, Warner, Royden, and some stationers in Paules churchyard, whom I in no sort can accuse nor will accuse by reason of his company; of whose consent if I had been, no question but I also should have been of their consort, for ex minimo vestigio artifex agnoscit artificem." (The craftsman recognizes [discriminates?] art by the slightest trace.)

Hariot did not defend himself in this; but he was not directly charged. In a way, he had stated his position in *A Brief and True Report;* in another, through the working papers which provide one trace of him.

Ralegh answered consciously in his *History*. There we find the response taken from the book of Daniel, where the four kinds of wise men are differentiated: wise men, astrologers, magicians, or soothsayers. Ralegh says, "Daniel in his second chapter nameth foure kindes of those Wise-men : Arieli, Magi, Malefici, and Chaldæi. Arieli the old Latine translation calleth Sophistas . . . or Physicos, or Philosophers, or (according to the note of Vatablus) Naturalists." He is speaking of the kinds of magic, or philosophy condemned, for he says, "As dogs bark at those they know not, so they condemn and hate the things they understand not."

When Ralegh writes this, he speaks of His Majesty; he is in a future age, writing of demons from within walls, not as he is now, among the pleasant fields of Sherborne, where he means to build a castle. Sherborne the loved. But in this future, he stretches his hand out to the sciences, remembering Nicholas of Cusa.

"Indeed not only these natural knowledges are condemned by those that are ignorant; but the Mathematicks also and Professors thereof : though those, that are excellently learned, judge of it in this sort : *In the Glasse of the Mathematicks that Truth doth shine, which is sought in every kind of knowledge; not in an obscuring, but in a neer and manifest representation.*"

In the plague years of 1592 and 1593, there were no plague-hospitals in the county of London. It was the arrival of the great carrack, the *Madre de Dios,* with her £150,000 of plunder — of which everyone but Ralegh had huge share, the merchants making one hundred per cent on their investment — that began the building of the first hospital.

On May 10, 1593, the Court of Aldermen ordered the next Common Council to move "that the surplusage of all such money as shall be raised of the sale of the Carrack goods allotted to this City over and above twelve thousand pounds may be employed toward the building of a house for receiving of infected persons." In April, 1595, it was not yet finished. In 1597, repairs were ordered, and a brick wall and gate were built. In 1603 — still unfinished. This was the pesthouse of St. Bartholomew's Hospital. In the summer of the same year, the plague was running through Hampstead, and the streets of London, where they scattered flowers for the burial of "maids of any sort" and wore rosemary for bachelors; the sick died under hedges, and in the Cages ("both in the Liberties and Suburbs") according to Sir William Waad, the prisoners were dying, sometimes three in a cage.

The riches of the carrack went out in various ways. One of the most fertile was that manuscript on China which was taken from the *Madre de Dios* and presented to Richard Hakluyt, and "the great Italian map, taken in the *Madre de Dios,* which I have translated and caused to be drawn for the company," the East India Company.

Hariot and Ralegh rode down to Cerne Abbas. It was late March; variable beyond the usual variousness of Dorset spring. The shepherds they passed herded flocks with a few newborn lambs, and many full ewes. In Long Burton, they rode along the wall, then past the common, and the farms and granges. First flowers were out in the roadside, thicker as they came to the lowlands beyond the hills near Great Minturn; and the place where three roads meet, at Little Minturn, was flooded again; the horses splashed. Up Cerne was far and high at the right, where Ralegh kept his hunting lodge.

Their company rode on. Last summer had been pierced by Marlowe's death, last fall by the birth of Ralegh's second son, named for him. Murder, birth, and God were the subjects of their speech; deeply, in talk through the night, Marlowe's death haunting them with its implications for Hariot of wizardry and his religion, which went so deep and was called by many atheism; and Ralegh's religion and his searching mind, which in politics was now suspect. Many thought he had been involved in Marlowe's murder, that Marlowe had indeed been murdered so that he might never speak about Ralegh, and that Ralegh — like Hariot — was an atheist, and that Ralegh was a liar. But Ralegh wrote,

> The mind in searching causes is never quiet till it come to God, and the will never is satisfied with any good till it comes to the immortal goodness.

Hariot and Ralegh were summoned to be arraigned before a Court sitting in Cerne. They rode down, and the hill with the Cerne Giant rose up on their left.

Out of the hillside, earth-graven through turf and soil to the chalk underneath, a White Giant stands and has likely stood since before Saxon times. Tall, 180 feet high, squarely drawn, small-headed, he stands over the countryside in power. Joachim Maass writes, "The natural possesses great magic, and when it appears in human form, exercises a magical power on all who come in contact with it."

In the Cerne Giant, this is a phallic power. The strong erect phallus, "which is primarily and obviously the 'intention' of the figure," is "well and firmly drawn" pointing straight upward; Cerne Abbas people know that "modern eyes, waywardly pre-occupied, do not seem to have observed that an axis scribed vertically along its length would follow a true east orientation." That is, this is a sight-line art which takes phallic power, human power, right to the rising of the sun at daybreak of the festival, and stands during all the rest of time to remind us of all power.

Cerne Abbas is the abbey town named for the early God (or as others say, for St. Augustine striking his staff into the ground of a well and saying, Cerno Deum, I see God — a "completely inaccurate and idiotic legend," our historian writes). The abbots wisely did not destroy the giant, but, thinking of a hoped-for pagan powerlessness, left him.

The town has always been connected with the old religion. And here were these interrogations, part of the hunt and struggle against "witchcraft."

The first of the occasions that had brought this local court down on Ralegh and his half-brother, Carew Ralegh, and Hariot, was a dinner-party of the summer before, at Sir George Trenchard's. They were arguing back and forth in the mixed sounds and talk of men at dinner, when the sound was stopped by Carew Ralegh.

"The soul," said Carew, "what is that?"

Three of the questions of the interrogatory, given in the name of Elizabeth, involved Hariot particularly. They were the first three, preserved in Harleian 6349, as :

1. Imprimis. Whom do you know, or have harde to be suspected of Atheisme, or Apostacye? And in what manner doe you knowe or have harde the same? And what other notice can you geive thereof?

2. Whom do you knowe, or haue harde, that have argued or spoken againste, or as doubtinge, the Beinge of any God? or what or where God is? And to sweare by God, addinge if there be a God, or such like; and when and where was the same? And what other notice can you geive of any such offender?

3. Whom you you knowe or have harde that hoth spoken against God His providence over the world? or of the worldes beginninge or endinge? or of predestination, or of Heaven, or of Hell, or of the Resurreccion, in doubtful, or contenciouse manner? When & where was the same? And what other notice can you geive of anye such offender? . . .

There were six more such questions, driven straight at this group of men associated with Ralegh and through him with Marlowe. The questions about God are rather like the questions about communism in our own time in the way they are framed for dogma and to *get* a person as prey; they are hunters' questions, with the same end the hunter has.

The hearings were held in the town of Cerne Abbas; the horsemen taking the left turning down Abbey Street from the square. At its far end is the abbey gatehouse, and down the lane, the river. The abbey's fish-ponds and gardens were here, divided from the town by the pib-stoned lane. A row of Tudor dwellings were quite new at the time of the hearings, and local officials coming in would stay in this block. The officials now were Thomas Howard, Lord Bindon; Sir Ralph Horsey; Chancellor Francis James; and two others.

Indictments had served their purposes before. In the time of

Henry VIII's commissioners, the information that the Abbot "matted with his concubynes" in the house of his cellarer in Abbey Street, had been given here. The place where the commission met was the Nags Head, a famous Cerne Abbas inn, which is thought to have included the house nextdoor.

This house can still be seen. It is called Barnwell's, and the Moores live there now. It is kept in warmth, color and kind hospitality, and Mrs. Moore has shown a stranger the room in which Hariot and Ralegh were heard.

Down the street is the shop of Hodges, the bootmaker, with its two bow-windows. This establishment was making boots for Ralegh when he lived at Up Cerne; and boots seem to come into this story.

Parsons, churchwardens, and curates were sworn in. John Jesopp, minister of Gillinghame, swore that he could say nothing of his own knowledge. "I have heard," he testified, "that one Hirryott of Sir Walter Rawleigh's house hath brought the godhedd in question. And the whole course of the scriptures."

Heard, you say? Of whom have you heard this?

"I do not remember."

Nicholas Jefferys, the parson of Wyke Regis, said he did not know of his own knowledge of any atheist in Dorset.

"But I have heard," he added, "that one Hariot, has been convented before the Lords of the Council for denying the resurrection of the body."

Another minister swore against Hariot — among all the testimony against Ralegh and Carew Ralegh. This was Thomas Norman of Weymouth Melcombe Regis. He, too, has heard nothing, but has heard Mr. Jones say . . . and Mr. Jones said about Thomas Allen of Portland Castle . . . and Allen was said to have torn two leaves out of a Bible to dry tobacco on . . . and Allen, said Mr. Jones' son, spoke "as if he denied the immortality of the soul."

"And I heard," said Norman, "that Hariot was suspected of atheism."

Some of this testimony is about a horse, taken for a post

horse by the Ralegh brothers from Jefferys, who begged for the
horse to be given back to him, saying he had to preach tomorrow, and had been gone a long time. He said that Carew answered, "Your horse shall preach before you."

And at dinner at Sir George Trenchard's, Carew saying, "The
soul? What is that?" Mr. Ironside spoke, and Ralegh spoke.
Ironside said, "It is a matter rather to be believed than dis-
puted."

And Walter Ralegh said, "Yet I pray you, for our learning,
let us know." The talk began, with Actus primus corporis
organici vitam habens in potestate, and what the divines said.
But what is that actus primus or immortal substance?

He again answered, "It is the soul."

Some men laughed. "Not sufficient answer." "Not like a
scholar." But Ironside said they were principia and could go no
further; and then they asked What is a man? But nobody could
remember what the answer was.

And Ironside's son says that this report is not like the conversation at all.

One other part of the examination is hotly argued, the two
women and Robert Hyde denying the whole thing. Francis
Scarlett, minister of Sherborne, swore that Thomas Allen's
servant Oliver was coming home from a sermon at Lillington
with Elizabeth Whetcombe and Mrs. Brewer. Oliver very sleepy
and objecting to the sermon — it was in the church where the
Ralegh baby had been baptized and at about the same time,
about Michaelmas. Mrs. Brewer was going on about what a
good sermon it was, and what a good man they had in the
minister.

"He used many words," objected Oliver; "he might have
ended in fewer."

Mrs. Whetcombe said stoutly, "He did nothing but out of the
word of God."

"The word of God!" said Oliver, "he said that Moses had
52 whores!"

"Whores says I," said Mrs. Whetcombe.

"Nay concubines," said Oliver.

Mrs. Brewer was exercised. "It was Solomon that he meant!" She looked down her nose. "Go home to sleep!"

Horsey never testified, even though he had been present at the dinner at George Trenchard's.

Francis Scarlett brings one other touch of Dorset into the record. A little before Christmas, he said, Robert Hyde the shoe-maker was standing in his doorway, saw the minister pass, and called to him. "Here is a company about this town," said the shoemaker, "saying hell is no other than poverty and penury in this world. And heaven is no other but to be rich, and enjoy pleasures.

"They say we die like beasts, and when we are gone there is no more remembrance of us."

He also said, "There is one Lodge, a shoemaker in Sherborne, accounted an atheist."

Was this a rivalry between bootmakers? Ralegh had his boots made in Cerne Abbas, at the shop which became known for this. The shop with the two bow-windows.

Ralegh has another word, in Ironside's testimony : "I have been a scholar in Oxford, answered under a bachelor of art; talked with divers; yet hitherunto, concerning the soul, have I not by any been resolved."

"I cited Aristotle," said Ironside.

"Obscure and intricate," said Ralegh.

"It must seem so to the most present," answered Ironside, "yet the reasonable soul is a spiritual and immortal substance breathed into man by God."

"Yes but what is that substance breathed into man etc.," Ralegh said almost to himself.

"The soul, quoth I," Ironside is testifying. And he tells of the argument that followed, in which he considers himself to have given proof.

"But we have principles in our mathematics," said Ralegh, "like the whole being bigger than the sum of all its parts, and I can show it, in a table, in a window, in a man."

"But soul is a spirit," argued Ironside, "and soul and God cannot be subjected to sense."

"Marry," said Sir Walter, according to Ironside . . . but Ironside's son said no, it was not like this, not the entire argument. In the testimony, it is Ens Entium, and Ralegh asking Yes, but what is this Ens Entium? and finally breaking off, saying, "I wish that grace might be said, for that is better than this disputation." Then Ironside went home with his fellow minister.

Hariot, thinking of his Maximum and Minimum, in terms of life and death (in terms of Marlowe?), wrote :

Minimum — That will kill me by piercing and running through.
Maximum — That which will presse mee to death.

The Inquiry was disappointing, the Cerne Abbas history ends, and no capital charge could be framed from the hearsay evidence.

Ralegh's ramifying wish had gone out actively since he took over the mana of Humphrey Gilbert when the news arrived in 1583 that his half-brother was dead. Within six months, on March 25, 1584, with Adrian Gilbert and John Davis, he had a new charter. The adventurers were incorporated under a name which expressed both longings of Humphrey Gilbert, and which prefigured the teaching of the star-captains by Hariot, and the School of Night. This was "The College of the Fellowship for the Discovery of the North-West Passage."

(As I write, in 1969, with Captain Button, Captain Whitlock, John Franklin, Baffin, all, long gone, the news is full of the flights to the moon — with men and with machines, in separate, national flights — and the planned voyage over the northwest route to the new-struck oil fields off the north capes of Alaska. Our Virginia, our Guiana. It has been pointed out that there was no gold in either place, but there was petroleum, there was steel. Only if they had found petroleum, they would not have known a use for it, the machines were not yet invented. They would have screwed up their noses, and made their faces, seeing it only as one more contamination for their drinking water.)

Ralegh's lieutenant on this voyage, Lawrence Keymis, was another lifelong friend of Hariot's, undoubtedly one of the captains taught by him. Keymis comes through to us in full male clarity at two moments only — now, going to Guiana, writing the *Song of Guiana* to Hariot and on his journey far inland to "localise the floating El Dorado legends in the uplands of Guiana between the rivers Rupununi, Essequibo and Parima" — and again in Guiana with Ralegh and young Wat when two of the three men met death in their two ways.

Hariot is supposed to be responsible for the map of Guiana, now in the British Museum, and described as "drawn by or for Sir Walter Ralegh." And it is to Hariot that Keymis dedicates his *De Guiana Carmen,* published with the account of the expedition by Hakluyt, with these Latin words at the head of the Latin poem :

Ad Thomam Hariotum Matheseos, et universae Philosophiae peritissimum (that's most knowing through experience, skilled, practiced)
de Guiana Carmen, Dat. Anno 1595
Montibus est Regio, it begins, quasi muris, obsita, multis;
    Circumsepit aquis quos Raleana suis . . . .
Surrounded by many mountains as if by walls, this land;
    Around it flows those waters that are Ralegh's.
Guiana has deep bounteous entrances;
    And the free neck carries a hostile yoke.
In these hills did the Spaniard sweat and freeze
    Seven years, nine times; nor yet grew strong.
Sacred power fate is in those numbers. It is his doom
    And ours: let him return to us, I pray.
The way made open and sponsored by Walter Ralegh
    In one month; how can I celebrate this deed?
Daytime, night-time; by the oars working, by sails,
    He brought achievement through by highest skill.
Whatever expense was needed, great ones, he spared not,
    Born to devote himself to the highest good . . . .

And the laborious, devoted, verse goes on :

> Discriminating Joseph kept vigil in his danger
>   Although there was desertion, brother for brother.
> Let fame fix on the many-colored coat,
>   So was this garment torn in evil-doings.
> You read and startle. Prick up your ears, and your spirit.
>   This land has gold, and gems the color of grass.
> It is always spring there; there the prodigal earth yearly
>   Teems, it puts down the sun in fertility.
> Our England, let England be rich, be happy throughout:
>   England, backing this, will bear fruit everywhere.
> The headless men, birds, fishes, and wild beasts;
>   I stop here; through strangeness they amaze and please.
> There we explore or nowhere. Therefore we ask:
>   God grant that we possess this promised land. Amen.
>
> Your most loving
L.K.

Hariot is called Matheseos by Keymis. This is not Mathema-tician, but appears to be related to "mathesis," the term that Bruno used in his *Insomnium* and in *Idiota Triumphans,* as Frances Yates says (*Giordano Bruno and the Hermetic Tradition,* p. 296). "It is highly significant," she writes. "For 'mathesis' . . . is not mathematics, but one of the four 'guides in religion' of which the others are Love, Art, and Magic." The word swims among its meanings of learning in general and (accented differently) magic.

Not only Hariot but Northumberland was called Matheseos. George Peele writes in "The Honour of the Garter" :

> Renowned lord, Northumberland's fair flower,
> The Muses' love, patron, and favourite,
> That artisans and scholars dost embrace,
> And clothest Mathesis in rich ornaments;
> That admirable mathematic skill,
> Familiar with the stars and zodiac,
> To whom the heavens lies open as her book . . . .

We come, through Hariot, through Northumberland — and

read John Davies' poem to him here — to the crown Elizabethan figure of the Magus, Prospero. Behind him stands
Faust; but Frances Yates asks another fertile question here.
How much does Shakespeare's conception of the role of the
Magus — that is, Prospero — owe to Bruno's "reformulation
of that role in relation to the miseries of the times?" The role
and its language — which

> "captures the voices of the gods."

When Ralegh came back from Guyana — and some of his enemies said he had never gone, he had been hiding in Cornwall,
those were West Country ores he showed today — he was forty-
three years old, "a beggar and withered," in his words. He had
no gold with him, only some samples to be assayed. He spoke
of "Guiana, and that great and golden city, which the Spaniards
call El Dorado, and the naturals Manoa."

His spiritual achievement was made. Chapman saw those
seven months as an achievement of Tamburlaine's kind. During
these years when he was close to Hariot and close to Ralegh,
he urged the Queen:

> Go forth upon the waters, and create
> A golden world in this our iron age.

The two were not brought together until the sixties of the
twentieth century, although Ralegh, promising gold, had actually written of the presence of "rocks of a blue metallic color,
like unto the best steel ore," in 1596. "To the Spanish explorers
it was 'El Dorado,' a land rich in gold and diamonds. Even
today, in some river valleys after a heavy rain, motorists occa-
sionally find precious stones embedded in their tire treads. Yet
for centuries piracy and tyranny, revolution and lethargy kept
most of Guyana's wealth inviolate."

During the Second World War, reports reached the Beth-
lehem Steel Company, part of the American hunt for new

sources of steel, that fliers over Venezuela were noticing that their compasses went spinning erratically. There was iron ore below! In 1941, a rich lode was found in El Pao; and later, a subsidiary company of U.S. Steel struck a high mountain of sixty per cent iron, making it "one of the richest lodes in the world."

Guyana, the new republic that was formerly British Guiana, has been developed since 1960 by these steel companies and by the Venezuelan government. One huge part of these developments is a $45,000,000, 370,000-kilowatt dam across the Caroni River. Another is a city whose population in 1970 was 100,000 people; this city is popularly known as Ciudad Guyana. A railroad runs from the city ninety miles to the mines, and the Orinoco has been dredged for the passage of 60,000-ton ore ships.

The organization that is in charge of this program is an autonomous company, the CVG — Corporación Venezolana de Guyana. This venture has been called one of the most imaginative that man has ever taken — in American commercial terms, "instant Pittsburgh."

The formal name of Ciudad Guyana, the "astonishing metropolis," is Santo Tomé de Guyana.

Later in Ralegh's life we will come to Santo Tomé.

Many times among his working papers, Hariot deals with problems out of Alhazen and Pappus. Alhazen was a link between Hariot and Northumberland, or it may have been that Hariot introduced the seminal work of Alhazen to the Earl. This moment of introduction marked a breaking-open in Percy's life, a threshold as distinct as the one Hobbes notes, much later, when he first found Newton. Percy writes of himself among the books :

Amongst the rest, as a destinie from eternitie prepared to crosse my desires, there lay an owld *Arabian* called *Alhazen,* which with some anger I angrylie removed, it flying open perhapps by reason of a stationers thred uncutt, yet superstitiouse in my religion that it was the spirit that directed me by hidden and unconceivable meanes what was good for my almost marking nothing I light upon a place where a figure seemed somewhat more irregular than his fellowes, which caused an awakinge.

This awaking of Percy's is one of the distinct moments in this history. It has some of the qualities of Descartes' chain of dreams. It surely binds Percy to life; and in his suffering and his rage, it offered the key elements to help to solve them.

He came to this experience with anger, necessary to him as a prelude to all his important deep psychic places. He needed this, as he needed the sensation of something from eternity to cross his desires. This he could take as a sign from his personal religion that it was a spirit directing him; and by means of beauty, "hidden and unconceavable meanes."

What is it coming to him, and from what does it free him? Bound by Aristotelian terms and traditions, as the schools were, Percy comes in this moment to his full imaginative life and his liberation.

There did I behold a demonstration declaring the hight of the aier with no small wonder, because it had eno bene taught me, *Nullum vacuum in rerum natura.* Unchaining my mynd from the former conceites to behold the project of this great promiser, I studied by still interrupted with the worthes of my Mistris which had sealed deeper impression in my memory.

This passage opens one of the links, not only between Hariot and Percy — and we will have more of *Vacuum* and *Nihil* — but between this kind of thought and the life of flesh. For, as the last sentence sets before us, Percy has set himself to make arguments that might come straight out of *Love's Labour's Lost,* for the discrepancy in life of mind and a mistress.

Keats, in his "night encounter" with Chapman's Homer, saw the edition that contains the poem to Hariot. His friend,

Thomas Hariot. Even with the wrong details, this is taken to be his portrait.

Moon drawing by Hariot, with photograph of moon (below).

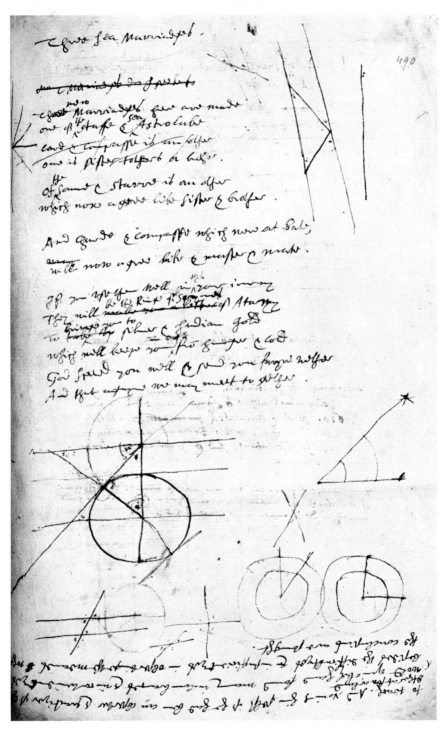

A poem among the diagrams. Hariot's "Three Sea Marriages" from his papers.

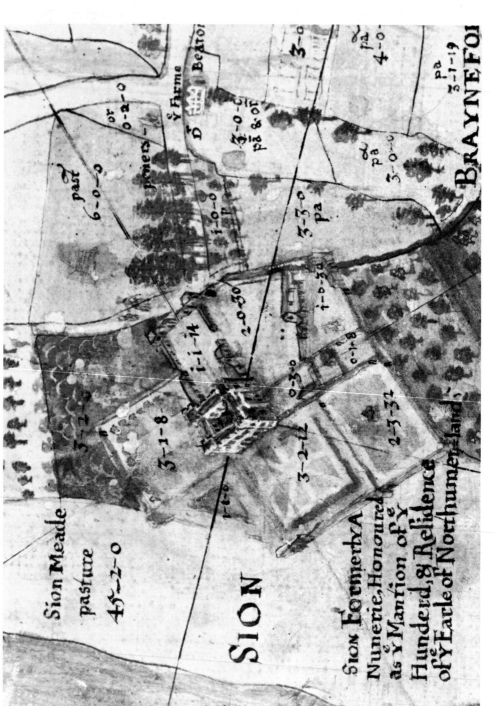

Glover's Plan, a picture map of Syon House showing where Hariot lived.

Sir Walter Ralegh with his son, Wat.

Queen Elizabeth

Henry Percy, Ninth Earl of Northumberland, young. Portrait by Nicholas Hilliard.

John Donne.

Giordano Bruno.

Taken to be the young Shakespeare.

Elizabeth Throckmorton (Lady Ralegh).

Dorothy Devereux (Countess of Northumberland).

Northumberland as The Wizard Earl. By Van Dyke.

Pleasure Trip

How They Catch Fish

Chief Lady and Child

Woman, Child, Doll

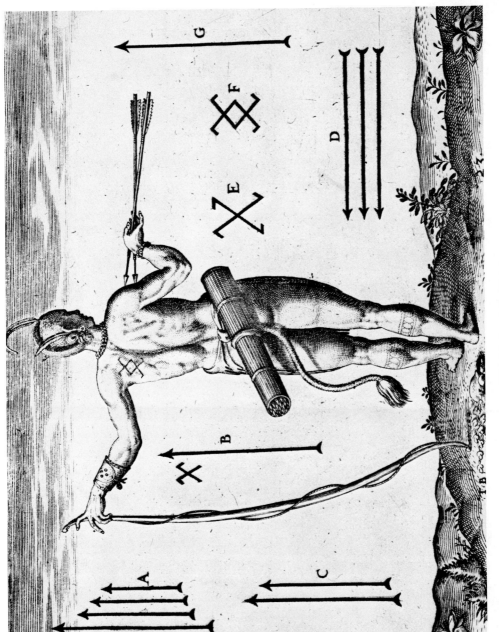

The Marks of the Chief

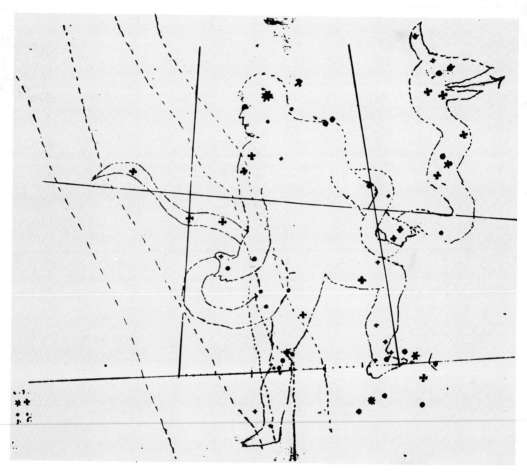

Drawing of the constellation Ophiucus. The struggle with the serpent.

Charles Cowden Clarke, and Keats found a copy belonging to an editor of *The Times* and parted "at day-spring" after reading. In that excitement, Keats walked home and wrote his sonnet, which Keats sent to Clarke to reach him at ten o'clock next morning.

The sonnet is a celebration of discovery. It begins in the terms of the young poet in his finding of Chapman — or of Homer through Chapman : this is the octave of the sonnet, moving through "realms of gold" : and then, continuing in the language of seeing with which the sonnet begins, the sestet moves to two other kinds of seeing, that of the astronomer,

> Then felt I like some watcher of the skies
> When a new planet swims into his ken;

and the other kind of seeing, that of the American explorer, the smiting of his own strong sight with discovery — and every schoolboy knows that Cortez has here been substituted for Balboa; but the curious thing is that in English history it is Hariot, and only Hariot, who combines in his one life the experience of astronomer and American explorer, although it is a necessary stroke of the poet to use the name "Cortez" instead of the other and the discovery of the next ocean instead of any other. The sky, the ocean — they are right.

> Or like stout Cortez when with eagle eyes
> He stared at the Pacific — and all his men
> Look'd at each other with a wild surmise
> Silent, upon a peak in Darien.

The poem, the planet, the ocean : these are the emblems of discovery. But it is of discovery itself that Keats is writing, and the deep inner event is found in its three reflections. "It is an internal sky, attained through meditations induced by the reading of a book," says the master-critic Kenneth Burke, of this sonnet. He suggests that "the poet is here coming upon a new internal sky, ... through identification with the enactments of Chapman's translation."

Keats binds the kinds of discovery — the inward crisis of finding in poetry, and the explorer's seeing of new sky and new ocean — in the same way that he binds beauty and truth (or poetry and science) in the binding that is his strength.

It is certainly not possible to assert that this conscious opening for Keats is related to the Chapman dedication (did he know who Hariot was? did he ask? was his question answered? or left unanswered, to haunt him with the word of Chapman's poem : "soul-loved," "perfect eye," "staring ignorance," "glowing and amazed eyes"?). It is not even possible to say that Keats read this poem; nor to find Hariot emerging from a poem on discovery. It is possible only to say that Chapman set his accompanying lines with *Achilles Shield*, and wrote over them, of the man who in himself made bonds among astronomy, many kinds of exploration, and poetry :

TO MY ADMIRED AND SOUL-

LOVED FRIEND

Master of all essential and true knowledge,

M. Hariot

The poem begins in full praise :

> To you whose depth of soul measures the height,
> And all dimensions of all works of weight,
> Reason being ground, structure and ornament,
> To all inventions, grave and permanent,
> And your clear eyes the Spheres where Reason moves;

To Hariot's eyes he sends blind Homer :

> This Artisan, this God of rational loves
> Blind Homer; in this shield . . .
> I send for censure . . .

It is to Hariot, for his praise, that Chapman sends the work. He speaks of being a servant.

> Virtue must wait on wealth; we must make friends
> Of the unrighteous Mammon

146

he says, and the entire system of patronage, in which both he and Hariot worked, glares in its other aspect. But then Chapman comes again to Hariot himself :

> Rich mine of knowledge, O that my strange muse
> Without this body's nourishment could use
> Her zealous faculties, only t'aspire,
> Instructive light from your whole Sphere of fire . . .

It is Hariot's wholeness, as well as his fire, that emerges.

> O had your perfect eye Organs to pierce
> Into that Chaos whence this stifled verse
> By violence breaks : where Gloweworm like doth shine
> In nights of sorrow, this hid soul of mine :
> And how her genuine forms struggle for birth,
> Under the claws of this foul Panther earth;
> Then under all those forms you should discern
> My love to you, in my desire to learn.
> Skill and the love of skill do ever kiss :
> No band of love so strong as knowledge is;
> Which who is he that may not learn of you,
> Whom learning doth with his light's throne endow?

Chapman says to Hariot — "your emperie of spirit and soul . . ." He says to him, "Yet your self shall shine . . ." He says

> And when thy writings that now errors Night
> Chokes earth with mists, break forth like eastern light . . .

He sees Nature crowned with Hariot's soul, whose brightness shows what true man is . . .

Again and again in Chapman's writings, the breathing of Hariot is felt. A key speech of Clarence's, in that curious play *Sir Giles Goosecap* (now attributed to Chapman), is close to Hariot, or to any man who binds science, poetry, exploration. The *Shadow of Night* is a poem that meets an assumption current among us, that "Chapman was one of a group of men, including Ralegh and Marlowe, who were interested in pushing science and philosophy beyond the bounds of contemporary beliefs and decorum, a group bound together by a common curiosity, suspected of being atheists and hence condemned by most of their fellows, but mocked by Shakespeare in his *Love's Labour's Lost* as 'the school of night.' "

The other direct reference to Hariot is in Chapman's Homer, whose Preface to the Reader says,

> Only some one or two places I have shewed to my worthy and most learned friend, Mr. Hariot, for his censure how much mine owre weighed : whose judgment and learning in all kinds, I know to be incomparable, and bottomless : yea, to be admired as much, as his most blameless life, and the right sacred expense of his time, is to be honored and reverenced. Which affirmation of his clear unmatchedness in all manner of learning; I make in contempt of that nasty objection often thrust upon me; that he that will judge, must know more than he of whom he judges; for so a man would know neither God nor himself.
>
> Another right learned, honest and entirely loved friend of mine, Mr. Robert Hews, I must needs put into my confest conference concerning Homer, though very little more *than I had* with Mr. Hariot. Which two, I protest, are all, and preferred to all. Nor charge I their authorities with any allowance of my general labour; but only of those one or two places, which for instances of my innovation, and how it shewed to them, I imparted.

What does "blameless" mean to Chapman? Guiana meant many things to him; see his poem *De Guiana*. It is gold —

> Guiana, whose rich feet are mines of gold,
> Whose forehead knocks against the roof of Stars . . .

It is to be created, "A golden world in this our iron age." And gold means many things, has many faces and voices,

> You will lose gold, for which you lose your souls —

Chapman knows gold and power :

> You that know death lives, where power lies unused —

He speaks of Ralegh here, in 1596, at the time of the second voyage, as sent to discover by Elizabeth —

Th' industrious Knight, the soul of this exploit,
Dismissing him to convoy of his stars.

Chapman, the poet of many-gleaming night in all its meanings;
of many-gleaming gold, and gleaming Homer, turns these in
love, gleaming on Hariot.

One shouting, brute, triumphant pain; and Essex, Ralegh,
Donne on the final raid on Cadiz in 1597, with the clear shout
of "Entramos!" and the throwing of the hat into the sea and
Essex and Ralegh, enemies and rivals and suddenly in one
sexual martial moment of coming-together, at last joined;
and then the fire, the men falling like coals into the water, the
sacking and burning of the whole town of Cadiz, so that it
had to be rebuilt from the ground. And Ralegh, struck by an
arrow-storm of splinters from the deck where a cannon-ball
ruined his knee so that he limped on a stick for the rest of his life.

But Donne said, after this : A third of my library is Spanish
books.

And the Spaniards say : But this is where the English learned
what Spanish wine is.

There is a sea between his demands and her commands.

It was after the middle of Michaelmas term; Elizabeth had
come to dine at Twickenham with Francis Bacon, who had
"prepared a sonnet" for her. She, thinking always of Essex in
Ireland, his demands, that sea; thinking of the surgings in the
realm, and of what might be a proper punishment for the book
about the first year of Henry IV. There was Bacon's sonnet,
"tending to draw on Her Majesty's reconcilement to mr Lord."
And the book which was a "seditious prelude to put into the
peoples heads boldness and faction," she raged. It could not be
the author whose name was signed, it must be some other
man; she would find him, and have him racked to pro-

149

duce the real author. And did not Bacon find treason here?

"For treason, sure I found none; but for felony, very many places."

"Wherein?" asked Elizabeth.

"The author has committed very apparent theft; he has taken most of the sentences of Tacitus, and translated them into English, and put them in his text."

The Queen persisted. She would have him racked.

"Nay, Madam," said Bacon, "he is a Doctor, never rack his person, but rack his style; let him have pen, ink, and paper, and help of books, and be enjoined to continue the story where it breaketh off, and I will undertake, by collating the styles, to judge whether he were the author, or no."

She asked continually about the case of Essex; Bacon answered ever that these were faults which the law might term contempts. He told her, "My Lord is an eloquent and well-spoken man; besides his eloquence of nature or art, he has an eloquence of accident, which passes them."

When Devonshire was named for the place in Ireland, and not long before he went, Elizabeth spoke again of these things, to Bacon, and Whitehall.

"Surely, Madam," said Bacon, "if you mean not to employ my Lord of Essex thither again, your Majesty cannot make a better choice," speaking of Devonshire. He was going on when Elizabeth interrupted him.

With great passion, "Essex," said she, "whensoever I send Essex back again into Ireland, I will marry you, claim it of me."

"Well, Madam," Bacon answered smiling, "I will release that contract, if his going be for the good of the state."

Toward the end of Easter term, things had come to a head. Elizabeth said to Bacon that she had found his words true. "The proceedings in the Star Chamber have done no good," she said; "they have rather kindled factious bruits than quenched them. Therefore I am determined now, for the satisfaction of the world, to proceed against my Lord in the Star Chamber by an information *ore tenus*, and to have my Lord brought to his answer. Howbeit," she assured Bacon, "whatsoever I do shall be towards my Lord, *ad castigationem et non ad destructionem.*"

Bacon answered her in words that carry their echo : "Madam, if you will have me to speak to you in this argument, I must speak to you as Friar Bacon's head spoke, that said : first, *Time is*, and then *Time was*, and *Time will never be.*"

It was late in November, with a little cold young moon shining for four hours, a still evening — "calm and variable," said the almanac — just before snow-cold. A good day to let the melancholic blood : Thursday, November 23, 1598.

Hariot was writing four lines of verse. He wrote them, went over them keenly, and changed their order, setting their numbers in the arrangement he wanted :

4. If more be more & lesse be lesse
3. Lesse by lesse brings lesse of lesse
2. Lesse by more brings lesse of more
1. More by more must needs bring more

He set the date under the four lines, took another sheet of paper, and wrote, making his changes as he wrote. Finally :

If more by more must needes make more
Then lesse by more makes lesse of more
And lesse by lesse makes lesse of lesse
If more be more and lesse be lesse

Yet lesse of lesse makes lesse or more
The which is best keep less in store
If lesse of lesse thou wilt make lesse
Then take the same from that is lesse.

But if the same thou wilt make more
Then adde to it the signe of more
The rule of more is best to use
Yet for some cause thou it refuse

So both are one, for both are true
Of this inough and so adeu.

At York House, the Lord Keeper was holding Essex for insurrection in his fury and welter; Anne More was there, and Sir George More of Loseley, her father, when he was in London. Donne had been with Essex at Cadiz and in 1597, in the Azores expedition, and now, in 1599, Donne was secretary to Sir Thomas Egerton, the Lord Keeper, and Essex was his prisoner. "A sort of semi-durance," Gosse calls the time, when Essex was under Egerton's personal charge for over nine months. In the last month of these, the trial of Essex was held at York House.

The following February, in the culminating act of Essex' life of flame and fascination and madness, he left York House, went the short way to his own house, and was followed by the delegation sent to recall him to his loyalty to Elizabeth. Egerton was a member of this group, and Donne was there in his train, although he was surely not admitted through the wicket to the confrontation. The Queen's envoys were surrounded; the courtyard was full and buzzing like a wasp's nest, says Camden, with Essex "half demented," shouting and whirling his arms, obliterated from view and rising high again. "Away my Lord," came the cry, and "They abuse you," "They betray you," "They undo you." Egerton then put on his hat and said loudly, "My Lord, let us speak with you privately and understand your griefs."

Essex left the delegation in his book chamber, guarded by men with musket, and the procession of the Earl and two hundred of his young men went through the streets of the City, Essex shouting, "For the Queen! For the Queen! A plot is laid for my life!" until Burleigh and the Garter King at Arms entered the City and proclaimed Essex and his accomplices to be traitors.

In the acts that followed, Essex, in torment, declared that England was being assigned to the Infanta of Spain. Being barred from return to Essex House, he turned aside to Queenhithe with those who would not leave him, and went by water to Essex Stairs. The Councillors had gone; and Essex set about to burn some papers and a book, and "a black bag that he wore about his neck."

His sister, Lady Rich, and his Countess were allowed to leave. Essex hoped for an hour or two to fortify the place by which they would go. Sometimes he thought of yeilding, sometimes he resolved to force his way out, being encouraged by Lord Sandys, "more aged than the rest," who said that "the resolutest counsels are the safest."

The Lord Admiral had besieged the house to landwards, and now began to consider the conditions upon which Essex said he would yield, saying that for these he would make intercession to the Queen. At ten o'clock at night, in torchlight, the Essex men came out. Essex and Southampton were taken to Lambeth, to the Archbishop's house across the river. The night was dark, and the cascades at the Bridge made it impossible to take the prisoners to the Tower.

The report of the "tumult" was brought to Elizabeth at dinner. Camden reports her as saying only that He that had placed her in that seat would preserve her in it; "and so she continued at her dinner, not showing any sign of fear or distraction of mind, nor omitting anything this day that she hath been accustomed to do at other times."

Eleven days later, at the trial in Westminster Hall, the confrontation between Sir Walter Ralegh and the Earl of Essex took place in full fury and legality, with Coke as Attorney, and Bacon calling on his friend and master to "confess and not to justify."

Too much happened: no confession would have changed the course of this agon. Among the things Essex had burned before his capture was the correspondence with James VI, in which Essex undoubtedly urged the Scottish king, as the successor named to England, to come and take the throne from Elizabeth. The crevasse of jealousy between Essex and Ralegh was full of teeth. Ralegh had written to Cecil his "tyrant" letter, always construed to be against Essex, and when James did come to the throne, he always called Essex "my martyr" and his vengeance against Ralegh uncoiled and uncoiled forever. But, perhaps most of all, the words that killed Essex were his own poison words against Elizabeth : "Her mind is as crooked as her carcass."

On the Saturday night before Essex was taken, Ralegh ordered Sir Ferdinando Gorges, the Governor of Plymouth Fort, to Durham House; but Essex advised Gorges to set a rendezvous on the river, on neutral water. Early Sunday morning, Ralegh came across the mists, unattended in his boat. Gorges, with two men, drew alongside. Ralegh at once advised Gorges, who was his cousin, to return to the fleet, but Gorges spoke of the action to come, and said there were 2000 gentlemen "who have resolved this day to live or die free men."

Ralegh did not see what they could do against the Queen's authority.

"It is the abuse of the Queen's authority by you and others that makes so many honest men desire a reformation thereof."

Musket shots barked across water. Four shots from a follower of Gorges missed Ralegh. Now Gorges saw four men putting off from Essex Stairs toward Ralegh; these men also had muskets. He told his cousin to escape, and Ralegh's boat rowed to Whitehall.

The four Court officials came to Essex later that morning, expecting an uprising in the City.

Now, at the trial, it was openly Essex against Ralegh at last. When Sir Walter was called and his oath given him, Essex said, "What booteth it to swear the fox?"

Debate and pity, but not long. Both Southampton and Essex were sentenced to be "hanged, bowelled and quartered."

In the Tower, he was reviled by his chaplain, Master Abdy Ashton. "However you would colour it with other pretences, your end was an ambitious seeking of the crown, the hope

whereof for your own raising made these men to follow, ani-
mate and applaud you; so that if by a true confession and un-
feigned repentance you do not unburden yourself of these sins,
you shall carry out of the world a guilty soul before God, and
leave upon your memorial an infamous name to posterity."

He now confessed his sorrow to the four Lords of the Council.
On the 23rd, the Usher of the Black Rod for the Order of the
Garter went to the Tower and pulled the George and the Gar-
ter from Essex' neck. His sisters, who had welcomed him back
to Essex House after his release almost a year before, are not
mentioned. But now Dorothy finds an agony to match Henry
Percy's impossible sorrow for his father. All the hopes from the
Queen having become an axe.

Ralegh was there, between seven and eight on Ash Wednesday morning. He saw Essex enter the enclosure for the scaffold,
a place three yards square, railed round, in the high court above
Caesar's Tower. Essex came from his lodging, dressed in a
gown of wrought velvet, a satin suit and felt hat, all black. He
was calling on God, and asking the three divines and the
others with him to pray for him.

Ralegh was asked why he was there, and declared that he
expected Essex to make objections against him, and he pro-
posed to answer. But the others begged him not to let Essex
see him as he was killed, "not to press upon the Earl at his
death," and Ralegh withdrew to the Armoury, and looked on
from behind the stone frame of a window.

Hariot was with Ralegh, or took down that day what
Ralegh told him of Essex' last words. The State Papers and
Camden give in full a long speech. Hariot has set down only
one sentence; it has the ring of truth in death. It is to be found
on a page of spherical triangles, among all the folios that work
out problems in triangulation for a globe. It is down at the
corner, upside down. There is no date, no comment; but these
are in full early-morning clarity, the last words of the Earl
of Essex :

> "Lord forgeve me this Horrible sinne, this bloody & crying
> shame."

Then he fit his head to the block, and said, "Executioner, strike home. Come Lord Jesus, come Lord Jesus . . ."

In the midst of which the executioner struck.

He had to strike three times, says Camden, but neither arms, body nor head stirred; then he lifted up the head saying "God save the Queen."

Camden's report ends, "The hangman as he returned from the Tower was beaten by the people, so that the sheriffs of London were called to assist and rescue him else he had been murdered."

In May and June, 1599, Hariot was occupied with an experiment, closely observed and recorded in the papers which we have. This work has elements of the chemistry of metals, possibly of close packing, and, in its terms, of alchemy.

The experiment was interrupted only once. May 6th and 7th are empty, because Hariot went to London. From internal evidence, it appears that the experiment was conducted at Syon House.

This is a transcript from his notes;

"The imposition was at 4h¼ after noon; the 2 of May being Wednesday. 1599. at which time the matter lay as above.

"As hy as the line in about the playne where the glasse beginneth to narrow, there were ———— drops at the [word illegible], but all clear above.

"At 6h, there were some broad beades of dew and loose bodies at a and b.

"At 7h there was a fine misty dew of silver color up to the line b, which is the very plane that the copper pan did circulate or compasse.

"At 8h I found a fine dew as hy as c which is an inch & a half hyer than b, with some of the hyest part turning into bigger drops.

"At which time I noted two drops, one south, & the other west, within ½ inch of the ———— [mother?]

"At 10h the next drop was proved to be longer & parallel to the matter.

"N——— there was a drop within half an inch of the mother and another East.

"NE there was a drop bigger than his fellows an inch & ½ above the others. Which as I was noting brake & trickled downe. Some from c then trickled down to b. About c there is nothing on the glasse but a silvery little thin mist.

"The long west drop before mentioned went down & vanished."

These observations continue until 3 ½ ho in the morning when Hariot writes "Ignis extinguitur."

"Terra. May 3.

"At 10 of the clock in the morning I found all in the same forme as I left it. The drops between c & b as before. The silver or milky dew between b & a also, but all the lower region under a which before was full of sprinkled great drops vanished and were now all gone. & a clear glasse.

The aforesaid easterly drops were also cleane gone

"Now only appearing under the S a round drop like a bubble.

"SE. 4 copper drops one lyeth upon another. W. some small drops. NW. a great drop . . .

———

"May 4. I looked diverse times. I found all in the same manner as I left but that the dew & drops in all playces were lesse . . .

———

"May 5. h 11 AM. The low part of the lake was clear. The other parts less diminished [?] . . . but in the same forme.

"I went to London.

"May 8. ♂. hor. 11 AM. I returned, at what time I found as I lefte it in forme but that the lowest parte of the second region, much of it was cleare of ——— between b and a where the silver dew was a great part as [?] yet . . .

"May 9.

"May 11. I found one of the southwesterly drops, that lay on the top of the silver region fallen down to the bottome, this way appearing on the side of the glasse.

"The little bubbles that were between S & E I saw were quite gone & between N & E unto the N not so big . . .

"Terra.

"May 13. hora 10. for an hour I gave fire in which time nothing did _____ but 2 hours after the fire was out all the lower region was full of a dew or little small drops."

The notes continue to May 18, when Hariot says he again went to London. "I left the Northerly lapis appearing somewhat above the superficies of the ♀ and somewhat dry, all things in the hyer region the same as before but somewhat diminished.

"May 22. I found the Northerly sulphur to have a reddish ring about that which appeared above the ♀ & within it somewhat whitish yellow."

May 24, at ten in the morning he gave fire. Nothing appeared for two hours; the lower region was thick with dew.

May 25; he is now writing more fully and with marked excitement.

Bruno before his accusers.

Yes, he had praised the infinity of worlds, believing that infinite divine power could bring into being an infinity of worlds.

Yes, he had praised Queen Elizabeth and called her *diva*; yes, he had spoken of fornication as the least of carnal sins; yes, he had quoted Lucretius, but never felt that man was of solely animal origin. He believed in a Godhead in the Father, the Word, and Love, which is the Divine Spirit; in essence, these are one; "but I have never been able to grasp the three being really Persons and have doubted it." The questions pour over him. He answers and answers. He makes the statement beginning "I hate and detest all the errors I have at any time committed as regards the Catholic Faith and the decrees of Holy Church . . ."

He saw everything in life collapsing around him, even when

he cast himself on the mercy of the Inquisition and asked that his punishment be private.

He was delivered over to the Nuncio, transported to Rome, and imprisoned for seven years, without books or writing materials. Was he in chains? Campanella was tortured twelve times; the last time lasted forty hours.

Bruno had against him Bellarmin, more famous as the opponent of Galileo. All the papers of Bruno's trial in 1599 and Bruno's manuscripts have disappeared.

A news notice for February, 1600 : "Thursday was burned alive in the Field of Flowers that Dominican brother from Nola, a pertinacious heretic, with a gag on his tongue because of the vile words he spoke without wishing to listen to the Comforters of others. He had been twelve years in the prisons of the Holy Office . . ."

One historian of Italian heretics says that Bruno spoke the words of Plotinus, " 'Vast power was needed to re-unite that which is divine in me with that which is divine in the universe.' "

Did he refuse the crucifix, now being used to torture?

"And the man who, in many respects marched generations ahead of his fellows had the evil fortune to influence directly only one great thinker. But that thinker was Spinoza."

There is a sign in Hariot's writings. It is a very small jotting which appears slowly as you look at the page. It is off in the left edge of a folio and it reads : "Nolanus de immenso et mundi." The book is there, in the locked White Room at Petworth House where, the story goes, Turner painted.

Try to find a copy of *De Immenso.*

Of the lifework of Bruno :

"The universe is all of a piece; the principles which obtain on earth are observed through space. Here lies his indisputable merit. He was the first to extend the Copernican theory to all the hosts of heaven. He did so with characteristic boldness. It was a marvelous sweep of the scientific imagination, for we must remember that Galileo and Newton had not yet come to supply their confirmatory evidence. He went further, to declare that the physical universe occupies infinity . . ."

But the man who wrote of the bonds, the authority on memory, comes to us as the figure of forgetting. When the news of his death reached England, it made no stir; it was hardly mentioned in print. Only as satire and parody does he come through in death and life. Is he the Bruno of the additions to Marlowe's *Dr. Faustus*, on whom Faust As Cardinal (in the same relation that we see today in the graffiti on New York walls, Pepe As Hawk) pronounces sentence :

> He shall be straight condemn'd of heresy
> And on a pile of faggots burnt to death —

and perhaps combined with Ralegh and Hariot in the characters of *Love's Labour's Lost,* where the verbalism, the distance from women and its closing in, the manners and exaggeration toppling into the ridiculous grotesque, give us Berowne and the rest.

Gagged he was on the Field of Flowers, burned and forgotten. But Hariot remembered; he knew the penalties before him, even in a Protestant — or rather a non-Roman Catholic — country. Hariot remembered Bruno. The mark dented deep on a page by a compass-foot seems to speak for this. And there are the Cantos of Mutability.

Henry Osborn taylor writes :

"Even the environing sphere of the fixed stars was burst asunder : Bruno's universe, one, infinite, moveless, had no limit whatsoever.

"And God? The universe in His unfolding, *explicatio* as Cusa said : enfolds him also, necessarily; for God is within it, not without. And then, in thinking of the abiding unity of this infinitely unfolded deity, Bruno turns (among other ways of thinking) to Cusa's *coincidentia oppositorum,* the union of contraries attained in infinite being. So God, as the world-soul, permeates and energizes and vivifies the universe . . .

"Proudly comforting and defending himself, when examined before the tribunal in Venice which was to deliver him to the Roman Inquisition, Bruno stated in his philosophic creed :

'I hold to an infinite universe, that is, the effect of the infinite divine power; for I think it unworthy of divine goodness and power to have produced merely one finite world when it was able to bring into being an infinity of worlds; so that I have declared that there are endless particular worlds like this of the earth. I regard it, with Pythagoras, as a star, like the moon, the other planets, and the other stars. They are infinite, and all these bodies are worlds, and without number; they make an infinity of worlds : the infinite whole in an infinite space, an infinite universe.

'Within this universe I place one universal Providence through which everything lives, grows, acts and abides in its perfection. And I understand this in two ways : that in which the soul is present in the body, all in all (*tutta in tutto*), and all in any given part. This I call *natura*, the shadow, the footprint of the deity. The other is the inconceivable way in which God, an essence, presence and power, is in all and above all, not as part, not as soul, but in a way that is unspeakable.' "

Many have followed Bruno — Taylor says "not exactly" — this man who brought all the modes of imagination into his system — which Taylor says is "scarcely a system because not founded on some rock of well-proven certitude." He was the pioneer of certitude that is based on something other than rock. He is our swimmer of infinity. Many have followed him, "not knowing whom they followed, yet swimming ever in those shoreless floods."

> Better be choked with English hemp,
> than poisoned with Indian tobacco,

goes the verse in front of *Work for Chimney-Sweepers*; and

tells of Della Porta, who commends the plant in *Natural Magic*.
The introductory poem tells

> Of the quicke sighted and refined Crew,
> Of new installed Knights Tabacconists

and of those

> They burne for Heretiques (O foule Impietye,)
> Cause they blasphemed Tabaccos Dietie.

This poem speaks of Trinidado, and of the Irish kern and the

> . . . wholesome simples of Guyana land

and exhorts us

> Go charme the Priest and Indian Canniballs,
> That ceremoniously dead sleeping falls,
> Flat on the ground, by vertue of thee sent,
> Then waking straight, and tells a wonderment,
> Of strange events and fearefull visions,
> That he had seene in apparitions.

It ends, after whipping the queen "with rods of steele,"

> Then will I never looke for greater gaine,
> Nor ever think my labour lost in vaine.

This is very close to the bone. The prose, too, is close : ". . . .
And herein I cannot but wonder much at the ouer sight of
some, who otherwise being learned and wise, yet in this
seeme very *Paradoxicall*, when as they contend to proue
Tabacco to be a great nurrisher." For it is manifest that it
taketh away nourishment. And it is not good for gonorrhea, as
has been claimed; it is not good for scurvy; and Monardus tells
us of the trances of the Indian priests. And tobacco should not
in any respect be used by the melancholy person. — It can
occasion a hasty and untimely death.

Hariot at Syon House in July, 1601 was making his experiments
in optics. These were part of a building interest, that went on

for years. It begins here with observations in refraction from water to air, two pages of calculations both of air and crystal, and air and water. Two days later, he goes on with the observations, writing his name on the page in the cipher he has developed. On another page, he is making calculations "upon my astrolabe" of the angles of incidence, "ab aere ad chrystalli" and "ad aqua."

In these observations, he sets himself problems, using air and water, air and glass . . . find the fraction . . . how much water should be extended to make the prime refraction. Then salt water. Then a table of observations for glass and water with oil of terebinth.

Later, in November, a set of calculations from air to glass; and, upside down, the first drawing that indicates the beginning of the study of close-packing. This first sketch is for a piling of circles (bullets?) three over four; but two of them are touching four others.

These observations continue for many years; the fruit of some of them are in the correspondence with Kepler. Hariot writes to Kepler in Prague, on December 2, 1606, thanking him for his letter with its many problems in optics, mechanics, etc., and providing a table in answer to Kepler's question regarding Hariot's opinion. Hariot answers with a table of his observations on refraction, giving the weights, media, radius of incidence and degrees of refraction in air, for fountain water, rainwater, distilled water, Spanish wine, Rhine wine, brandy, salt water, *petroleum rectificatum*, oil of terebinth, and olive oil; and sal gemmae, crystal, glass, sugar, and gum. The notes for these observations are to be found in his papers. Of these thirteen diverse media, Hariot speaks of the weights, the relation to the perpendicular, and what the evidence of the eyes affords in relation to mathematical law.

"Et numeri isti sunt ita accurati ut plus unitate non fallunt. Posui illos ut judicetur de raritate et densitate . . .

"Lege, compara, perpende parum, et sis memor legum refractionum . . . Falluntur ne oculi, praesertim cum mathematicis legibus et dyoptris constriguntur? . . . Sit paradoon opticum, sed verum . . ."

Isn't it therefore always refracted as it is in the beginning? Answer . . . "Sed quid hoc, et quo modo? hope and wait a moment. expecta et attende parumper. Reuertamus ad initium ubi incipiebamus."

"Ita placuit in argumentando ludere." And he goes on to the rainbow, and "likewise of many physical things in their own places, if God gives us time and health." In the meantime he will wait patiently.

But he must say a word about the rainbow, of reflection in the concave surface, of refraction in the convex, and "I have said nothing of the waiting mysteries. Bene vale. London. Decem. 2. Your friend

Tho : Hariot"

"Probably the most interesting application of Hariot's atomic theory," Kargon writes, is "in the field of optics."

Hariot has written, in several places, among his now shuffled papers, phrases and sentences and recipes in a cipher which he seems to have developed for his own pleasure and for use with Nathaniel Torporley, in whose papers and in whose hand the cipher also appears.

The cryptic writing is very close to that which immortalized a freed slave of Cicero's, Tullius Tyro, who made the first method of shorthand, using marks which are arbitrary to designate whole words. Some historians, says Alexander d'Agapayeff, "say that he only perfected the method which was already known to the poet Ennius, nevertheless the characters used in Germany as late as the tenth century were called Tyronian after him."

Through the mistake of a monk, going by some resemblance to Armenian writing, the Tyronian characters in an old psalter were described later as being in "Armenian." Hariot's writing was also called Armenian. His cipher was broken by Dr. Ethel Seaton, who has written about this secret script, and given the signature of Hariot, "Watr Warnr" (probably not a signature, but in Hariot's hand), a trial sentence which is used in several languages — that first sentence describing creation, from Genesis — "In the beginning God made heaven and earth," shown in cipher here as "yin [t]he bigining god mad hevn and." Dr. Seaton speaks of the Notae Romanum Veterum, printed in 1603, of which Hariot may have seen a manuscript which could have a source for his cipher. The first use preserved in his papers is dated Syon · 1602 · July 20.

Frances Ricketts, the cipher expert who worked with Leslie Hotson on breaking the Japanese code during World War II, has worked with me on other instances of the Hariot script. The name of Randal Knevet is here, out of context and un-explained, although the Knevet family may have had a member in Northumberland's circle. Another name is that of Thomas Malsat, to whom I have as yet no clue; nor to a pair of words that seem to come through as "tymiu nostra." The recipes are alchemical, both Dr. Turner's, one for spirit of wine, one for pewter.

One marginal note in cipher that has been impossible so far to read may be a clue to Hariot's personal life in the spring of 1599. On a sheet of observations for the period lasting from early May to late June, he notes, to one side, writing the last word in cipher :

"from the 7th of June I was with-----"
The name looks rather like "Clinth."

On July 22, 1601, he writes at the head of a page, and these are the only words in cipher,

"ratyo calculi"

Another jotting in cipher seems to be about the rainbow — part of the work that appears in the correspondence with Kepler.

The author of *Natural Magic*, read by Hariot and close to Hariot's imagination, Giovanni Baptista della Porta of Naples, made a cipher used by Cardinal Wolsey, and another more complicated one copied by Blaise de Vigenere as a code (like the one suggested by Bacon, and given always in clusters of five letters). And the Duke of Brunswick-Luneburg — related to that Duke to whom Bruno dedicated *De Immenso*, published a code, using for his cryptic name, Gustavus Selenus — moon-man — of Luneburg, moon-town.

Hariot was working with "magic squares" on the names Henricus Princeps, Silo Princeps — and Sir Nicholas Carew wrote from Ireland, "If I only had Hariot to work with cyphers, or Levinus."

Bacon communicated in cipher; and John Wallis, Hariot's mathematical inheritor and defender, became famous as a cryptographer for deciphering the papers used at the trial of Charles I. The papers, captured at the battle of Naseby, were letters from the King to his wife; they carried plots against Parliament and his denunciation of the Roundhead leaders. It has been the deciphering of these letters that has been cited as the instigating factor leading to the charges which condemned the King and were the final excuse for his beheading. John Wallis, who has written extensively for Hariot (and against Descartes as his imitator, not acknowledging him but pirating his algebra), became archivist of Oxford. It is impossible, one would think, that biographical notes on Hariot, and perhaps some of Hariot's own writings, might not be found among Wallis's archive at the Bodleian, although my search has turned up nothing.

Another mathematician from whom threads go to Hariot was used by Henri IV to break the ciphers of the Spaniards in their secret correspondence concerning the Netherlands, part of Italy, and their possessions in the New World — that is, Florida, Mexico, Central America, and all of South America as well as the islands of the Caribbean. This mathematician was Vieta, whom Torporley served as secretary in Paris. Vieta used the frequency law to find the key to this alphabet. After two years, the Spanish found that the French Foreign Office had been reading all letters, in all their variations, sealing them again, and sending them on.

Characteristically, the Spanish accused Henri IV (a Protestant) of having magicians at his command (Vieta) and of "invoking the help of the devil . . . by calling up the spirits of those who had known the cipher during their earthly life."

But a new Pope sent the complaint to a commission of cardinals with a wry note of "urgent recommendation." The investigation has not been completed.

The only portrait that we have that has ever been called a likeness of Hariot is a painting of a man of middle age, looking out at us with a penetrating clear gaze out of blue-grey eyes. His face has great control, discipline; the long English nose has strong nostrils, the mouth is closed and grave, the clipped moustache and pointed beard not heavy, the light-brown hair growing over a high clear forehead, the ear seen in this three-quarter portrait beautifully formed, with the man's hair beginning to curl slightly over the top of the ear. One's own look returns to his eyes : the observing, noticing quality in them is very strong.

He is dressed simply in a figured black cloak with shoulder rolls. His ruff is simple, too; three rows of soft white. Linen shows at his cuff, too; and in the left hand is a pomander, the orange stuck all over with cloves which was held to be smelled for pleasantness and to ward away the plague. The painting's background is dark green.

If you look closely, you see that the pomander is of a texture different from that of the rest of this painting, which is 18½ by 14½ inches and hangs in the house of the President of Trinity College, Oxford.

The object which was originally held in this man's hand has been sanded away, and the pomander has been painted in.

In the upper left corner of the background was painted the legend AN. DNI 1602. AETATIS SVAE 42, Hariot's date and age given correctly. In February, 1957, the painting was cleaned, and a different number for the age was revealed under the first. It now reads AETATIS SVAE 3 2, with a bump between the two separated numerals, now of course impossible for Hariot. Was there a mistake, painted over in correction? What is the bump of paint? Why are the numerals separated? Could there be something under the pomander?

Mr. David Piper, curator of the National Portrait Gallery and my authority on the English face, kindly had the portrait X-rayed when President Norrington of Trinity generously allowed it to be brought from Oxford to London. Mr. Piper's report is that the painting is an authentic object, that X-ray of the numerals showed nothing, that the bump is a lump of the same paint as the rest of the background, that the pomander was clearly painted after the rest and nothing is visible through it.

This portrait has been accepted as Hariot's likeness in several quarters. A reproduction hangs in the Fort Raleigh Museum on Roanoke Island; another is printed in Stefan Lorant's *The New World*. Both are identified as Thomas Hariot.

The painting is now listed as *Unknown Man*, in the Oxford Portrait Catalogue.

Mr. Piper says that the clothing is Dutch, and the subject may very well also be Dutch.

The question of the portrait is like many others in this history, mysterious, equivocal, capable of at least two interpretations, and of extreme interest taken together with the other live and mysteriously moving pieces of this evidence. It is possible to swim among many unknowns.

From the account rolls, we apprehend stroke by stroke the life at Syon House and London. The life on the river is given to us : feriage on Thames at Istleworth; for the carriage of household stuffe from puddleswharfe to walsingham's house; from Charingcrosse house to essex house; from Syon House to the water syde; from Petworth; horse hire and horse meat . . .

Tobacco; tobacco pipes; pistols, head for pike, gold for a golden hatched Rapier and dager; Salomon Butler at Delphe for a guilt Rapier. George Percy traveling into Ireland.

To Sir Walter Ralegh's son a white curled feather.

To Sir Francis Veres his players in Holland, to Mr. Vincent a preacher.

And for trimming of 4000 leaden soldiers. This is the game that was played for years, first at Syon House and later elsewhere. It has been called a children's game by all the historians of the Percy family, but it is clearly something more. The War Game, the Kriegsspiel, is said to have been invented much later, and to be played on maps of the battlefields; the pieces used being the bars and abstract signs of battalions and regiment. But this game, of many pieces for soldiers and officers — there is a listing in the accounts for men and for pikes — shows a military intelligence at work. The notes in Hariot's working papers bear this out.

For cutting down the wilderness in the birch walks; for setting maps in frames; for making the riding place in the orchard; to ye Mason for making yo : Lo : closet in the garden; for making a pair of stairs. For the late Sir John Parrott in Wales; and Syon rent. Velvet, caps, bands, silver, holland, silken ribbon.

To Mr. Hariot for his pension at £80 by year, for two whole years ended at Michaelmas, 1601 li 160.

To Mr. Charles Frank upon an Adventure into ye Lowe Countries in a Wherry; to Mr. Story for ridinge of yo : Lo : great horse. To Francis Henson for bookbinding. To lawyers . . .

When John Donne came to the Earl of Northumberland for help, he was desperate. At the age of twenty-eight, he had come to a stop, for the time being, in his poems — the marvelous lightning-twisted, fierce poems of the Songs and Sonnets and the early Satires. He had come to a stop in his warfaring; he had gone with Essex to the Islands, to Cadiz. He had tasted the airs of exploration, and was aware of Ralegh and "Guiana's rarities."

The thing hath travell'd, and, faith, speaks all tongues. He had spent his inheritance and found many women. Now he was secretary to Lord Egerton, the Keeper of the Seal, and had been in that post at a great climax in his life, the execution of Essex. Here was another climax; for he had fallen in love with Egerton's niece, Anne More, the daughter of Sir George More, the master of Loseley House in Surrey, and Lieutenant of the Tower of London.

There were qualities in George More — his impulsive drive, his insatiable energy — that should have brought him close to Donne, and that did attract the Queen, who visited Loseley four times.

Of Anne, at seventeen, we know that Donne, shaken by all the events of 1600, was in love with her when she was sent away from York House, and saw her in private several times when she came down to London. Just before she was to return to Loseley before Christmas of 1601, she and John Donne were married in the presence of five persons. Days later, Donne was asking the Earl of Northumberland to help in telling the bride's father. Of the Earl, Gosse says, "his love for acting as a go-between in delicate affairs amounted to a dangerous passion." His passions were at the surface : his unreined curiosities and loathings, his battles with his wife in the early days of her backing the cause of James of Scotland; his feud with Francis Vere, and the challenge with rapiers that was now over his head, and had been building ever since their quarrel in wartime in the Netherlands. He was effective and brilliant, and his intelligence and power were deeply attractive to Donne. It was to the Earl that Donne now turned to avert the disgrace before him for breaking Sir George's objections to him as a changeable and poor faithless waster. With Donne's long and curious letter announcing the marriage and begging for forgiveness and the happiness that More might find it "easy to give," Northumberland on the second of February went to Loseley.

Northumberland carried his argument for Donne and his bride to a wild father, who raged against the poet and went at once to Egerton to have Donne dismissed, and to have Donne and the marriage witnesses thrown into separate prisons. From the Fleet, Donne wrote again to his father-in-law, who now was trying to have the marriage annulled. Ill, his career ruined, his marriage threatened, Donne began to write in an entirely different tone; and this submission changed the course of his life. It gave him back his wife; his illness had caused his release from prison; broken, "poor and repentant," he wrote letters to More, to Robert Cotton, and to other friends. Northumberland's appeal was beginning to take effect, but very slowly; for both More and Egerton had moved punitively and fast. As a matter of fact, they had both overreached themselves in fury. Egerton's wife, the Countess of Derby, and her daughters, may also have had a great deal to do with the movement of softening that now followed. Sir George More was the first to come to approval of the marriage. But he had argued with Egerton to dismiss Donne; Egerton could not bear to lose face through inconsistency.

Donne was married, then, he was with Anne; but his life was now to be spent, first at Pyrford and then at Mitcham, of whose manor Sir Nicholas Throckmorton Carew — his brother-in-law and Ralegh's relative — was lord, and near to the mansion of Sir Julius Caesar, who became his lifelong friend. In London, Donne kept rooms in the Strand, and part of his time he lived and wrote there, while the birth of his children and the growth of sickness and poverty commanded the Mitcham household.

Northumberland seems always to have kept the consciousness of Donne, many of whose interests met those of Hariot and Ralegh, as well as others close to the Earl. This period, for him, marked the veering of his support at last to James, in brief agreement with his wife as Elizabeth's strength faded to dying. The Earl, in attendance on the Queen's last Progress, writes from Sir William Clarke's house at Burnham,

"Wednesday night the Queen was not well, but would not be known of it, for the next day she walked abroad in the Park lest any should take notice of it . . . The day of the remove

Her Majesty rode on horseback all the way, which was ten miles, and also hunted; and whether she was weary or not, I leave to your leisure."

A larger warfare was that of the Border, which was torn by blood feuds resembling the Corsican vendettas, endless raids and murders and challenges rolling back and forth over an entire countryside. The hope was that the Border could be held.

Public opinion was against the Infanta; and Arabella Stuart was ruled out; Northumberland said that there must not be a succeeding Queen, the people "fearing they should never again enjoy another like unto this." In his correspondence with James of Scotland, Northumberland was sending his kinsman, Thomas Percy, as the trusted bearer of messages.

At the end of Elizabeth's life, he writes to James, ". . . . For a twenty days she slept very little. Since, she is grown very weak, yet sometimes gives us comfort of recovery; a few hours after, threatens us with despair of her welldoing. Physic she will not take any, and the physicians conclude that if this continue, she must needs fall into a distemper; not a phrensy, but rather into a dullness and a lethargy."

Now, in his powers of reconciliation, the drama of meetings, Northumberland was beginning to be preyed on by his enemies; but James was for him; and at this time, Francis Bacon wrote to Northumberland of his "great capacity and love toward studies and contemplation of a higher and worthier nature than popular" and asked if he might be any use to your lordship by my head, tongue, pen, means of friends. Hariot was a member of this household, and Bacon was aware of Hariot. Now Elizabeth dies; James succeeds her; and Ralegh falls.

Ralegh in his carriage was almost lynched on his way to the trial. The moment that James had come into England, it was clear that he considered this essential Elizabethan more than an enemy. From his first pun, made to Ralegh's face when he rushed up from Devon in March to an audience and James said, "Rawley! True enough, for I think of the rawly, mon!" to the quick building up in James' mind of Ralegh as devil-figure, is it Spanish? what is it out of this gallery, this dark man, breathing smoke?

He was stripped of offices, first of Captain of the Guard with its pride of place, then — after a temporary increase — of the governorship of Jersey. Between these, he lost his licensing patent, and the income from taverns. He had a large revenue from part of every drink taken publicly; and the drinkers hated him. Then Durham House was snatched from him, after 20 years, during which he had improved the river front and put £2000 into the fixtures of the building. He wrote to the Lord Keeper Egerton, saying that the meanest gentleman in England would have had six months' notice. He made late appeasing gestures to James; but soon he was under house arrest. By late July, he was in the Tower.

Plague summer in London : and an increase of over 1000 deaths a week. Ralegh tried to kill himself the day after he was imprisoned, but the table knife with which he stabbed himself in the right breast left only a painful wound. During the fortnight in which he was healing, he could hear the bells ringing for plague victims. The bells never stopped tolling. In the streets, people with running sores could be seen, in hatred trying to infect others by strewing contaminated gloves, handkerchiefs, ruffs. Families took their bedding and went out into the country. The court of justice was removed to Winchester. One out of every six in the City was sick or dying of the plague. Infected ale-houses were not shut up. Londoners went out to the outlying towns, and died under the hedges; in Hampstead, they would fall in the yards and out-buildings, and there were barns around London where many would run to die. The jails were infected. There was an outbreak of 30 prisoners in Southwark; they were caught and put under stricter custody.

At the end of July, Ralegh was well and asking for Hariot. John Peyton, an officer of the Tower, writes to Cecil:

"Right honorable my very good Lord, Sr Walter Rawleg (torn, about 'his hurte') w in these two dayes perfectly whoole, he doth styll contynewe pplexed as you leafte hym, he is desirous to have M^r heriott come to hym, whereon I cannot conceyve any incovenyence if shall so stand wth the LLs, thier honorable pleasures. My Lord Cobham his spirites are exceedingly muche declynes, he is growne passionate in lamentatyon & sorowe, his onely hoope is in his ma^{ties} mercye, and y^r mediation. I am exceeding gladde to heare that my good frend Sr George Mor shall succeed me in this place whom I wyll assiste in all things that shall be wth in my powres . . . Towre this 30 of July 1603."

The plague reached the Tower in September. Three prisoners died in three days, and Sir William Waad, the lieutenant, sent away his wife and children, but told Cecil that he meant to ride it out himself.

On the 12th of November, Waad conveyed Ralegh to Winchester for trial, allowing him to travel in his own coach. The town had seemed deserted. From the houses, groans and mourning cries could be heard. Those who walked in the streets kept near the center channel; some chewed orange peel or angelica root; some smoked tobacco; you kept to windward of anyone who looked infected. Coaches were hung with rue to keep the leather and the nails plague-free; the nostrils of the coach-horses were plugged with herb-grace.

But as this coach moved through the City, crowds formed. They shouted hatred at Ralegh, and yelled in the name of Essex. Ralegh was cold to this; they screamed along the line of his progress, and forced the coach leaning. Wade said it was "touch-and-go whether Ralegh could be brought alive through such multitudes of unruly people as did exclaim against him."

The trial took place in the Palace of the Bishops of Winchester, with Coke, the attorney general, conducting the prosecution. Ralegh was allowed no counsel. The town was crowded, and lawyers and clients "were made to pay through the nose for food and lodging." Ralegh pleaded Not Guilty to the charges, of raising sedition (and not mentioned was the story that James had heard, that Ralegh was for a commonwealth instead of Scottish rule), of various Spanish complicities, and concerning a treacherous book; of plotting in Durham House to give the throne to Arabella Stuart.

Ralegh said : "My Lord, I pray you I may answer the points one by one as they are delivered, by reason of the weakness of my memory, and sickness."

This request was refused. It was the general feeling, says Hume, that he was guilty but that the evidence was not strong enough to convict him.

Coke set forth the case, mocking and insulting Ralegh continually, "Thou viper, thou traitor; I will prove thee the rankest traitor in England."

There was the matter of a confession and a retraction of the confession by Cobham, and the Bye-plot was dragged in.

Coke said : "After you have taken away the king, you would alter religion.

"Thou art a monster, thou hast an English face, but a Spanish heart."

"Let me answer for my self," said Ralegh.

"Thou shalt not," said Coke.

"It concerneth my life," Ralegh said.

The piling-up of vituperation went on; with Coke making his case on the kernel of suspicion, the arrogance of Ralegh, and that curious quality in him that is blazing out of his poetry always, a transcendent quality that in his life was anti-Spanish and venomously so, but that was seen by the opposed type of Englishman as "Spanish heart"; the quality that comes through in passionate war, attracting and obsessing men and women of one side with imaginings of men and women of the other side, their dreams, their inventions and products, that flood across all barriers when the war is over; the Elizabethan explosive.

Ralegh called for two accusers to be confronted with him, according to English law, out of the Old Testament. "Is it not strange for me to make myself Robin Hood or Jack Cade? I knowing England to be in better state to defend itself than ever it was. I knew Scotland united; Ireland disquieted, where of late our forces were dispersed; Denmark assured, which before was suspected. I knew that having a Lady whom time has surprised, we had now an active king, a lawful successor, who would himself be present in all his affairs.

"The state of Spain was not unknown to me. I knew the Spaniard was discouraged and dishonored. I knew the king of Spain to be the proudest Prince in Christendom; but now he comes creeping to my king my master for Peace."

Coke heaped testimony on testimony. Ralegh called again for Cobham to be brought face to face with him in court. "Campion was not denied to have his accusers face to face."

Coke : "He is a party, and may not come; the law is against it."

Ralegh : "It is a toy to tell me of law. I defy such law, I stand on the fact."

Ralegh had studied in the Temple, but this is his own truth and style of mind. To a lawyer, it is the last straw.

The jury was out for 15 minutes.

Popham, before speaking the Judgment, spoke of having thought it impossible that one of so great parts should have fallen so grievously. He spoke of the monopoly on wine, and the others. "It is best for Man not to seek to climb too high, lest he fall; nor yet to creep too low, lest he be trodden on. Two vices have lodged chiefly in you; one is an eater ambition, the other corrupt covetousness.

"Ambition in desiring that grace you had beforetime. For your covetousness, I am sorry to hear that a gentleman of your wealth should become a base spy for the enemy, which is the vilest of all.

"You have been taxed by the world with the defense of the most heathenish and blasphemous opinions.

"You shall do well before you go out of the world" — and

then Ralegh knew what was coming, but only part of that—
"not to die with these imputations on you.

"Let not any devil Hariot, nor any such doctor, persuade you
there is no eternity in Heaven. If you think thus, you shall find
eternity in Hell fire."

He ended piously, "If the fear of God in you had been answerable to your other great parts, you might have lived to have
been a singular good subject. I never saw the like trial, and hope
I shall never see the like again."

The burden was falling on Hariot again. His life and thought
was being used to drag down Ralegh, as Marlowe had been
dragged down. The sentence was still to be read.

"But since you have been found guilty of these horrible
treasons, the judgment of this court is, That you shall be had
from hence to the place whence you came, there to remain until
the day of execution; and from thence you shall be drawn up
on a hurdle through the open streets to the place of execution,
there to be hanged and cut down alive, and your body shall be
opened, your heart and bowels plucked out, and your privy
members cut off, and thrown into the fire before your eyes;
then your head to be strucken off from your body, and your
body shall be divided into four quarters, to be disposed of at
the King's pleasure; and

"God have mercy upon your soul."

One of the judges, Gawdy : "Never before has the justice of
England been so depraved and injured as in this trial." Ralegh
had been the most hated man in England, they said; now, they
said, he is the most revered.

He was Essex now. "Never was a man so hated and so popular in so short a time."

One of the King's observers reported : "Whereas when I saw
Sir Walter Ralegh first, I would have gone a hundred miles to

see him hanged, I would ere we parted have gone a thousand to save his life."

Ralegh asked only that his death be honorable, and not ignominious. The court promised him to do their utmost endeavors. The court rose, and the prisoner was taken again to the castle.

Part of the work of which we have the signs in the letters between Kepler and Hariot is to be found in his working papers in notes made later in 1604 and in 1605, when he is working on refraction, from air to crystal sphere to air, air to water to air, air to glass to air.

These notes begin in August, 1597; his arms are out toward Baptista Porta at the beginning and toward Kepler in this period. They begin with the tables of angles of refraction from air to crystal to glass, according to Della Porta.

On August 11, 1597, Hariot makes a table of angles of refraction from air to crystal or glass, according to Baptista Porta. That is Gianbattista della Porta, whose *Natural Magic,* with its suggestive and beautiful section on optics, had reached him.

The next day, he notes, "Partes of my staffe dobled," and gives us the table of angles of refraction. Again, on the 21st and 25th of August, 1597, Hariot goes on with his observations of refraction. On the 21st, he notes: "Partes of my staffe single."

Very early, Hariot is experimenting with a prism given to him by Mr. W. Cope (this sets the date before Cope was knighted). The description and diagram of "Mr. W. Copes cristall" give us a concavo-convex prism. Ab is concave, ac is convex here; "ab being parallel to the horizon it sheweth the colours not lustrous as in the light of a glass window — ab perpendicular do shew as lustrous as in that of glass . . . the colours double though in the same order; and the thinges in it now double."

Since these working papers are bound together all in confusion, lacking even the chronological order afforded us by the dates written on some of them, I am referring to them here in whatever order I can let them have which Hariot has shown us by date, internal evidence, or their relation to his Kepler correspondence.

Now follow the observations : prisms, glass spheres; a group of optical observations, *ab aqua ad aerem,* made on July 20, 1601, at Syon; a group of air-crystal calculations, and another of air-water calculations, made on that same day; and then at 10:30 in the morning two days later (h.10½), two words in Hariot's cipher, ratio calculi.

There is here a double row of spheres, three over four, perhaps the beginning of a drawing of piling of round bullets again, like the other close-packing diagrams.

And with it, upside down on the sheet, notes *"Ab aere ad glacie"* dated Novem. 20 · 1601.

The papers proceed with the tables of water to crystal; of crystal to water, with the angles of incidence taken "upon my astrolabe"; *ab aere ad chrystalli ad aqua* (part of this table is taken from earlier observations).

There are here a statement of universal problematic elements of refractions of radii, and calculations, air to crystal sphere to air, air to water to air, air to glass to air. The statements on sight through concave glass begin to be formulated, and *De visione recta et flexa : per aspectum et intuitum.*

Then suddenly this description of the laws of the rainbow, beginning

> A man sitting in the middle of many spheres that are equally distant . . . shall seem to be in the middle of a concave sphere.

This deals with transparency and the shape of the sphere. Hariot says that this is common to all the spheres "in the adverse parte of the sonne," and ends

> The reflexion that is from the rayne concave is only from that part that makes equal angles with the eye after the reason of a concave sphere and the diameter of the rainbow is according to the diameter of the eye.

These observations alternate with notes on concave spheres used as burning glasses (under *De Cono Vitreo*), but I shall go on with the observations on refraction.

On November 2, 1604, Hariot is writing : "A note of sal gemma. I observed the angles of refraction of sal. gemma upon my astrolabe, and find at the angle of incidence of 60, 50 40 the same refraction as of glasse or crystall."

A note deals with an instrument ordered : "I had my new instrument of lynes frō the cooper in brasse — Decemb. 21 · 1604. The pece was 1½ inch square and ⅓ of an inch thicke. Two sides were ground and polished.

"Decemb. 29 · 1604 — I had a peece of gumme arabicke polished of 1½ inch square and about ⅓ of an inch thicke; I also had prepared a piece of yellow amber. Upon my new instrument of lynes from the cooper, I observed at the angles of incidence $\overline{10}$ · $\overline{20}$ · $\overline{30}$ · $\overline{40}$ · $\overline{50}$ and found the same angle of refraction as of crystall or glasse exact in both — videlicet of amber and gemma. crystall

       glasse
       sal gem.
       amber
       gum"

On February 19, 1604/05, he was observing refraction from petroleum to air.

Hariot made observations of colors on the 8th, 9th, 10th, and 11th of April, 1605. His notes give the angle of glass as $\overline{58.0}'$ and the angle of incidence $\overline{51.1}'$. Superficies vitri distantia a charta — 6 foote — 12 foote

flanedo a termino charta 1½₅ ynches — 0.4 inches — 2 inches
rubido a termino charta ½ ynches 1 inch

I observed with the angle of 60 of glasse and sal gemma and found them all one.

Then the calculations, and colors through various angles of water. Then a table for glass and water with olei terebinthui, aqua salsa, spiritus vini. The results of these may be found in his letters to Kepler.

He calculates color through oil of terebinth. He sets himself these problems : air and water, air and glass; find the fraction from air to glass. How much water, he asks, should be extended to make the prime refraction ab aqua? He sets himself problems with perpendiculars, with the angle from the orb of the moon, from the sun.

Now we come to burning glasses — although eight years later, at Syon, Hariot was continuing these observations of refractions from air to wine, amber, gum, crystal, salt : all equal, he says on December 30, 1613.

And he is reading Alhazen's fifth book.

Measuring the effects of burning glasses at 1000 paces—that is 5000 feete, he writes, or 10,000 halfe feete — and the diagram is here, with the wide-spread focus on the objecta from oculis, and the other focused on the objecta and wide on the oculis. Per illos duos modus for the two acts of sight.

"A concave sphere doth burne in a circle to any point in the axis; and the eye shall see a reflected circle forme or rather be set out by it. Here rainbow and burning glass come together in their laws."

Problems in *perspeculo polyconico,* problems of the telescope.

De cono vitreo : "So many sonnes do burne . . . No glasse can burne other than by reflection or fraction; not unto 23 times his breadth; when he hath his best forme . . ."

Again, the cone of minima combustione, the cone of minimal potential.

"The greatest actual heat upon any materiall poynt is the heat of 84, 525 sonnes.

"The greatest potential heat that can have being is the heat of 169,050."

He is reading Alhazen and working the problems of page 196.

He is drawing the angles of refraction of his staff in water, "Baculus in aqua."

The constellation Serpentarius, the Serpent-Bearer, is called by its Greek name, Ophiucus, now, by us. It is the thirteenth zodiacal constellation and is at least 5000 years old.

The drawing of this constellation which Hariot kept with

him is of a strong, broad man with his back to us, gripping in his hands the coils of a snake spread across the sky, his crested head rearing up higher than the man's, tongue out, not forked but arrow-headed. Two vast currents pour down the sky, touching the man : they are bays of the Milky Way, one from the south and one from the north. These currents carry some of the large number of clusters and nebulae within the constellation, which contains very few stars, but is rich in globular clusters, very faint and very far from us.

Of the stars, there are Rasalhague — the peak and head of Serpentarius — the Sabiks ("The Conquerors" in Arabic) and the Yeds, the hand stars on the western border.

In the foot was a great nova which burst into visibility on September 30, 1604. It was seen by Kepler, and was reported in his book of 1606; it was visible for 17 months and was called Kepler's Star. It was one of four bright novae seen in Ophiucus. The Yeds are the country of novae, these bursting energies that seem to mean continual creation and the defiance of entropy. Near Rho Ophiuci, above Antares, there is a region of dark nebulae, systems of dust that hide the light of stars.

The sun and the planets are sometimes "in" Ophiucus, although it is not listed among the twelve of the Zodiac. The constellation has been seen as a man and snake by people of many cultures, and has been interpreted as an arrangement that means a man carrying a snake, with two meanings. It has been thought of as Laocöon who understood that the Wooden Horse at Troy was dangerous and a spy-carrier and must not be admitted into the city, and was wound about and crushed to death by a snake sent by gods on the side of the Greeks; and the constellation has also been seen as a man carrying the serpent of wisdom, Aesculapius, bearing the snake that means healing and has become the sign of physicians. The snake's power is venom curative or poisonous.

Hariot writes, referring to Kepler's work : "Kepler in his 1604 book of Nova Stella in Serpentario, p. 58 seq."

It is Hariot's constellation, of the man undergoing the struggle with wisdom, of the region of clusters and nebulae.

3

The Patteran

PART TWO

On that November day, Thomas Percy came riding hard from London to Syon House, past the roads with the cattle grazing, the start of heron near the river, and to wait upon Northumberland at noon. He had been in London without letting Northumberland know that he had returned early from the north, where he had been collecting rents for the Earl. He was a tall and handsome man, prematurely grey at forty-six, with fine large lively eyes; bold and grave, gentle and quiet too. He had been the Earl's collector for some time, and was his distant cousin, and a born Protestant. He had became a Catholic, and had Jesuit friends; he was one of many Catholics around the Earl, and had been carrying messages to James, who as King of Scotland about to become King of England, was a hope for leniency toward this group who had been persecuted in England. At the accession of James, there were many hopes for peace; but the bewildering various meanings of peace were illuminated harshly after two years of James, and England was up to its eyes in the many plots which may be gathered under the name of "The Spanish Plot," the By Plot, the Main — under one or the other of which Ralegh and many more are in the Tower.

During the past months, Thomas Percy had changed visibly; say that the arrangement of his psyche had altered. He had a reputation in Cheapside for drinking, and for women on Bankside. But in a disastrous time, he had found the Jesuits, or they him; and he was fighting the flesh, hating women, hating drink, and hating the King, who had used him, making promises about tolerance and kicking them all away.

His friends were now Kit Wright, his brother-in-law; Catesby, the Winters, Father Garnet, Guy Fawkes. It is the moment of the Gunpowder Plot, which began as James was riding down; before that, in Flanders and Spain and the English colleges at Cleves and Douai; in the hope that the Infanta could come to rule in England under two papal breves saying that only the one whom the Pope should appoint might lawfully be the ruler.

This was a plot made by English converts, with no help from Europe. Philip of Spain would not again risk a fleet; Lerma thought it could be bought rather than risked.

The plot, as it was made, was the maneuver that would kill James in the way most to horrify him, if he should find out. It was the way that his father Darnley had met his death in Kirk of Field. If Ralegh was the devil-figure to James, this was the death-figure : death by explosion.

The plot, of course, was to blow up the House of Lords with the King, his wife and son, the Council and the peers, by a simple stroke of engineering — under the large building to lay a train of gunpowder; a familiar mode of death, used now in Flanders, killing trenches-full at Ostend.

The whole familiar story will not be told here except as it concerns the people who chiefly are followed in this book. It is a story deep in the English unconscious, and conscious mind and memory too; look out a window in London on any night of November 5th, after seeing the children say to you, "Penny for the Guy" all day, and see the red fires flare through the mist as the effigies burn.

They needed a cellar beside the House of Lords, and an attractive responsible young man to rent Vinegar House, leaning against the Prince's Chamber, part of the House of Lords. The train of powder could be set right under the throne. Percy was a Gentleman Pensioner, he could talk to the landlady, Mrs. Whynyard; but she would only rent with references, and the man who was brought in was the young Dudley Carleton, the charming, advancing, seductive secretary to the Earl. It was on his word that the conspirators got a lease for twenty pounds, and four pounds a quarter rent. During the preparations ramifying from that center — the frustrations, the transport of materials, the delays and close shaves (Bacon and Hamilton met in Vinegar House) and the spread to White Webbs, to Flanders and through England, there was a counter-stir at Court. Cecil and Northampton were working to establish the sole power in the king, and let Spain know that they and their party were the ones with whom it must deal. Men were mustered; Cecil, remembering the Essex rising, closed the theatres.

A week before the day set, the letter warning of the plot reached Lord Monteagle, at supper with a friend of Winter the conspirator. The friend was given the letter to read aloud. It warned of God and man and "a terrible blow" and urged him not to go to Parliament. Monteagle, at ten that night, rode to Whitehall, and by the middle of the night, Cecil was on to the plot; he began to check and slowly found the evidence; he prepared King James to believe that he himself, the threatened king, had solved the crime and was about to net all the criminal murderers.

On November 3rd, with their plan known to the men closest to James, the conspirators were blind to their own danger. Percy returned to London, bought one of the new fine watches for Guy Fawkes so that his timing might be perfect, and sent Kit Wright up to Syon House to hang around the stables and try to learn from the grooms whether Northumberland knew that Percy was back from the north. Kit Wright brought back the word; one of Percy's servants had spoken to a man in the Earl's service and Percy decided late that night to go up to Syon the next day, Monday.

He sits here at dinner with the Earl, and Sir William Lower, the duchess' son-in-law and a brilliant warm friend of Hariot's, and probably with Hariot and his friend Nathaniel Torporley, judging by the arrests following.

"Thomas Percy," said Northumberland, "sauced me with a gudgeon" — he lied to the Earl to get money out of him.

The conspirator looked around the table : there were the Earl's brothers Charles and Alan, Sir Edward Ffrannces, his retainers Edmund Powton and Giles Greene, and Captain Whitlock.

Northumberland had cause long after to remember the conversation at that table. He did not pay attention to it at the time. Thomas Percy turned to Lower, and asked, "What news of the Parliament is there?"

Lower answered, "None that I heard of."

Percy took a little paper out, and said, "We have more news in the north than you have here." He was carrying a list of some articles of the Commissioners. Later, when they understood what had happened, Northumberland's party realized that Percy was trying to find out whether word of Monteagle's letter had filtered through.

The Earl asked Percy to stay for supper; it was then that a page came in, and spoke at Percy's shoulder. There was a man in the yard, wishing to speak to him. Percy went out, and the talk continued. In a few minutes Percy came back, made some excuse to the Earl, and left for the last time. The man in the yard was Guy Fawkes; his horse was steaming.

That evening, at Vinegar House, something had happened that "had at once confirmed and removed his fears." He had been in the vaults under the Prince's Chamber when torches came through; it was Lord Suffolk and Lord Monteagle. It was a curious small party : Suffolk the Lord Chamberlain and another Catholic peer, without guards, talking and laughing, walking along as if making a routine check. Fawkes stood very still; they must come right past him and his stores; he watched their faces. When Suffolk came up to him, he asked Fawkes who he was, and who owned the heap of coal and wood. Fawkes used the name he had been going under, Johnson, and told them he was Percy's man; the fuel was for his master. Suffolk made a joke about Christmas fires, and went on. Fawkes stood there with double feelings : they were onto something, they had come down into the vault on a search; but it had been in the lightest manner, and they had gone away assured that there was nothing out of the way there. However, he had been followed, and it was time to go back to London.

Near Tothill Fields, they parted. Percy joined two of the conspirators to tell them all was well.

Fawkes went back to the vault, laid the train of gunpowder, checked the new watch that Percy had given him, and lit the lantern. As he was going upstairs, he was suddenly seized; they bound him and searched him. Men of Sir Thomas Knyvet, Justice of the Peace for Westminster and Warden of the Mint, who had been called to this service by Northampton days before. He was standing over Fawkes, looking at the slow matches and the touchwood, which had been taken from him; and the wound-up watch. A man was coming up the stairs, bringing the lantern, just blown out; its wick was still smoking.

"What are you doing here?" Knyvet shouted at him.

Fawkes knew his entire landscape at once. He had served as a soldier; he knew cloisters; his auburn hair redder by torchlight, his sandy beard, sunburned, bound, doomed, he said, "Had you but taken me inside, I should have blown you up, the house, myself, and all."

The plotters with Percy had gone to sleep. The news that Fawkes was seized brought them out into the streets. In Montagu Close, under Monteagle's window, Kit Wright heard a lord shouting, "Come with me to Essex House! I am going to call my Lord of Northumberland!"

By now, Northumberland, a member of the Council, was in session with the lords; and a messenger had emerged and dashed up Fleet Street. The conspirators knew that he had gone for Percy, whom Kit Wright found, and gave the word to, and the two men rode off.

All day long, rumors came back : Percy had been seen by Archbishop Bancroft, crying that London was up in arms. Popham said an arrest was imminent at Gravesend. Waad,

Lieutenant of the Tower, sent word that Percy was riding northward.

The squires supporting the plot at Dunchurch, and in Wales, heard first that everything was going according to plan in Westminster. But as the conspirators rode through the country, stopped for confession and absolution, and rode on to Staffordshire, their supporters began to understand.

They paused after crossing a river to dry their powder, which was soaked; this was at the kitchen fire at the house of one of their band, in Staffordshire. A live coal fell into the platter, and in the explosion they were scorched, burnt. They were ragged black ghosts, in agony. The house was surrounded, and a company of armed men were firing into the court. They were wounded, shot down; Kit Wright was killed, and his brother. The others were wounded and on the ground. Four were taken prisoner. Percy and a friend were still on the ground while the others were being tied up, when the local men burst into the court, stripped them naked, stole their clothes and ornaments. They died, thirsty, bleeding, freezing, their wounds shivering open to the frost.

Waad, the Lieutenant, had Guy Fawkes on the rack. He had not been able to get a confession from him. The King had written 16 questions, none of which he had answered. The lords had waked all night; he had slept. Thirty minutes of stretching, and he did it; shaken, quivering, he said he would tell all he knew. Later that day he said he would talk to Cecil; and if you look at his signature on that statement, the rambling, tormented "Guido" and then he could not write — it will tell you.

Ben Jonson, standing in the Council chamber, denounced this plot as a Catholic poet. He was thirty, a big ardent man speaking for the laymen. He had become a Catholic seven years ago; he had fought against Spain in the Low Countries, and he was still against Spain; but he was horrified at murder engineered in the cause of God. He too spoke to Cecil, and undertook to work with the priests to help to hunt the conspirators. But nothing came of this.

At a meeting of the Council, it was determined that Northumberland — because of the dinner with Percy, and later because he had employed Percy without the customary oath — be "for the time placed under restraint" in the custody of the Archbishop of Canterbury at his palace at Croydon. Cecil wrote to the King's representatives at foreign courts, an equivocal letter reporting the commitment of the Earl and minimizing its importance.

Northumberland wrote from Croydon on the 8th of November, a statement about Thomas Percy which was backed up by the Earl's Auditor Ffotherley; and on the next day, he writes to the King, conscious of having giving offense but in no way expecting that James thinks he was in the plot :

Y^r Ma : in y^r function uppon earth is a God : your self owt of y^r justice and mercy seeks to imitate that great Master. He forgives those that repent. I avowe that I am sorrie in my minde of y^r displeasure (now got by my passions, and never imbraced in my thought with the lest joy in Intention) I beseche y^r ma : therefore hold on that imitation the world takes notice of in you in this case of mine

Save, I humbly crave y^r ma^{ty} the bird in my bosome : I meane my loyalty . . .

On the 10th, Northumberland heard that Thomas Percy had fallen wounded. It had been argued that a guilty man would have hoped for his death and silence; the Earl wrote to the Council, urging good medical treatment be given Percy, "for now he will tell truely." There is no record that a deposition was ever taken from Thomas Percy; however, the suspicion that he had worked with the Earl began to fade. Popham began to take a new tack, but all that came through was the fact that Percy had been a trusted courier from King James, and the promise from James of toleration for Catholics, urged by Northumberland in the hope of James's good reception in all of England.

Now the attempt was made to implicate Northumberland with Ralegh. Here, the Earl backed away again, saying, "He never had letters from me since his troubles."

King James, on the 27th of November, committed Northumberland to the Tower, there to wait trial in the Star Chamber. His castles in the north were seized; he was removed from all office, fined £30,000 — a sum greatly multiplied in twentieth-century currency — "and that he shall be returned Prisoner to the said Tower of London, from whence he came, there to remain Prisoner as before, during His Majesty's Pleasure."

His wife, boiling with horrors, imperious, fighting, humiliated by the Earl again and again, saw him go into the Tower where her brother had been killed and her first father-in-law imprisoned. Every provocation and loss reached her again. The rioting before Essex House and down Fleet Street had been transformed into this new rioting and dread. Dorothy Devereux with her lost brother, that demigod, her lost babies and the new living children, deserted and mocked for a shrew and now deserted again, betrayed again by the Tower, changed phase. It was too much; she crossed a threshold. The marriage went into a new place, and a faithful volcano sprang in her.

She would work for him, argue for him. Her anger would fight for him. This frightfulness could be beaten down. Surely the King saw she was Essex' sister, surely the King knew they had quarreled on his side, she had quarreled with Ralegh even when the Earl held him as his friend.

The charges were reduced from "heynous treasons" to "matters of errors." Surely Henry Percy would be out of the Tower soon.

James spoke of the Gunpowder Plot as his masterpiece. He took the fact of its frustration to mean the thwarting of his personal doom. The doom was derived from his mother, his relation to her, and her death by decapitation, the identical death that hacked Elizabeth's mother; from his father, who was exploded, and whom he never knew. James saved himself

from his devil-figure, the Spanish-looking devil breathing fire—
which he equated with smoking tobacco—by locking up
Ralegh; and he saved himself from being blown up by having
such advisors as Cecil, Northampton, Monteagle and the rest.

His doom through his mother and his father, his beliefs
about kingship and love, were the pallor of his relation to
women, and more deeply, in wildness and extravagance, his
relation with men.

His masterpiece of logic and the aversion of doom is com-
memorated in the Powder-Plot Room. This is a room in the
house of the Resident Governor of the Tower, Queen's House;
a room with oak panels, lit by a large window on the river.
A famous room, with shields of the Cecils, Howards, Blounts,
Somersets, Humes.

The walls are covered with invocations. One is clearly by
King James :

> James the Great, of Great Britain
> King, Illustrious for Piety, Justice, Prudence,
> Learning, Fortitude, Clemency, and other regal virtues;
> Of the Christian Faith, the Public Safety, and Universal and
> auspicious;
> Queen Anne, most serene daughter of Frederick the Second,
> invincible King of the Danes;
> Charles, Duke of York, to every virtue divinely disposed;
> Elizabeth, sister of both; most worthy of her parents;
> Hold these as the pupil of thy eye,
> Guard them, protect them from the wicked,
> Keep them fearless in all alarms
> Under the shadow of thy wings.

Then there are the panels. A votive panel from Sir William
Waad, heavy, pretentious, as anti-Catholic as the Fire Monument, finally ending with the treasonous hope and the miraculous detection, and his everlasting thanks.

There is a panel with the list of the conspirators' names. Then
there are illustrative panels, showing the Knights of the Garter
in their high offices—Cecil, Charles Howard, Blount, Henry

Howard — preparing to question a prisoner, and if gentle means would not evoke an answer, to proceed to the rack.

There is the panel with the line in Hebrew and in Latin which may be translated : He unfolds and brings into the light, from the obscure night, things deep in the vast earth and hidden in the darkness of fate.

And, last, there is a wooden bas-relief portrait of James over the mantelpiece. The face looks out with a look of bronze. It is not the relief that is powerful and curious, but the words under it. Suddenly, the deep life of James is spoken for; this is one of the few places where this man is seen at the psychic depth and height of man. These are the words as they stand, suspended forever :

VIVRE SANS REVE QU'EST CE

Hariot was arrested, as was Torporley, not for any connection with the Gunpowder Plot, but for casting the King's horoscope; it was still a matter of the king's fear.

LIVE WITHOUT DREAMING WHAT IS THIS

At the moment of the Gunpowder Plot, Hariot was engaged in casting the King's nativity with his Shropshire friend, Nathaniel Torperley. Torperley was not yet rector of Salwarpe, but always he was of the line of English divines whose concern is cast far past his village and his spiritual duties; or, rather, he takes his place among those who, like George Ripley before him, include other forms of imagination and reality in their lives. Torperley had worked with Vieta, the French mathematician, as secretary in Paris, and brought back to England word of the work in algebra which was bound in, locked in, to Hariot's explorations in unities and numbers.

But, in November 1605, it was the King's horoscope with which both Hariot and Torperley were involved.

Hariot was lodging at Essex House when his friend asked

him to "set the nativity." His answer was that he could find the exact time of the King's birth because there would have been cannon set off at Edinburgh right after the birth was announced.

Not having an *Ephemeris,* Hariot asked Torperley to spare him the trouble of calculating the houses, the "journate of the planets" by bringing him the chart of Stadius — which Torperley did — and Hariot drew up the horoscope and put it up at Essex House.

It was very likely that one of the household, in the storm over the Gunpowder Plot and the implication of everyone around Thomas Percy, informed on the existence of this horoscope, for on the 27th of November, Torperley signed a statement in answer to nine questions regarding this unlawful act. James had expressly forbidden the casting of his nativity, and Torperley confessed that the end of all casting of nativities is the judgment to be made on them.

He swore, however, that Hariot did the work for the sake of the art of understanding the truth. One reason Hariot gave was that it was his desire to see how the horoscope agreed with James' happy fortune in coming to the crown.

When it was cast, they asked Torperley, did you look upon it? Yes, he did, was the answer.

And what use did Hariot make of this nativity? Torperley, seeing the implications, said that he knew not, but that Hariot told him None.

Now came the question that showed who the real quarry was: How often, they asked Torperley, had you talked with my Lord of Northumberland? Torporley said, But once, which was at Syon before Queen Elizabeth's death.

Then Torperley told of Hariot's giving him the date of birth of that longed-for son of Northumberland who died; he confessed that he cast that son's nativity; and then, quailing, added that he was "not very sure of this."

His examiners hammered the question home : Did you not cast it a purpose to judge? Torperley rallied. He would not say that he did not; but he would say that he did not (the manuscript says "now") judge.

After this answer, which seems to have turned away the anger of the examination, there is no sign of Hariot's being followed by the charges, nor of Torperley's paying any penalty.

There are stories that James' dread of witches extended in a curious way to his own horoscope. Not that it was his own dread, this time. For Tycho Brahe, who was held by James in great respect and for good reason, and Kepler, as well as Hariot, acknowledged astrology as a branch of their own science of astronomy, and cast horoscopes. It is possible that the chart of his birth which James is reputed to have carried about with him was drawn by Tycho Brahe.

When James — as James VI of Scotland — sent to Denmark for a bride, it was the elder daughter of the King for whom he asked. In 1585, when the negotiations began as Hariot was sailing to the New World, it was for the Princess Elizabeth James was hoping; but in the exigencies of European diplomacy, she was given to the Duke of Brunswick. Anne, the younger sister, was twelve years old, "and howbeit Madame Elizabeth was the more beautiful, the Princess Anne was far from unlovely and for her age was taller and more fully developed than her sister."

Among rioting in Edinburgh four years later, the marriage was settled. It was solemnized by proxy late in August. At the end of the month Anne set out for Scotland, but her ship was driven by storms away from course. She was taken to Oslo where James sailed six weeks later with the Chancellor and 300 persons and celebrated the marriage on November 23rd. A month of festivities followed, and then James and his new Queen, with whom he was now deeply in love, travelled through Norway and Sweden. On January 21st of the New Year they crossed the Sound to Elsinore.

They stayed in Denmark late into the spring of 1590. On the 20th of March, James went to visit the great Tycho Brahe at his island observatory of Hveen. He arrived at eight in the morning, and stayed until three; Brahe entered in his diary : "Rex Schotiae venit mane H.8, abiit H.3." This meant a further link for James. Hanging on the library wall at Uraniborg, Brahe's house at Hveen, was the portrait of George Buchanan, James' tutor, the poet, humanist and historian whom James later repudiated as he began to love Lennox. Buchanan, with Peter Young, brought up the young James; both men were strong links with Denmark. Among the friends of Tycho Brahe's at this time was Rosenkrands, the Danish statesman; a cousin of his was Axel Gyldensterne, governor of Norway. Brahe had drawn Prince Christian's horoscope; the Duke of Brunswick asked for one; it may have been after this visit that Brahe drew King James' horoscope. It was now that James promised Brahe copyright in Scotland for thirty years for his writing, and wrote for Brahe at Uraniborg :

> Est nobilis ira Leonis
> Parcere subjectis et debellare superbos.
> Jacobus Rex.

What was in James' horoscope that he did not want seen by his subjects? In his birth chart, the moon is in Leo. Virgo is rising, with the Sun and Mercury in Cancer.

Two successive hours have been given for the time of his birth. Between nine and ten o'clock is as close as the biographers care to come. Sir James Melville of Halhall was Queen's Messenger and carried the news to Elizabeth of the birth between ten and eleven. George Buchanan wrote that Mary Queen of Scots gave birth somewhat after the ninth hour from midnight.

Critical, reserved and shy, a perfectionist, logical, but with reason not serving him once he became emotionally involved with an idea, says a 20th-century chart. "There seems to have been some underlying mental strain . . . which resulted in tenseness, depressive moods; he was also self-willed and perverse . . . Critical periods of upheaval, sudden endings and new beginnings, with resulting inevitable strain . . . Strong

physical desires and a sensuous nature . . . Friction, inadequate
emotional satisfaction, with resulting explosive and careless
behaviour . . . Little continuity of effort. Venus was in Taurus.

". . . Lucky, and was protected from anything particularly
awful happening.

"There was much kindness, intuition and understanding, and
yet complete obstinacy and rigidity."

There probably are very few scientists, or people educated
in rationally governed conduct, who will allow for this mode
of interpretation. Although its vocabulary will be different,
this horoscope must be very like the nativity cast by Hariot, and
it offers a few answers to questions.

In the front pages of a little book, now in the Rosenbach
collection, this has been written (before the printed collection
of Gabriel Harvey's writings, in a contemporary hand) :

"The planets be to the Signs, as the Soul is to the body : and
the Signs to the Planets, as the body to the Soul. *Erra pater.*
The one without the other, can do nothing. The A. B. C. of our
vulgar astrologers, especially such as are commonly termed
Cunning men, or Arts-men & some call them Wizards . . .

"It is not sufficient for poets to be superficial humanists : but
they must be exquisite artists, & curious universal scholars . . ."

More, of Chaucer, Digges, Spenser, Ronsard, Bartas. And
of the lack of skill with spheres, staff, astrolabe, and the other
instruments of science.

"But one sees it is otherwise today with Digges, with Hariot,
and with Dee." *Aureum calcar non rudium amealorum.*

The house in which Hariot lived at Syon was built before
1606, for in the accounts of 1606-07 Mr. Ingram records £20
spent for making a brick wall between the towre of her la :
lodgings and mr. heryotts house. This wall is measured four
years later, from her La : Garden to Mr. Herryotts house as

95' by 23'. There is also a bill for carpenters employed on a dormer window in Mr. Herriott's house.

We know from Hariot's will something about the rooms of that house. The parlor in the north, with a wooden box of maps at the northeast window; and the closets on the north side, with the furnaces; the library there, with its big table.

Among the drawings and plans of the grounds at Syon, there is one that shows a small house along a wall at the right side of Syon House. Tall trees grow there today, and there would seem to be no marks of Hariot's living quarters and laboratory. An air photo taken in summertime shows only the line of trees; but it is possible that a closely-read winter air view would allow the differences in earth that show that a building stood there to be visible.

Additional evidence is in Hariot's working papers, where one page shows the floor plan for five rooms of a house whose outlines appear to be the one in the drawings. These floor plans are drawn to show only one feature, the doors and the directions in which they open. They are freehand drawings. One can see plainly the chamber, the long study, the dining room, pantry, and kitchen.

In Hariot's working papers is the note, "for Virginia" and the 1606 voyage :

<pre>
        Bartholomew
Cap.   Gosnold   Mr. Percy
        Roger   for Virginia
Mr. Stranson
</pre>

with diagrams of prisms on the rest of the page.

Hariot's observations of the comet of 1607, a comet that much later came to be known as Halley's comet, were used more in Germany than in England. Two hundred years later, a young astronomer's first published paper was a reduction of Hariot's work. This paper was singled out by Olbers and von Zach. It may have been his own praise that began to drive

F. X. von Zach to become a champion of Hariot's and to try once more for the publication of his work that Hariot had long ago desired.

In Germany, von Zach, using the 1796 astronomical congress as a base, founded the first review of astronomical achievement. From Gotha the "Monatliche Correspondenz" went out into Europe.

Ralegh's agreement to transfer his interests in Virginia was by a contract calling in "the trading classes, the capitalists, whose aid later made possible the successful founding of the James-town Colony." It was Ralegh's double-edged spirit that insti-gated it, and the circumstances of his life : the despair and the conviction that England and the West were destined for a rich involvement; and the prison of these years.

The merchants and captains who took over from Ralegh were given one hundred pounds by him and special trading privi-leges. He reserved one-fifth of all gold and silver ore, for himself and his heirs. Richard Hakluyt was of these men; Sir Thomas Smith, first president of the East India Company and Captain Gosnold's brother-in-law, another.

When peace was made with Spain, the way was open for two companies, one in London, one in Plymouth, that would hold a charter for colonizing Virginia. The territory described in this charter, granted on April 10, 1606, extended from the Cape Fear River, North Carolina, to Bangor, Maine, in a strip includ-ing the offshore islands to 100 miles at sea, and mainland to 100 miles west of the coast.

Instructions given to the colonists in November gave the government to a council subject to a royal council of thirteen in England. Residents in Virginia were to have the legal rights of those who lived in England. The next month, further instruc-tions were given in a sealed document. Under Captain Newport while at sea, the settlers were to make a prescribed government, to choose the greatest westward-flowing river and "find the other sea; to look for minerals;" to write an account of themselves and the country, and specifically not "to write any letter of any thing that may discourage others."

The men stood in a great range. They were sent on a commercial and colonizing venture, in a spirit very different from White's and Hariot's, although it was in the hopes of the 1585 expedition. George Percy, the younger brother of Northumberland, was high in the ranks. The flag ship was commanded by Captain Newport, with 71 men; Captain Gosnold had the *Godspeed* with 52 men; and a pinnace, *Discovery,* carried 21. There were no women.

Sir Walter Cope said, in London : "The eyes of all Europe are looking upon our endeavors to spread the gospel among the heathen people of Virginia, to plant an English nation there and to settle a trade in those parts."

There was John Smith, who had soldiered in Turkey; he was 27, a year older than George Percy; Captain Wingfield, who had served in Ireland and the Low Countries; Captain Gosnold, who had sailed to New England for Ralegh. Smith, who was hardy, active, and used to the life they were now in, had little use for many of the others; and in the miseries of the first summer, these attitudes were deepened and inflamed. George Percy, whose ribbons and capes and plate we know from the Alnwick Account Rolls, had loved Virginia at first. In April, at the entrance to Chesapeake Bay, he wrote : "Fair meadows and goodly tall trees, with such fresh-waters running through the woods, as we are almost ravished at first sight thereof."

But after the first months at Jamestown, the Indian attacks, and the friendly visits, the hardships of the summer : worm-eaten barley, brackish water, diseases, fear and hatred, irritation with each other, and finally the death of 46 — almost half their number — by September, George Percy, the big, dark man, with his deepset brown eyes, living in the crude little house at Jamestown near the wooden church, wearing his Dutch beaver hat with the cypres band and the rose when he could, having with him five suits of silk, broadcloth, velveteen, and a best silk suit with taffeta facing, gold lace, gold buttons — George Percy knew there were never Englishmen left in a foreign country in such misery as these men were in this new discovered Virginia.

Part of the misery was the imbalance of their company. Out of 105, there were 12 laborers, and 4 carpenters against the wilderness.

Torture was among them; the wheel was used to break their bodies, one died chained to a tree, with a bodkin run through his tongue. George Percy tells of deaths like rhymes: "The 15th day, there died Edward Browne and Stephen Galthorpe. The 16th day, there died Thomas Gower Gentleman. The 17th day, there died Thomas Mounslie. The 18th day there died Robert Pennington, and John Martine, Gentleman."

When the second ship arrived, two women were on it — "Mistresse Forest and Anne Buras, her maid" — and more gentlemen. There were also several goldsmiths. "The worst mischief," said one of the planters, "was our gilded refiners, with their golden promises, made all men their slaves in hope of recompence. There was no talke, no hope, no worke, but dig gold, wash gold, refine gold, load gold" and load "a drunken ship with so much gilded durt."

John Smith had been up the Chickahominy where he was captured by Powhatan and condemned to die. Pocahontas, his young daughter, may have saved him; his brains were not clubbed out, and some bond of love was made. Powhatan was the friend of Smith from that moment forward; and peace was kept between this prime chief and the English while Smith lived in Virginia.

On his return to Jamestown, he was sentenced to be hanged by a lawyer on the Council against President Ratcliffe's instructions. Captain Newport, arrived early in January, at that moment saved Captain Smith, who was the town-builder and corn-planter of the next period. Smith wrote to England: "When you send again, I entreat you rather send but thirty carpenters, husbandmen, gardeners, fishermen, blacksmiths, masons, and diggers up to trees' roots, well provided, than a thousand such as we have."

They had no scientist, no Hariot.

Of Virginia, Smith mapped, listed resources, made his demands in the form of advice for colonization.

Of Virginia, he said : "Nothing is to be expected thence, but by labor."

Of Cape Hatteras, in this century. Hart Crane:

> To that deep wonderment, our native clay
> Whose depth of red, eternal flesh of Pocahontas —
> Those continental folded aeons, surcharged
> With sweetness below derricks, chimneys, tunnels —
> Is veined by all that time has really pledged us . . .
> And from above, thin squeaks of radio static,
> The captured fume of space foams in our ears —
> What whisperings of far watches on the main
> Relapsing into silence, while time clears
> Our lenses, lifts a focus, resurrects
> A periscope to glimpse what joys or pain
> Our eyes can share or answer — then deflects
> Us, shunting to a labyrinth submersed
> Where each sees only his dim past reversed.

A roaring of lions across the moat. This is a palace, a zoo. A place of execution. Hell, with good company.

When Ralegh entered the Tower for his long years, he was celled in the Bloody Tower, that wet cold place of murder. Two years later, Northumberland entered too, never to leave until after Ralegh's lifetime.

What will you allow prison to be? Cramps, nightmares. A memory machine. Ralegh would walk on the wall-top, and the sailors cheered as the ships passed, until he was forbidden that riverside. In the stone, the narrow stairs, the sense of thick blood (thick enough to build with), the carvings of other men's signs, names, dates. Rebels, priests, dangerous women.

They were all here, they are here in these times of Ralegh
and the Wizard Earl, who late in his imprisonment made his
list. Ralegh down twice (liberated for Guiana and his ships,
but that is years away), the Lady Arabella, the Earl of Somerset and Lady Somerset for the Overbury poisoning; Guy
Fawkes and the Gunpowder people; Overbury himself "for
refusing to go Ambassador" who stayed to his death; and the
priests and the Jesuits; the Ralegh people, and the page to one
of them; those who tried to help Arabella to escape; William
Seymour, for marrying Arabella; Mr. John Cotton, "for suspicion of writing a book," and Sir John Yorke and his lady "for
the play in his house in Yorkshire; Peacock, for witchcraft,
and a sea-captain for going to Guiana" being commanded to
stay. A hundred and thirty-one persons on this list, Keymis
and Digby, Cobham, Grey, all.

The watermen outside, bringing the bottle tribute, those
black leather wine-bottles called bombards, two out of each
cargo going to the Lieutenant of the Tower. John Taylor, the
water-poet, writes :

> From Water unto Wine : Sir William Waad
> Did freely and for nothing turn my trade.

And he cries out :

> O Bottles, Bottles, Bottles, Bottles, Bottles,
> Plato's Divine workes, not great Aristotles.

Hariot came to work with Ralegh and Northumberland.
He was never under sentence, excepting one short lost time;
but voluntarily he came to the Tower, and a great part of his
life was here. Bacon wrote : "Sir Walter Ralegh experiments
in chemistry; and along with him the Earl of Northumberland,
professed patron of learning; both of them intimately connected with Thomas Hariot, the great mathematician : valuable
allies all, if they could be procured."

We know their lives from words like these, from their own
words, from the stones rubbing our shoulders as we walk here,
and from the account rolls.

"Now, my Lords, as the Summer groweth on, I find this little Garden, that lieth all the Day upon the Sun, to be very close; these Galleries very noysome with the Savours from the Ditches. . . . These lower Parts are so wet after every Shower of Rain, as there is no stirring . . ."

We know the days. We know the payment to Waad for Northumberland's privilege to "make his own diet" in the Tower, that is, his own cook and supplies; and pendant rubies for the ears of Waad's daughter, bought by Dorothy Percy; and books, paper, and ink — books from John Bill; books of law, statutes, pleas, the Italian books, the histories; a wall to be built at Syon to Hariot's house; tobacco, cinnamon water, an instrument for the making of ponds, devised by Mr. Warner; journeys to Syon and London and the Court about his Lordship's causes; the preacher of the Tower; the groom that was hurt; repairs at the Tower, such as payment to bricklayers employed in paving Northumberland's walk upon the wall; building for Lord Percy in the Tower, mending the chimney in the kitchen, rent for the Brickhouse on Towerhill for the Countess; the barber for Northumberland and the corn-cutter; Scavengers at the Tower, 4*s*. 4*d*.; the household expenses for the London house; his Lordship's stillhouse at the Tower; bread for a year, £52 18*d*.; barrels and hogsheads of beer, £80 4*s*.; beef, mutton, meat tongue, meat foot, calves' heads, Maribones, £140 16*d*.; butter £35 14*s*. 1*d*.; eggs £13 5*s*. 3*d*.; flour, sweet oil, Cape olives, apples, pears, cream, artichokes, peas, gooseberries, lemons, oranges, filberts, salt oil, meal, Limoges mustard, salad herbs, westphalia oysters; to John Hall and James Turner, grocers : loaves of Madeira sugar, 37 lbs. at 16*d*. the pound; to John Davies for a hogshead of small Canary wine, claret, Rhine wine, white wine, malmsey, muscatel, Bastard wine, red wine, £118 3*s*.

Northumberland, thinking of his nightingale garden at Syon.

The rent for the auditors at Tower Hill and Essex House. Charcoal and sacks and loads of coal. To Dr. Turner for a

pomander against the plague. Dozens of bottles for the Frontig-
nac wine, and corks for stopping them. Horses, and even a
"gray fleabitten nag bought in Smithfield, £4.10s."

This Tower, where they come together, more than at any
time in their story. Ralegh, Northumberland, the prisoners.
Their wives, Dorothy Percy and Elizabeth Ralegh, and the
withholdings, the quarrels about money of the Percies (open
and taken to Knollys and to Court) and the great marriage
of Lucy Percy and Hay, that was to set Northumberland free,
a Prospero deliverance that he refused, it coming from a Scot
belonging to James.

The children : that Lucy, and Algernon Percy, the son.
Questions of the Tower, that they think of here behind stone :

Tell me Death —
Virginia — why was it let go?
How can the sons be shown the world?
How will the daughters live? And this is, though
   they seem not to know it, How can the daughters
   be shown the world?
What can become of these wives?
What stars look down?
What is the history of the world?
How to escape this prison, without escaping?
Can the Prince save us? This prince, the hope
   of the world, who loving Ralegh almost
   receives his freedom from King James,
   almost receives lost Sherborne, but takes
   a fever, is not saved by Ralegh's elixir,
   and dies, dies — Prince Henry, the hope
   for a new civilization.
What is this marriage of a beauty to a King's
   favorite?
What is the roaring of those lions, with these
   men in the cells?
Who goes to bed with each other in this prison?
What are the cries in the dark garden of the Tower?
What are those cries coming from the lowest cells,
   where the torturers are very busy?

What are the cries from the river?
How does the plague reach into all bodies, and
    what is the sound of that plague-bell?

The questions and the children, for they are questions. It is Hariot who will educate them, the self-committed, who passes into this prison and brings up Algernon to become Admiral and to rule the Caribbean, Bermuda, Virginia, all the doomed rich future full of promise and deep in this story. Hariot, Ben Jonson, Hues, and Warner, who devote their own lives to this overshadowed Tower time. As the editor of this book, John Simon, now does in an American jail with a black American prisoner, making a book out of tapes.

Hariot worked in this way, bringing materials, making calculations to be used by Ralegh, helping Northumberland. Did he work on the clock on the Tower wall, or measure the walks of these caged animals, Ralegh and Percy . . . this "caged bird," Prince Henry said of Ralegh. Did Hariot make that picture of time? Did he build Ralegh's laboratory, the little house on the grass of the healthier, drier side? These are the accretions on which live pearls, stories. Do we take them as myth or history? Where do we believe?

The world is here. The New World is asleep. Hariot makes the leap in this prison from the New World to the moon. He makes his great picture of the moon. He observes and maps and makes his leap.

The moon over the Thames.

This prison is an island and the world.

One of the accusations against Hariot that became famous had been used against him mightily in his lifetime — of one piece with the charges of wizardry, atheism, and "jugglery." It came up in Anthony à Wood's maunderings about Hariot's religious belief and the way in which he imparted this to the Earl of Northumberland and to Ralegh while the "compiling" of the *History of the World* was in process in the Tower.

"He could never believe that trite position Ex nihilo nihil fit," says Anthony à Wood of Hariot.

The debate over *nihil* goes as deep as the balancing of *to be* or *not to be*. It is recorded in the copybooks and in Shakespeare, whose long drama of nothing is the pivot on which the beginning of the action of *King Lear* turns.

Nothing will come of nothing.

Will it? Of what is the world made? You? The Universe?

Hariot writes : "Omnia fint ex nihilo & ex nihilo nihil fit — non contradicant."

All things are made of nothing and out of nothing nothing is made — these are not contradictory.

Francis Bacon, who has been seen as far removed from wild dreams by those who do not think of his hopes nor of his last act, his descent from his carriage to take up a handful of snow for the preservation experiment on the chicken (and it takes someone with great practical poetry, Bert Brecht, to tell that story), speculated on the great school he might found. He wrote, in the *Commentarius Solutus,* of

the setting-on work my Lord of Northumberland and Ralegh, and therefore Hariot, themselves being already inclined to experiments.

Francis Bacon appears to modern readers as a son of day, caught later in logic, but the false logic of the bribe refused, or the bribe taken but not honored. As a man of myth, he is a son of night; or, rather, he says that Eros is named thus, but not truly. He calls him Cupid, and declares that this is the most ancient of all the gods; of all things, except Chaos. "Though he was thought by some to be the son of the Night, he had no parents." This is very different from the lineage of Venus, the daughter of Saturn, who had castrated his father Uranus and was in turn castrated by his son Jove. Cupid is "the appetite or instinct of primal matter . . . the natural motion of the atom; which is indeed the original and unique force that constitutes and fashions all things out of matter."

But the movement of atoms, not being generated, is — after God — "the cause of causes, itself without cause."

Cupid is shown as a young boy to declare the simplicity of the seeds of things.

To know the seeds, that is great indeed.

He is naked to show that atoms have no physical qualities which we can — by sense alone — perceive.

The atom has long-range powers in space; these are his arrows.

And he is blind.

These were the years when Bacon wrote of myth and of the primal quality of all bodies, movement. He stands to us for the new naturalism; but into this went his years of the Sphinx and her claws and the questions of travellers; and of Orpheus, who is lost and beaten down, like those philosophers who lose in the contest with nature anrd then retire to solitude. Then they found cities; then, their influence is exerted over mankind, to civilize us.

Bacon writes of Oedipus and Prometheus and Pan; of the way of experience, Pan's chase, not lit but guided in the dark as if by a hand; proceeding by "varying, exchanging, extending, inverting, constraining, joining, connecting, and selecting experiments" — the method of discovery.

Bacon describes the alchemists as similar to "those husbandmen who searching for treasure turned the land up and rendered it fertile." Casting back to the Argo, there was the story that the Golden Fleece was a book, on parchment, that contained the secret of the philosopher's stone. And casting back further, we are given the identity of Joseph and Hermes Trismegistus, which may come nearer to the statement at the core of this art : there is transformation of all things, our dreams are the language of transformation.

James wanted to make peace between England and Spain; but he also wanted civility along the Borders, and in the early years of his reign, he was able under pretext to imprison the Earl and to "straighten" and pacify the lands he hoped would become the "middle shires" — with one king, one faith, one language; one law, one parliament, one people alike in manners and allegiance.

"In 1607, James boasted that the Borders, once desolate, lawless and bloody, 'are now become the navel or umbilic of both kingdoms, planted and peopled with civility and riches. Their churches begin to be planted, their doors stand now open, they fear neither robbery nor spoiling. They now live every man peacefully under his own fig-tree.' "

Within a few years, however, his prerogative was challenged by Coke, who stood for the common law and not the idea of divine right, nor the ordinances of the Book of Judges, nor the Roman law of Scotland. James believed — all through his huge quarrels with Coke — that he held the judgeships, the commandment and the oath, and that all judicial authority flowed from the King. This was backed philosophically by Hobbes, who says in *Leviathan* that all honor rests in the king, and that all men are equal in that their honor is so held, and their allegiance is to fight for their king.

Coke answered the King when he said he would defend the common law. On the contrary, said Coke, the common law defended the king. James trembled with anger. Coke's words, he shouted, were those of a traitor . . . "His Majesty fell into that high indignation as the like was never known to him, looking and speaking fiercely with bended fist, offering to strike him, which Lord Coke perceiving fell flat on all fours, humbly beseeching his Majesty to take compassion on him."

Hariot wrote out, copied out, in his working papers this of the Elizabethan corporations :

There is great difference betwixte a corporation privileged for only trade; and a corporation privileged for planting and trade; and a corporation privileged only for planting. Of the first we have examples of many corporations : the Muscovy company, Turky, Barbary, Guiny, Spaynishe, and others which now become well to stand profited by their trade and expand well.

Of the other two we have not no especiall example that have not proved well, Sᵣ Humphrey Gilbert for planting and for trading in Norumbega and Sᵣ W. R. for Virginia.

Hariot was familiar with the work of Josephus a Costa. With a drawing of a rose of the winds, among his papers, and a naming of the winds according to A Costa : Tramontana, Greco, Levante, Sirocco, Mezogiorno, Garbino, Ponente, and Maestro, the Mediterranean listing, he gives us the translations :

N	Tramontana	Septentrio	Aparetias
S	Mezzo giorno	Auster	Notus
E	Levante	Subsolanus	Apeliotes
W	Ponente	Favonius	Zephyrus
NE	Greco	Aquilo	Boreas
SE	Sirocco	Vulturnus	Eurus
SW	Garbino	Africus	Lips.
NW	Maestro	Corus	Argestes

Part of the training of anyone reading charts or texts on navigation.

He also sets down 20 textual corrections to Josephus.

Diego Columbus left some money to a Lisbon tobacco-merchant in 1523; the Spanish and Portuguese will laugh at the lateness of the English.

Hawkins saw the Indians of Florida using tobacco in 1565, and it is said that Hawkins brought back the knowledge. But Howes, who went on with Stow's *Annals,* adds that "Sir Walter Ralegh was the first that brought Tobacco into use, when all men wondered what it meant." This wonder recurs with every new intoxication — every stimulant. The sedatives do not excite this curiosity; but chocolate, coffee, tea, and in our time again, marijuana, hashish and the rest — and still tobacco. It was Ralegh who brought it over from a medicine to a fashion. His habit began after Hariot brought it back.

Ralegh smoked while Essex went on the way to his execution; Essex called for tobacco on the Islands voyage, in 1597, when the enemy was approaching, and when the first volley was heard, "cast his pipe from him."

Shakespeare nowhere mentions tobacco.

In 1597, tobacco cost 35*s*. a pound; in 1599, £4 10*s*. was paid for that quantity. In 1602, five pounds cost 50*s*.; in 1603, an ounce of pudding-cane tobacco (comparable to plug tobacco) cost 3*s*. Virginia was second only to Trinidado in popularity, and Orinoco came after that.

But in 1604, King James' *A Counterblast to Tobacco* appeared, and with it a duty on tobacco of 6*s*. 8*d*. on every pound entering the country. The king railed against the "barbarous Indians," the "two or three Savage men" who "were brought in, together with this Savage custom. But the pity is, the poor wild barbarous men died, but that vile barbarous custom is yet alive." He saw the use as "vile" and went on to speak of "the force of that natural Self-love in every one of us . . . as we cannot be content unless we imitate every thing that our fellows do . . . like Apes, counterfeiting the manners of others, to our own destruction. For let one or two of the greatest Masters of Mathematics in any of the two famous Universities, but constantly affirm any clear day, that they see some strange apparition in the skies : they will I warrant you be seconded by the greatest part of the Students in that profession . . ." He echoes Hariot in talking of the drowsy lazy belly-god.

In our time, we are familiar with the calculations of coming world populations dense enough to strangle the cities, to use up any foodstuffs that exist — these predictions never deal with potential — and still go starving, to crowd beyond all easy habitation every inch of earth. Hariot, at the edge of the seventeenth century, made these reckonings :

The number of persons y^t may stand on the earth—424, 705,528,000,000 — figuring of acres 250,000 = 5$\frac{5}{11}$ acres (note; rivers & waste included as before)

The issue from one man & one woman in 240 yeares may be more than can inhabit the whole earth. /Supposing the first man & woman have a chylde every yeare, one male & an other female./ 2. That the children when they are 20 yeares old & upwarde doe allso every yeare beget a childe, one yeare male & an other yeare female./ 3. That all are living at the end of 240 yeares./

The number of males (5034303437
females (5034303437
persons 10068606874

That in 400 yeares upon the former suppositions, there will in all be more men than can stand on the face of the whole earth. In (my table) I finde that in 340 yeares they will make a number of 14 places. Therefore in 400 yeares they will make a number of 16 places which is more than can stand on the face of the earth.

This is a demonstration of the speed of multiplying; our equivalent of the famous answer of the vizier who was to be rewarded for his services, and asked only for as much grain as would satisfy these terms : on a chessboard, 1 grain on the first square, 2 grains on the second square, 4 grains on the third, and so doubled each time. Not enough grain in the kingdom to fulfill his requirement.

Hariot continues, calculating space and population for England alone. "That in every 40 yeares there is . . . a new generation. Therefore in 6000 yeares there are 150 generations. Therefore there have ben of persons in 6000 yeares 7 000 000 000

150   1050 000 000 000.

There being 50 000 miles square in England there there [sic] may stand in England 300,000 000 000 persons./ The former number is three times greater & therefore theyre place of stand-ing must be allso three times greater than England."

They made anagrams to amuse themselves.The changes rung on letters are scattered through these papers. Sometimes words are chosen to stand for series of numbers, sometimes for lines of poetry; again and again, for the letters of his own name :

Thomas Hariotus

Tu homo artis, hus
homo hus ut artis
homo hasta utris
vitus
vutis
humo astra hosti
trahis hosti musa.
O trahit hos musa.
Oh, os trahit musa
oho trahit musus
oho, trahis, mutas
oho, sum Charitas

and again

Inopinabilis mars
and

oho, trahit musas
oho, trasit mutas
oho, sum charitas

Among his notes on the Gospels, he cites two verses of John 8 : verse 25 for God at the origin, in the beginning and the nature of intelligence; and verse 44, "diabolus a principio homicida," where devil, murder, and the beginning come together.

In February, 1610, Donne applied for the post of Secretary of Virginia — John Chamberlain writes that Donne "desires to go." We have no record of the first time that this wish took form, nor of the reasons why Donne was not given the post, comparable to that of Hariot with the Grenville expedition. Virginia had just gone through the terrible "Starving Time" under George Percy, and Donne would almost certainly have spoken with Hariot and Northumberland about the country and his chances. He wished to be sent with Lord Delaware to Mulberry Point.

Donne lived at Mitcham during this time, and went when he could to London, staying in his rooms in the Strand, ill and poor, and concentrated on poems. From 1609 to 1611 is the period of his *Pseudo-Martyr,* with its attack on recusants and on Bellarmin.

In April, 1610, on two successive days, Donne was given Master of Arts degrees at Oxford and at Cambridge.

Donne would be made a Doctor. King James was not going to leave Cambridge until this was accomplished. But Donne was a Son of Night, and a Shadow-Man. In one of Chamberlain's letters, reaching us in full immediacy, he writes to Dudley Carleton, "John Donne and one Cheke went out Doctors at Cambridge with much ado after our coming away by the King's express mandate, though the Vice-Chancellor and some other of the heads called them openly 'filios noctis' and 'tenebriones' that sought thus to come in at the window, when there was a fair gate open. But the worst is that Donne had gotten a reversion of the Deanery of Canterbury, if such grants would be lawful, whereby he hath purchased himself a great deal of envy, that a man of his sort should seek 'per saltum' to intercept such a place from so many more worthy and ancient Divines."

This jump was something for which Hay always took the

credit. He thought that his persuasion "first begat" in Donne the "purpose to employ your extraordinarily excellent part in the affairs of another world."

Ignatius His Conclave seems to have followed this period, although its exact date is uncertain. It is surely written after Galileo had the telescope and published *Star Message,* for Donne offers his ecstasy on the summoning of Galileo of the stars. There is no word here of Hariot. But there is a curious couplet in the Holy Sonnets.

Donne has changed phase. He has written his poems; now it is sermon-time. In this prose he speaks of Galileo, of Kepler, of Tycho Brahe; but never of Bruno, never of Hariot. He writes : "And with the same ease as you passe from the earth to the *Moone,* you may passe from the *Moone* to the other *starrs,* which are also thought to be world, and so you may beget and propagate many *Hells,* and enlarge your *Empire,* and come nearer unto that high seate which I left at first." But these words are in the mouth of Lucifer. He is speaking to Ignatius about Galileo and his glass.

In Donne's poems, there are several namings of astrologers and astronomers

> whereas they spie
> A new-found Starre, their Opticks magnifie . . .

He asks us, in his poems

> Know'st thou how blood, which to the heart doth flow,
> Doth from one ventricle to th'other goe?

He does his reverence to her

> Who could not lacke, what e'er this world could give,
> Because shee was the forme, that made it live . . .

He does not speak of Ralegh; these lines run with Ralegh :

> Shee, shee is gone; she is gone; when thou knowest this,
> What fragmentary rubbidge this world is
> Thou knowest, and that it is not worth a thought;
> He honors it too much that thinkes it nought.

Thinke then, my soule, that death is but a Groome,
Which bringe a Taper to the outward roome . . .

These appeared in 1612. Who comes first? who after?

And new Philosophy calls all in doubt

goes on to

And freely men confesse that this world's spent,
When in the Planets and the Firmament
They seeke so many new; then see that this
Is crumbled out againe to his atomies.

Donne does not speak directly of Hariot; but these lines
are in the fifth of his Holy Sonnets, which begins

I am a little world made cunningly
Of Elements, and an Angelicke spright,
But black sinne hath betraid to endless night
My worlds both parts, and (oh) both parts must die.

Everything of the split and the betrayal and the being whirled
together and condemned are here. At once we move in this
full energy to an invocation. The Holy Sonnets have many
invocations; most are to God, some to angels or to the soul
of the poet. This speaking, however, is different in nature : the
poet is speaking to someone with disinctly human functions :

You which beyond that heaven which was most high
Have found new sphears, and of new lands can write . . .

Who is this who looks beyond the sky and writes of "new
lands"? I know of only one person in Donne's age who combined both of these. Or does he mean us to think of one of
the star-captains? He moves to an image of sight :

Poure new seas in mine eyes . . .

(No, not sight; but weeping and washing)

that so I might
Drowne my world with my weeping earnestly,
Or wash it if it must be drown'd no more :

New spheres, new lands, drowning.

Donne was never allowed to go to Virginia, nor to Ireland.

He did go again to the Continent with James Hay, when Hay had already been created Lord Doncaster and sent on a peace mission that was half parade, half laughing-stock.

His life and world would have to be changed, but from within. Donne never lost interest in Virginia. But he failed in his plan to transform his life, the life of his family; ill, penniless, unable to make his life move, he was caught between Mitcham and the Strand.

He had applied for the work that Hariot did, twenty years before. Older than Hariot, without training for it — except, perhaps, the work with Egerton and the brief time as Member of Parliament — he was refused the position of secretary of Virginia.

The man who would make all things new.

Chamberlain writes to Dudley Carleton that Donne seeks to be preferred secretary of Virginia. There is no further word. We do not know why he was refused, nor what Donne was told about the reasons.

But at this time, Sir George More at last paid the dowry so long withheld from Anne Donne, and there was at last no further pinch of money.

In December, John Pory, a friend of Donne's and also a Cambridge man, brought a letter from Sir Henry Goodyer about the money confiscated to the Crown. The letter spoke confidently about how easy it would be to get a good part of this money for Virginia. "You see," he continued, "that as long as there is any life left in the nest, I never leave laying."

Pory was becoming known as an industrious, helpful and energetic man, basically different from wild Jack Donne, who now was not writing the lyrics of his youth — Ben Jonson said that he wrote his best before the age of twenty-five — but *Biathanatos* of last year. Not solid. Not at all the man to go to Virginia.

He was not sent; a hundred boys and girls that were starving in the streets were sent. Donne wrote

O my America, my new found land . . .

218

It was a woman who was his new world.

He wrote

> We have added to the world Virginia, and sent
> Two new starres lately to the firmament.

Much later, as Dean of St. Paul's, Donne was a contributor to the Virginia Company. And, after Hariot's death, Donne preached a famous sermon to that Company, urging them, during a time of financial trouble, to cast far ahead. "The Plantation shall not discharge the Charges, not defray it selfe yet; but yet already, now at first, it shall conduce to great uses . . .

"You shall have made this *Iland,* which is but as the *Suburbs* of the old world, a Bridge, a Gallery to the new, to joyne all to that world that shall never grow old, the Kingdome of Heaven. You shall add persons to this Kingdome, and to the Kingdome of Heaven, and adde names to the Bookes of our Chronicles, and to the Booke of Life . . ."

"Bless it so in this calme," he prays, "that when the tempest comes, it may ride it out safely."

But it was to Donne's friend, John Pory, that the post of secretary for Virginia went.

The Indians of Virginia, says Hariot, think of the sun, moon, and stars as "petty gods" with the other gods of a principal order made first as instruments of creation, and "one only chief and great God, who hath been from all eternity."

But the moon, the moon, the first sight of whom none of us can remember, has always until the week in which I write this page, been the white intact; the untouched — but in this year by man-made machine — the longed-for, the cold, the witness of grief, of joy by night; reminder of the sun, of many things; related to earth, thrown off — is this Eve cut out of Adam's side — or between this planet and some other planet?

battered by meteors? carrying concealed properties? keeping
one face averted until man flew to the other side in these years.
And here in this country, in so deep an England-and-Spain, a
Montague-and-Capulet relation with Russia, even this Soviet
flight was doubted by shopkeepers, who said to me that the
photos were false.

My edition of Lucian is called *Trips to the Moon*. Not only
do we come to one contemporary use of "trip," but this small
book begins with "Instructions for Writing History," and "A
True Report," which binds together the parts of our relation
to the moon : observation, fantasy, history, or whatever we call
that attempt to sort out the past which lives in the present and
which I call "traces."

Well may they say war is the parent of all things, that's
Empedocles talking, when one action can make so many historians.

It is the easiest thing in the world for a man to write history
if he can but say what comes uppermost, says Lucian.

These men (the ones who only praise) seem not to know that
poetry has its particular rules and precepts; and that history
is governed by others directly opposite, says Lucian.

In history, nothing fabulous can be agreeable, says Lucian.

But the moon, the moon. Not always the white intact, sometimes the bending goddess in the cave of Latmos, curved over
the young man.

And the fearless eye-witness, the historian of fact, the one
who makes "a kind of diary"? A diary of the moon; a noc-
turnal until we move into space, that's into day.

I shall at least say one thing true, when I tell you that I lie,
says Lucian.

"Once upon a time, then, I set sail from the Pillars of Hercules,
and getting into the Western Ocean, set off with a favorable
wind . . ." Out of a certain impatience of mind and thirst after
novelty, with fifty like-minded companions.

The storm comes now, this is a storm-born voyage. Seventy-
nine days of tempest here. Then an island, calm and bright, a

pillar, a river of wine, and "large vines full of grapes." They slept one night on shore. The next day a most violent whirl-wind rose; the ship was lifted up. Hang they did, for seven days and nights; and then landed on a tract of land, "round, shining, and remarkably full of light."

Now come the men who ride on vultures, and the emperor of the moon, who is Endymion. That spot, he told us, which now looked like a moon to us, was the earth. Here my edition of Lucian has a note : "Modern astronomers are, I think, agreed, that we are to the moon just the same as the moon is to us. Though Lucian's history may be false, therefore his philosophy, we see, was true (1780)." Another follows : ("The moon is not habitable, 1887.")

The story follows; I will not tell it here. But after it comes the *Icaro-Menippus,* the next step, as we all have always known. The next step after the moon is Jupiter.

Menippus

It is no dream, I assure you; I am just arrived from Jupiter.

Menippus found that "everything here below, such as riches, honors, empire and dominion, were all ridiculous and absurd, of no real value or estimation, considering them, withal, as so many obstacles to the study of things more worthy of con-templation, I looked up towards nobler objects, and meditated on the great universe below me; doubts immediately arose con-cerning what philosophers call the world . . .

"I beheld the stars, scattered as it were, by the hand of chance, over the heavens; I saw the sun, and wished to know what it was; above all, the nature of the Moon appeared to me most wonderful and extraordinary; the diversity of the forms pointed out some hidden cause which I could not account for . . ."

And the philosophers he asked "only threw me into greater doubt and uncertainty, by puzzling me with atoms, vacuums, beginnings, ends, ideas, forms, and so forth."

He meets Empedocles; he sees the earth, here a sacrifice,

there a burial; some at war, some betraying each other, some tilling their fields, some making journeys, some merchandising, some robbing and plundering, the Spartans flogging their children, and the Athenians perpetually quarrelling and going to law with each other. "It was just as if a number of dancers, or rather singers, was ordered to leave the chorus, and sing his own song . . . You may imagine what kind of a concert this would make."

The discordant music of the earth.

He carried a message from the moon to Jupiter. It is the god, you know, and not the planet. It is we, in our own time, who dream of going to Jupiter once the moon is reached in life as in dream; as Galileo, as Hariot, did in the same year by telescope; Galileo not knowing that he would face the Inquisition, but Hariot already full of similar knowledge, both of his patrons, those handsome men of power and pride, prisoners in the stone rooms of the Tower.

Hariot's drawings of the moon have come down to us as a few pages on observations made at Syon dated for day of the year, and hour, and one saying that he saw with difficulty because of his rheum.

There is another drawing of the full moon, everything very clear and as we know it. There is no word nor signature on this moon-map, also among Hariot's papers at Petworth. But the assumption made is that this is Hariot's drawing, made in this year of the spread of the telescope and of the publication of *The Star Messenger*. The crater of Copernicus is clear, with its radiating marks. An astronomer who was shown this drawing, with no hint of its provenance, guessed at a date 150 years later, and at an instrument of a power that had not been developed until long after Hariot's time.

Born two years after Hariot and surviving him, Francis Godwin (1562-1633) wrote between 1580 and 1632 the story of a moon-flight. It was not published until after Hariot's lifetime (in 1638) and became popular, going through many editions in England and in three translations. Godwin's *The Man in the Moone* tells his story as autobiography. A Spaniard, Gonsales, is put ashore at "St. Hellers" and trains "a certaine kinde of wild *Swans*" to come to him, to perform tricks, to carry burdens, then a lamb, and finally the "Engine" that can carry him on a nine-day flight to the moon.

The people on the moon send their children who "doe amisse" to the earth, where they are exchanged for other children. The place where the moon-children are left is "a certaine high hill in the North of *America,* whose people I can easily beleeve to be wholly descended of them, partly in regard of their colour, partly also in regard of the continuall use of Tobacco which Lunars use exceeding much, as living in a place abounding wonderfully with moysture, as also for the pleasure they take in it, and partly in some other respects too long now to be rehearsed."*

Swift follows, and Cyrano de Bergerac; and very soon our own time. As I write, it begins to be the morning of the day of the first manned moon-flight.†

I had looked at the drawing of the whole moon by Hariot many times, in England and in New York. It was before me on the table; I looked at it long, its spreading seas, the hatching of darknesses, the craters. It is a map as well as a drawing, I remember; it is really that, and to be used. I bring out another map with which Hariot is identified, the map of Virginia credited to John White, and bearing White's name on a legend at the left of the engraving made by De Bry. On the table, side by side, the two maps seem to have very little in common.

*Goodwin, Francis, *The Man in the Moone,* Hereford, 1959. The quotation comes from p. 105 of the 1638 ed. A preface, by E. M., to the 1638 editions says, "That there should be *Antipodes* was once thought as great a *Paradox* as now that the *Moon* should bee habitable. But the knowledge of this may seeme more properly reserv'd for this discovering age: In which our Galilaeusses can by advantage of their spectacles gaze the Sunne into spots, & descry mountaines in the *Moon.*"

† This passage was finished after the rest of this book.

One is signed by water, the ocean, the Sound and all the water-formed sand-bars and the shallows; the many rivers and Chesapeake Bay . . . not as many rivers as Guiana, also mapped by Hariot.

Suddenly something jumps out of the maps, with that startling abrupt movement by which I recognize the authentic, a movement that is no movement at all, like the famous moment in Zen doctrine when the snow is let fall from the branches of trees. An identity seemed to leap out before me from the maps. From one, the circles which we know as the craters of the moon, and named for astronomers. From the other, the circles which are the palisaded villages of the Virginia Indians. Both with their vertical lines — one to show steep darkness, the other the stockade of poles. Both circles very human, part of the bonds that link Virginia and the moon through human perception. Through Hariot. Through ourselves.

[*1610*]

At midnight, at Syon, that October night, Hariot saw for the first time one of the moons of Jupiter. It was Wednesday, October 17, 1610, and he records the first three sightings, then and twice more at intervals of one hour. He draws a diagram of huge Jupiter, keeping its diameter in relation to the one moon he sees (drawn as an asterisk) and he notes its distance as three minutes from Jupiter. He writes at the head of the page : My first observation of the new planets.

A month later, he is in London, "at Neales in black friers." It is Friday, November 16th, from 9 to 10 in the evening of a cloudy night with several heavy showers, and some clear patches. He sees Jupiter rise on the eastern horizon and begin his low ascent, with one moon 9 or 10 degrees away, at what we now call one o'clock. He draws this carefully, and puts a dot in line with the moon, but close to Jupiter. "Sometimes I thought I saw an other 3′ or 4′ of."

Still in London the following Monday, at 9 o'clock he makes

another sighting, and sees the large moon, one of the four Galilean moons seen for the first time in Padua at the beginning of the year by Galileo, who announced the discovery in *Starry Message* in March — news that leapt through Europe.

Hariot sees the large moon — Ganymede? — four or five degrees from Jupiter.

The next Wednesday, November 28th, he is again home at Syon. At 9 o'clock, about the time of its rising, Hariot sees the same moon 1½ degrees, or a diameter (he notes) from Jupiter; and he makes other sightings on December 4th and 7th. At 9 o'clock on Friday, December 7th, he notes one sighting, and another at 5 in the morning (sunrise is not until almost 8 a.m. in England at this date) he sees two "well and perfectly." This time he says who his companion is. "S.W. [Sir William] Lower also saw them."

On the 11th, Tuesday, he observes at 9 in the evening and again at 6 in the morning. He sees two moons, "the utmost fayrest and about 9' or 10' frō ♃ in centro. The other 5' a centro ♃ but the others before and after frō the [word illegible to me] of ♃."

He is playing, too, the word games that he does during these nights. He and Nathaniel Torporley had started some time before, on the other side of the page, with the words set for anagrams :

salve umbistineum geminatum Martia proles

He wrote an alphabet below the line, and marked off each letter occurring in it, and then added at once :

Imensi tu vult.

Then the four anagrams that Torporley made.

The game is revealing in its range and combinations dealing with verbal meanings, inkblot meanings which being verbal in nature carry that force, with the visible preoccupations of the player.

Hariot had written :

> Galilei prosopopeia ludibunda.
> Penem meum minus stabilem arsa virago tulit.
> Penem immensi stabilem tum vult arsa virago.

Now, on the side of the page with the observations of the satellites of Jupiter, he writes his own name in Latin, Thomas Hariotus, and three anagrams to which he comes back all during his life :

> oho trahit musus.
> oho trahis mutas.
> oho sum charitas.

The last sighting on this page is on December 12th, as Jupiter is beginning to seem to go backward. On this night, Hariot watched at 9 and at 6 in the morning. He saw two moons, one about 6′ away; then, in the morning, he saw one "easterly and cleare, 3′ or 4′ from Jupiter; "one other westerly, as I thought, 10″ or 15″ from Jupiter."

Hariot does not note the nature of his telescope, nor its power, nor the date of its making — nor information on how he acquired it. Did he buy it? make it? did Kit Tooke grind the glass?

The astonishing thing that struck watchers in Europe, holding their new telescopes — known before, used in Holland, but not before brought to these powers of magnification — was that they seemed to be looking at themselves for the first time. They were looking at a solar system. This is how it is, they said, and these "planets" do move around Jupiter, not around the earth. The four moons were named for Cosmo de Medici by Galileo, dedicated to a patron. But it was Galileo's name by which they would be known; until, power by power, the ability to see and make refracting telescopes developed, and much later reflecting telescopes. Then something further became visible. There were not only the four Galilean moons, there were others; and this is not an analogy with the solar system, for two of these newly seen moons travel in a direction contrary to all the others, and were evidently acquired by different means, and possibly at different times, from the larger moons.

Galileo was not a revolutionary in religion, but in science. Bruno, your revolutionary entire, ventured back to Italy, to Venice, and was dragged to Rome and burned. Descartes brought into his thinking the system he wanted to destroy; and if you dream along with Descartes on a winter night in 1619, you will understand why, deep in yourself.

Bacon wanted new discoveries and powers, and saw this as "the true and lawful end of the sciences." He wrote :

> Now among all the benefits that could be conferred upon mankind, I found none so great as the discovery of new arts, endowments, and commodities for the bettering of man's life. For I saw that among the rude people in the primitive times that authors and inventions of discoveries were consecrated and numbered among the gods . . .
>
> Above all, if a man could succeed, not in striking out some particular invention, however useful, but in kindling a light in Nature — a light which should in its very rising touch and illuminate all the border-regions that confine upon the circles of our present knowledge; and so spreading further and further should presently disclose and bring into sight all that is most hidden and secret in the world — that man (I thought) would be the benefactor indeed of the human race — the propagator of man's empire over the universe, the champion of liberty, the conqueror and subduer of necessities.

This is Bacon at his most inclusive of himself, using everything he cares for, in science, myth, history, and his own audacity, the hero as subduer of necessity, mocking the tabu against hubris, setting forth Hariot, Gandhi, Freud, Keats, any hero you hold.

Coleridge makes a resonance of this when he says, "A new light was struck by Hariot," and it seems impossible that there is not more to be found of Hariot in Coleridge, since everything he says of Bruno would seem to lead us back to our man.

Recognition of Hariot in England did not rise to the surface until another lifetime of the alliance of great capacities, this time, between Coleridge and Humphry Davy.

In 1796, the two poets, Coleridge and Southey, with Poole, volunteered as subjects for Davy's experiments in nitrous oxide, the beautiful stimulant which provides dreams of so profound a perspective and so catenary a form that their joy is probably not to be surpassed by anything in waking or intoxication. Coleridge, in his dealings with the history of ideas, comes to Hariot : he speaks of the tendency to concentrate on one principle that chances "to exercise a predominant attraction." He begins his monologue with Gilbert, "a richly gifted contemporary of Bacon," and the work with the magnet, and then goes on :

> Shortly after, a new light was struck by Hariot, followed up by Descartes and others; and the restoration of ancient geometry to its lawful rank and dignity, aided by the modern invention of algebra, transferred the ascendancy to the science of mechanics, which ended in placing the mechanical, or atomic philosophy, on the philosophic throne.

He speaks of the domination, in its wide spread . . . and soon he begins to make his own moves toward unity, moves only partly understood even by his friends and supporters. "In the Hebrew poets," he writes in the crucial letter to Sotheby, "each thing has a life of its own, and yet they are all one life. In God they move and live and *have* their being; not *had,* as the cold system of Newtonian Theology represents, but *have.*"

If you think of the telescope as it seems to appear in the world, it arrives as a scientific instrument, yes, and also as a toy. The story says that about the year 1600, a child was moving around the Lippershey shop, in Holland, picking up lenses there and looking through them. We are not told the name of this child, and the story is told as legend; but this kind of play is a source. At the moment at which we stare now, the child looked through the lens in his hand at another lens in the window. "He noticed" (the words are Bernal's) "that it made things outside seem nearer.

"The fact that no scientific genius was required to invent the telescope shows that it was long overdue. The need for it had always existed, but nothing was done because it was not thought to be realizable."

The notion of "overdue" is curious, rather like saying that a man is "born too soon." There is really no way for either to be true. But the statement "nothing was done because it was *not thought to be realizable*" appears to me to be an excellent statement of a flaw central to our way of thinking. No; there is another flaw. It is central to our education, and only that. The proof is exactly in this history : it was a child who saw that a new arrangement could make a new perception. He had not been trained to believe that this was unrealizable. This legend has the power of a myth. Between this child and Hariot we have the double source of the period stretching from whenever you please to our own moment, with all the forces of penalty on the other side, burning Bruno, stopping Galileo — (no; he submitted) — forgetting Bruno, forgetting Hariot. Not forgetting Galileo. He had the power to be remembered, to bring the Copernican theory through.

And the child had not learned that far sight was not realizable.

Hariot searchers are beginning to ask : Is it not possible that Pocahontas may have had the telescope before Galileo?

That is, of course, that Hariot says he brought perspective glasses to Virginia. We know his instruments were lost in the shoal water, or left behind. Did some chief have one, and did he give it to his daughter? Was she as ready for it as the Netherlands child in Lippershey's shop?

Thoreau has the clearest sight of Ralegh's speech, and says of this in his Journals, in terms of the America where Ralegh never arrived, farther west than his men ever knew :

"There is a natural emphasis in [Sir Walter Ralegh's] style, like a man's tread, and a breathing space between the sentences, which the best of modern writing does not furnish. His chapters are like the English parks, or say rather like a Western forest, where the larger growth keeps down the underwood, and one may ride on horseback through the openings. All the distinguished writers of that period possess a greater vigor and naturalness than the more modern, — for it is allowed to slander our own time, — and when we read a quotation from one of them in the midst of a modern author, we seem to have come suddenly upon a greener ground, a greater depth and strength of soil. *It is as if a green bough were laid across the page,* and we are refreshed as by the sight of fresh grass in midwinter or early spring. You have constantly the warrant of life and experience in what you read . . .*

"Every sentence is the result of a long probation. Where shall we look for standard English but in the words of a standard man? The word which is best said came nearest to not being spoken at all, for it is cousin to a deed which the speaker could have better done. Nay, almost it must have taken the place of a deed by some urgent necessity, even by some misfortune, so that the truest writer will be some captive knight, after all. And perhaps the fates had such a design, when, having stored Ralegh so richly with the substance of life and experience, they made him a fast prisoner, and compelled him to make his words his deeds, and transfer to his expression the emphasis and sincerity of his action."

The work of Galileo and Hariot, coexistent and complementary

* Italics mine — M.R.

230

in many ways, is far apart in fame, in published work, and in the long persevering drives of the Italian, coming openly forward as a center and pioneer of the new science, and of the buried Englishman who went as an explorer to his new world, and then lived a half-life in a prison to which not he but his friends were condemned.

Was there a direct link? Lower's phrase, "our diligent Galileus" — that sounds near.

Did Galileo write to Hariot? Did Dudley Carleton, or Winwood, or Aylesbury later in the Low Countries, or any embassy to France or Venice or Rome, carry these messages? Will Hariot's letters to Galileo float up in some Italian flood? Or die, if they exist, as pulp underfoot? A search is being made for them.

Galileo, Kepler, Hariot. We know another triangulation for Galileo and Hariot. Both were concentrated on the moon. Mapping, drawing, in that acute pyramid. Then another, for these astronomers fixed on Jupiter and the planets of Jupiter now first to be seen through the telescope; this far system, the bands of Jupiter, the red spot and the apojove. Shall it be said : they communicated through Jupiter and the moon?

The moon comes up in different dreams in our century. These years, men without the qualities of Hariot — who is to us a hero of the counter-culture — have gone to the moon and reported bareness in a time of the clash of dead wars to which are sent our young. But the young are dreaming, this summer, of a moon as fertile and unbegun and to be lived out as Hariot's Virginia.

Men who loved Hariot were carrying out observations for him on the western coast of Britain, in Cornwall and Carmarthen.

William Lower, the son-in-law of Dorothy Devereux, is another man who took Hariot as master and teacher. He watched, bought perspective glasses, and wrote often to Hariot at Syon House. From his letters we have quite another view of the work at Syon and London and the lifetime of this man who became one of the real windows into Hariot's life — Cornish-man, Member of Parliament, brother of a lost playwright, Nicholas Lower.

And friend to young Protheroe, the deeply-sighted, the lynx-eyed, who is still spoken of in Wales as "the inventor of the telescope." John Protheroe is another member of this younger group. We know that he worked with furnaces. For glass? For alchemical experiments? We know too, from Protheroe's will — in Somerset House — that he was Nathaniel Torporley's friend, and paid him a pension.

These glasses were part of a heresy. You could not prove that you saw anything, said the celebrated professors, you could not go out to the star and demonstrate. You could only show it again through your warped glass. In this time Bellarmine — who eleven years before wrote Bruno's condemnation and sent Bruno to death gagged and burning — Bellarmine gave an audience to Galileo and the long creeping process began. "This," says de Santillana, "had nothing to do with the scientific issue," toward which Bellarmine believed himself to be open.

But this is pivotal moment in the history of science; and the relation of scientists to power; and religion, and philosophy, and the connections between person and person, the biography of imagination.

Lower writes from Traventy to Hariot :

March 4th, 1611.

Sir, — I never loved huntinge till you furnished mee with dogs, I will henceforward prove another Nemrode; indeed I sought both arkes and tangents in the tables by proportion onlie; so, in a worde, you have made me see my faulte; in two or three more you have taughte me to amende it; onlie your curre dog Petiscus will not come into my sighte : but after a weeks vaine anger and points in seekinge for him, I found at last it was not the poore curres faulte, but Mr. Bills, that, sendinge me the second edition of the Origonometria, sente me onlie the tables; so as turninge the pages 75, 76, 78, 79, of the first edition (which is all I have) I found no such thinge as you sited, nor no such examples as you added. This is not the first time that Bill hath sent me imperfect copies; I pray let him understand so much. So you see I am defeated of the curre dog, savinge what I pick out of your letter, which indeed is not enough to give me satis-faction. Let Kitt, when he goes next to London, speeke to Bill, or att the Blackfriers, for a perfect copie of Petiscus; my brother the captaine will send it to me speedilie. The touch that you give of your doctrine of differences or triangular nombers, . . . me of them, wherin to understand somethinge, I will one day bee a begger unto you. Your dog, that hunts by the sines onlie, and I am growen familiar, and he is an excellent dog; but your she bitch hath no fellow for . . ., onlie she is slow; I had not lost hir, but knew hir goodnesse wel enough : the reason why I did nott use her in the former workes, was because, beinge in way of calculation by the tables onlie in that practise, I endevored to cleare that way of all rubbs; also because I conceaved it to be the shortest, I hastned (so greedie was my desire) to see the issue of my worke so that by the assistance of thes dogs of yours I grow so confident as to undertake to pursue in chace anie game : but then onlie I shal be sure that nothinge doe escape me, when you shall please to imparte unto me a betch of your triangular kinde.

I need not bee so curious to send you my doubts *in individuo,* for howsoever you satisfie me in private as you have done now, nevertheless, because you require it, I have sente them in two supplements, the one unto my letters that you have alreadie, the other unto thes, which, unless you had remembered me of, I should have omitted againe.

My worke is crowned now you allow of it, and indeed ther wanted in mee nether will nor industrie to accomplish it, nor in you will nor skill to instruct me, in the sacred wayes of arte; be you therfore ever of me unconquerablie respected, or be I not att all.

You have recomforted mee much to intimate that anie greate difference in my workes will discover a farther misterie; for I was almost dismaied to find thes second observations give an Aphelie different for the former 3 or 4 degrees.

Of this later worke I send you all the numbers given and found, and had also of manie more by this time, if the impossible issue of this last worke had not stayed my proceedinge till I receaved your censure of it. As you direct me I will proceede to doe them all, for I am growen verie experte in this calculation. I did not mistake that $\alpha\beta$ in the diagramme I sent you was double the eccentricitie, and therfore, before the recepte of your letter, in this second worke I had placed β att the center, and ω att the the centrorde, not onlie that $\alpha\beta$ mighte still remaine with Kepler the single eccentricitie, but to make it also corresponde with your vice royall probleme beare with this imitation. Concerninge the Joveall starres I writte nothinge of them last, because I had nothing to writte; for indeed, although both I and the yonge philosopher att Hawkesbrooke have often and in verie cleare nights (when Presepe was most plaine to bee seene without the cylinder); when wee, I say, have often diligentlie observed Jupiter, wee could never see anie thinge; I impute it to the dullnesse of my lighte, for onlie with your greate glasse I could see them in London.

That you have made so manie exellent observations of them I am most glad of, for you have gotten the starte of all in limitinge ther periods.

Ther periods are verie merveilous, especiallie that of *Jovi proximus,* whos scituation also is no lesse merveilous, beinge not one diameter of Jupiter of from him. Of thes thinges and thos other *mirabilia quae indies juvenis,* I longe to bee with you to discourse of them. My wiffe is well. Now you know all my comfortes. I have lost my second boy also, and wel neere eighty catle of the murraine, and the die still; now you know all my discomfortes and losses. Farewell, and lett not the hugenesse of this missive discourage you from reedinge of it; doe it at leisure and by peeces accordinge to your best opportunities, and sometimes use the power you have in me, which is to dispose of mee accordinge to the utmost of all or anie of my abilites.

Your faithfull frind,
William Lower.

By the helpe of your dogs, I will revew all thos workes of anie that exhibit the distance in the ellipses, equal or neerest to the same distance found before (for the workes uppon the former positions of ♂ in the eccentricke, which were onlie to find out this, I thinke you care not for); and when I have perfected them, I will send them unto you, with all the numbers given and found, whether the quesite consent or no, since you so require it.

Traventy, April 13th, 1611

I so overwhelmed you the last time with a longe letter as it is just I should make you amends now with one as shorte. To send you none at all (which perchance had bene best, consideringe the use you have of all your time) I could not consent unto, out of the addiction and delight I have to bee still conversinge with you; therefore I wll onlie signifie how it is with us, and so an end. My course of calculation I have stopte untill I heare from you; the two greate causes of my stay I declared in my last letters. I fell since into Vieta's last probleme of his second apendicle. Apol. Gal., and compared his way with yours that you last gave me : but to confesse a truth I can have my will of nether; and the probleme appeares to me not universall, but requires determination; for let the *b a* given have the same sides *a b, a c,* that Vieta's hath, and let v' s'' be the same that Vieta gives; now I will give a $\triangle$ that shall have thes sides, so as it shal bee impossible to find anie pointe from whence lines drawn unto the corners be in the given rate, and that is by giving a $\triangle$ with the same sides *a b, a c,* but in such position as the $< b a c$ be $>$ or $<$, then Vieta's $< b a c$, in such measure as Vieta's two circles doe nether cut nor touch. This rubbe put me out of this course, whereuppon I betooke me to your problemes for the distinguishinge of the sides of $\triangle^{\text{les}}$, whether the summe or difference of the sides and the angle adjacente or contained with the other side were given in this. I proceed still with much pleasure and satisfaction. I have also putt in order all thos propositons which you also gave me, but I had copied in lose papers and with ill diagrammes, so that all the thinges stand well; and so I thanke God doe we also, excepte my catle, which have al this winter bene persecuted with the murraine; since Christmas verie neere I have lost 100 beastes, — Vieta's sacrifices to the witch Melutina for the invention of one probleme. But I skarce keepe my promise with you. Farewell. I am al yours.

William Lower.

To his especial good frind, Mr. Thomas
Harriott, deliver thes.

Friday, July 19th, 1611

Since you incourage me so much I will proceede in thos calculations of ♂, and as I finish anie I will send them unto you; indeed to find the issue so . . . . . and in the later so impossible to be reconciled, had utterlie discouraged me, but that now by your letter I perceave ther may bee good use made even of ther discordance, therefore of this I will say no more till I send you more. The leasure that the countrie life affordeth us here, hath given me meanes to run over manie things since I left the course of calculation, but amongst others the 3 vexations of scientificall mortals hath held me most, to wit, the squaringe of the circle, the dublinge of the cube, and the philosopher's stoone. From the first I am come of handsomelie enough, and have made myselfe much sporte in the discoverie of mine owne parallogismes, but in the later I stick still, and am like to make you sporte here. I come fairelie of, but indeed I have here much *otium,* and therefore I may cast awaye some of it in vaine pursuites, chusinge alwayes rather to doe somethinge worth nothinge then nothinge at all. How farre I had proceeded in this, I ment now to have given you an account, but that the reporte of the unfortunate Erle's relapse into calamatie makes me believe that you are enough troubled, both with his misfortunes and my lady's troubles; and so a discourse of this nature would be unseasonable. Neverthelesse, give me leave to crave a worde or two in answer of thes doubts, whch I will beesilie propound as followeth: —

1. First whether ☉ and ☾ be bodies so difficulte to be dissolved as alchemists affirme, I meane by dissolution (as I thinke they doe), that they must bee petrifyed and distilled?

2. If they may bee dissolved, whether with one simple alone or with manie?

3. If they may be dissolved and petrifyed, whether ther recti-

fyed partes, beinge conjoyned againe, will be multiplied in virtue?

4. And lastlie, that which should have bene asked first, an sit elixir?

But at this time, this much is to much. I am sorrie to heare of the new troubles ther, and pray for a good issue of them, especiallie for my ladie's sake and her fine litle ones. So for the presente I rest, as of old,

> Your true frind,
> William Lower.

*To his especiall good frind, Mr. Thomas
Harriott, att Sion.*

This age thought in terms of opposites — as did the ancients, as do we. The banner of this thought was "To be or not to be." In the lists of qualities, and they are double lists always — they are doubled among Hariot's papers which I have called his "loose papers" but which the British Museum calls his Mathematical Papers — they go from Being and Essence, Action and Rest, Power and Impotence, as if he were showing someone the classifications. But then one comes to something that is so strong a statement that it may be taken as the emblem of his lifework. This lifework that begins in science and voyage, making connection with the people of his discovery, that deepens as Virginia fails and founders, as Virginia is betrayed and lost, deepens past the imprisonment of his friends, the outcast state of his astronomy, his hope and his politics — deepens to this diagram, small at the bottom edge of a folio page :

non est   est

in his way of dealing with them, not either/or, but with the line drawn through the points over *to be* and *not to be,* and then :

non est   est

as we might think of life, in the potential best of our time. To be *and* not to be, with life at the center.

4

The Island

he white striding magic of *The Tempest* is at the other pole from *Dr. Faustus*. These two plays, however, share a universe of powers, contraries, gratification by magic, renunciation.

In the Revels Accounts, *The Tempest* is down for payment on Hallowmas Night (November 1, 1611). It was presented at Whitehall before the King by the King's Players, and again at Whitehall in February, 1613, one of 14 plays performed during the marriage festivities of Princess Elizabeth and the Elector Palatine. It was thought that Robert Greene's Friar Bacon fed into the qualities of Prospero. Dudley Carleton says, "And it has been thought that the character of the royal and learned Prospero was typical of the literary and recondite studies of King James." Ralegh is in the Tower, but people remember the club he instituted at the Mermaid : Shakespeare and Jonson were two of the men who drank and talked among that company.

What is this play? What is within the relation of commanding Prospero to Caliban and Ariel? What forces of storm, island, music, torment, love? What island? Who is Prospero? Caliban? Ariel?

Caliban. Who is he? Why, he is himself. A monster, who is for music, against books; lying slave, abhorred slave, the entire population that is subject to Prospero.

> A freckled whelp hag-born — not honour'd with
> A human shape

What is that, to an Elizabethan Englishmen? An Irishman? An

anagram of cannibal? He wants freedom, as does Ariel; he wants his master destroyed, in his person and symbolically, in his magic.

> There thou may'st brain him,
> Having first seized his books,

he says, and

> Remember
> First to possess his books; for without them
> He's but a sot, as I am . . .
> Burn but his books.

However, he has the range of a man : this slave, attempting murder and rape, crammed with resentment, is also filled with music, with dreams, with longing for dreams and music :

> Be not afeard; the isle is full of noises,
> Sounds and sweet airs, that give delight, and hurt not.
> Sometimes a thousand twangling instruments
> Will hum about mine ears; and sometime voices,
> That, if I then had waked after long sleep,
> Will make me sleep again : and then, in dreamng,
> The clouds methought would open, and show riches
> Ready to drop upon me; that, when I waked,
> I cried to dream again.

Stephano's answer :

> Brave kingdom to me, where I shall have my music for nothing.

Caliban is not to be equated, any more than Ariel, or Prospero. But there is a drawing in Hariot's papers, of a child with his head down in his body, his eyes staring goggle up, hummocks of hair, animal ears, shoulders malformed.

Also, of the Magi around Northumberland, one was Walter Warner, who Aubrey says "was both Mathematician and Philosopher, and 'twas he that putt-out Thomas Hariot's *Algebra,* though he mentions it not.

"Walter had but one hand (borne so) : Dr. John Pell thinks a right hand; his mother was frighted, which caused the deformity, so that instead of a left hand, he had only a stump with five warts upon it, instead of a hand and fingers. He wore a cuffe on it like a pocket."

Prospero makes his choice. Not like Faust who goes down trying too late to renounce. In calm, resuming an old life, he puts away revenge and magic. He has not used his magic, as far as we are told, for journeys or for women. He has not used it towards his daughter, to whom he is a teacher; he has not used it to change the island, which to him is a cell.

The driving-away from oneself of the irrational forces that have, until then, been counted on in place of human powers — this is the choice that Prospero makes. It is a renunciation; but it is a renunciation for the sake of returning, for the sake of governing and of moving to a higher human power. Prospero had lived on an island, in "a cell," with a daughter, a spirit, a slave, and his books.

Faustus, in Marlowe, sold his powers. Cheaply, for twenty-four years. That was his choice, and at the end there is no choice. In a later *Faust,* Goethe has set another reconciliation. It is seen plainly in the death-scene (Part Two, Act V) : Faust overseeing the digging that will wall off the sea and extend the usable land, set the boundary of the conscious life further. Mephistopheles undermines this work, with all the rest. He knows that Faust works for him and his devils, that Neptune — "that Devil of the Sea" — will have the feast.

> In every way you're lost and lorn;
> To aid us every element is sworn,
> And ruin is the end at last.

The last answer of Faust is the plan to drain the poison-marsh along the mountain-range, to give space to many millions.

> Of freedom and of life he only is deserving
> Who every day must conquer them anew.

The word "free" is the trigger here, as it is for both Ariel and Caliban, as "forlorn" is the trigger for Keats, to call him back to his "sole self." Curiously, the resolve brings Faust to his trap, to the

Verweile doch, du bist so schön

that finally delivers him to death. In his downfall, it is the eternal power in its female form that draws him upward in his rescue.

Prospero's way is still renunciation. He abjures his magic; he requires only "heavenly music, and then

> I'll break my staff,
> Bury it certain fathoms in the earth,
> And deeper than did ever plummet sound
> I'll drown my book.

The last moment of the play is the last command to Ariel : to make calm seas, auspicious gales, and the rendezvous with the royal fleet. And then freedom,

> then to the elements
> Be free, and fare thou well!

And with the word "free" the play has ended. However, there is one further relation, a further freeing. It rests between Prospero and the audience, invoked for the first time.

> Now my charms are all o'erthrown,
> And what strength I have's mine own . . .

It is not Ariel's power, but ours, that must fill his sails. It is not the powers of white magic, but ours, that can give Prospero what he needs — a need never spoken before, a profound necessity that undoubtedly speaks for Shakespeare in the magician-ruler :

> And my ending is despair
> Unless I be relieved by prayer,
> Which pierces so, that it assaults
> Mercy itself, and frees all faults.
> As you from crimes would pardon'd be,
> Let your indulgence set me free.

With the double naming of "free" and the storm of applause that is invited and that follows, the play ends.

The play is itself; its people cannot be chained to other figures, its meanings cannot be chained to prose or philosophical meanings. These meanings are in their music, and move there.

Only certain questions can be reached. In the running-down of the sources of Shakespeare's plays, clear correspondences are seen between Gonzalo's speech concerning the ideal commonwealth, and Florio's translation of the essay by Montaigne "On the Cannibals."

The structure of the play has been compared with that of *The Beautiful Sidea,* a German work written in the years before 1605, with its magician, its beautiful daughter, its attendant spirit — the Devil, here — its enemy, and even its log-chopping scene.

For the tempest, we are always referred to two accounts of the shipwreck in July, 1609, on "rocks" off Bermuda (this must be coral; there are no rocks here) and the subsequent building of ships in which the voyagers sailed on to Virginia. The two accounts are Jourdain's *A Discovery of the Bermudas, otherwise called the Ile of Divils,* and William Strachey's story of the hell of darkness, the sea that gave battle unto heaven, the sparkling blaze of St. Elmo's Fire, the cry of Land! and running the ship ashore upon the dreaded islands of the Bermudas, where "tempests, thunders and other fearful objects are seen and heard."

Strachey's account was in manuscript in 1611; and Richard Wilson says, in his edition of *The Tempest* : "It is difficult to avoid the conclusion that either Strachey had borrowed from the play or the play from him."

The tempest is itself : roaring, war, mutiny, noise, sea and sky in chaos; but itself in relation to other powers : music and survival. There is a howl like this in *Lear,* where a man who knows female power only in a daughter is overwhelmed by storm on the heath and in himself. These are actual storms.

However, details are given to us here. We are shown that this is not Bermuda; Ariel has done his errand "from the still-vex'd Bermoothes," so that we know we are anywhere but there. Yellow sands; there are coral sands there, and yellow sands edge Virginia; but they edge Titania's country too, she sat on "Neptune's yellow sands." This geographical and chronological folly is nightmare.

But there is something here. What is Ariel? Spirit, air, but suffering. What has been his suffering? Imprisonment in the past, when he was the servant of Sycorax, the blue-eyed hag, Caliban's mother. This was punishment for Ariel's refusal to act her commands, "her earthy and abhorr'd commands." What were they? We are told only what the penalty was : confinement in a cloven pine, painfully, caught in the witch's death. Prospero found Ariel in torment, and by magic opened the pine. But Prospero threatens. If Ariel murmurs against him, Prospero will

> rend an oak
> And peg thee in his knotty entrails, till
> Thou hast howl'd away twelve winters.

Ariel will be meek, be invisible, be swift; and in two days, free. Ariel sings the song of the stilling of the waves, to a chorus of dogs,

> Come unto these yellow sands,

and this music, like the storm, cannot be placed on the air or the earth. The human man is stilled by it; in his weeping,

> This music crept by me upon the waters
> Allaying both their fury and my passion

and it begins again, singing the other side of horror, the sea-change of the drowned father, the pearls, the coral made of grief and rot. Ariel sings transformation.

Offer the glints and possibilities as questions : what names are these? what powers? What is an island of this intensity of bondage and at the same time the chance of return, of rule and marriage and a kind of after-life?

G. Wilson Knight, in his book that is full of clues and music, *The Shakespearian Tempest,* speaks of this play, "saturated in thought of sea-adventure, far coasts, amazing discovery . . . *The Tempest* is Shakespeare's imaginative genius mapped into a universal pattern; not neglecting, but enclosing and transcending, all his past themes of loss and restoration, tempest and music.

"At long last, a union of sea and earth in gentleness, blessing the bridal union of Ferdinand and Miranda. Nature's sweetness succeeds tempest. And all is here finally restored and forgiven. The ship is 'tempest-tossed' but not lost . . . So sea sorrow, roaring, and howling are blended with miraculous survival.

"This last vision encircles all former visions like an arching rainbow, vaporous and liquid, diaphanous, yet strangely assured and indestructible. And it contains a description of magic art necessarily apt to Shakespeare's work as a whole. *The Tempest* reflects the whole Shakespearian universe. Its lord, Prospero, thus automatically speaks as might one whose magic art had set down the plays of Shakespeare" :

> Ye elves of hills, brooks, standing lakes, and groves
> And ye that on the sands with printless foot
> Do chase the ebbing Neptune and do fly him
> When he comes back; you demi-puppets, that
> By moonshine do the green sour ringlets make
> Whereof the ewe not bites, and you, whose pastime
> Is to make midnight mushrooms; that rejoice
> To hear the solemn curfew; by whose aid,
> Weak masters though ye be, I have bedimm'd
> The noontide sun, call'd forth the mutinous winds,
> And 'twixt the green sea and the azur'd vault
> Set roaring war : to the dread-rattling thunder
> Have I given fire and rifted Jove's stout oak
> With his own bolt; the strong-based promontory
> Have I made shake, and by the spurs pluck'd up
> The pine and cedar : graves at my command
> Have wak'd their sleepers, open, and let 'em forth
> By my so potent art. But this rough magic
> I here abjure; and, when I have required

Some heavenly music, which even now I do,
To work mine end upon their senses that
This airy charm is for, I'll break my staff,
Bury it certain fathoms in the earth,
And, deeper than did ever plummet sound,
I'll drown my book.   (*Solemn music.*)

There is a reverberation : the deep life of Shakespeare, that aspect of life which it is now fashionable to call "inner"; I will not make division here between inner and outer, but call it his life, and this reverberates against other lives of his time, before him — and, with these powers at work, after him. End the oppositions. "The opposition of tempests and music is itself regarded as provisional, since tempests are part of 'great creating nature,' and indeed themselves a music."

Prospero is seen by Knight as a man "whose stature is politically important" — as "superman" (with Queen Elizabeth as "royal child," representing harmony in bright eternity, part of a double-ended figure whose other end is dark eternity, making a figure which the crystallographers know and call Tsuzumi, after the double-ended Noh drum of Japan). These meanings are double-ended — at least double, I say, for I believe there are many more than two. Perhaps we see two, easily, because of our bilateral symmetry. At any rate, Prospero is ruler, in the prison of his island, wise man, magician able to renounce his magic when it has served its purposes.

What is this island? What, in England, is an island, cut off by magic and water from the rest, where amazing events, further imprisonments, take place; from which release may also by magic come? Is not the Tower of London such an island?

What sonorities are here? What does the name Prospero have in it, along with the overtones of fortune and hope, and perhaps even the prospective glass, through which magically the future could be seen? Are there sounds here like Hotspur, and like Percy?

And of the Magi, the spirits around the great prince Percy,

is there one that has a name like Ariel? It is nonsense to look
at Hariot for these qualities and this name.

But where is the instigating event behind

> I'll break my staff . . .
> I'll drown my book.

What staff was broken? What book drowned? The loss that
overtook Hariot in the last moments in the shallow waters,
after the four-day tempest; a loss beyond which he imagined
and went forward. This may have been his style from the
beginning. In what we know of him, it was established here, in
the destruction of his mathematical instruments—cross-staff,
which was called "staff" in all his writings — and of his "book,"
his own particular magic, the notes on Virginia. After that
tempest and loss, a reconciliation came : the joining of memory
—"as far forth as I know and can remember" — and the out-
reaching imagination, that goes deep into imprisonment and
out beyond the air of the world.

It was not a conscious will to break, but rather a use of the
drowning and breaking. But Shakespeare uses this in the tradition around him, that of Faustus, in a world and religion where
renunciation for the sake of life is a way to move. Hariot's was
the same kind of renunciation in another form. His commitment through whatever loyalty, whatever attachment, that kept
him in the Tower, though not condemned.

These attributes : the name, and Hariot rings strangely like
Ariel — the book; the staff; gather a music around them. They
carry no proof. They need confirmation; there is more to come.

No connection between Shakespeare and the School of Night
can be demonstrated. But his own patron, glittering Southampton, was also in the Tower now. And there had been *Love's
Labour's Lost,* the mocking taunting parody of these men in
their learning trying to build walls, to exclude women, to exclude all the world except vanity. *The Tempest* is the great
reconciling play of the end. Is it possible that it represents more
of a reconciliation than we knew, and that everything political

249

in this age, who's out, who's in, and everything philosophical at which he had tilted as a young man, had risen in its next phase for Shakespeare, that the storm transformed had at last become music entire?

In the mud of the Thames, near London Bridge, are found pilgrims' tokens and sometimes the lead soldiers of an earlier time. At the palace of St. James, in the Armoury, there were models and toys in the first years of the seventeenth century. The histories of model soldiers, however, doubt that the large version — the "war game" — was played during this period, and the documentation of the European Kriegsspiel begins much later.

Part of the life of the Tower, however, included just such a war game. Was it for the training of young Prince Henry, or Algernon Percy, who was being brought up on the exercises of ranks and files? Or for the amusement of Northumberland and Ralegh, confined in the small rooms of stone, with only the Tower yard for field? Authoritative men have spoken to me of their doubts that there was anything beyond a few rows of soldiers deployed here; nothing that could be called a war game. However, one listing in the Account Rolls at Alnwick allows a strong gleam to fall across these ranks of soldiers and officers — centuries before H. G. Wells played on the big floor, or the children of the twentieth century played with their toys of bombs, rocket, moon invasions. In these lists, one comes across the following : the money spent

> for tryminge of 4000 leaden soldyers

This is before the Tower, among the rolls of Christopher Ingram from 12 Feb. 1599 to 27 March 1602 (O.S.). There are other items for lead brought to his lordship's use for the "manikyes" and for quicksilver, verdigris, and copper; and for stuff to make flags and moulds of brass to cast the "manykeys" and for drawings of 28 postures of men of war, and for wire to be drawn for the pikes of these soldiers.

During this period, Hariot's pension stood at 80 pounds each year, ending at Michaelmas.

Other charges are for ribbon, cinnamon water, spurs, tobacco, and tobacco pipes, scrivener's fees for copying, and bookbinding; colors for map-making, and maps of Antwerp, Ostend, Netherland, and the battles; water-carriage for passage and for carrying chests of books between London and Syon.

Hariot was in prison in the months of the Gunpowder Plot reaction. He was involved in litigation relating to Ralegh's finances at least once. The records of this suit are in the Public Record Office. In Hariot's working papers, there is one note, 6 pages after he has worked out unequal progression of sines for Sir William Lower (although, in the haphazard sequence of these papers, the pages may be far apart in date).

Here, another Lower is set down : Mr. Nicholas Lower, who according to the note is to be found "at a Duchmans within the mercury on Cheapside."

The list of those involved in the subpoena :

      April 26.   ho. 7.ᵃ
        first subpena
      Serjeant Harris
      Mʳ. Martin
      Mʳ. Walden   George mʳ. Sandersons
      Mʳ. More   man

    Mʳ. Karlile
    Mʳ. Walters
    Mʳ. Darrel   . . . .*
        Grindstones   Bish. of Elyes book
         mappes   Wright
         globes   Thesauro politico.2 .
                 . . . . in platina*

*Words not legible to me.

There are many notes among Hariot's papers of the working out of the generations of Genesis. They begin :

Ex Septuagint

	Adam	post Seth	vixit
	230	700	930
	Seth	post Enos	
	205	707	912
	Enos		
	190	715	905

to the generations of Abraham, and far beyond. They are in their finished form in Book Two of Ralegh's *History of the World,* in the pages of time-charts at the end.

From Hariot's observations :

Syon. 1611. April 9   De ☽ · ▢ ·
  clock or watch

Ho. 6.30   I observed the moon my an instrument of 10/1, and the line of division of light and darkness was far fro right. & more without instrument by daye light.

Ho. 6.58   The sunne set. Then I set my minute watch.

Ho. 7.30   Chr. observed ⎤ sensibly crooked
    8.0   I observed. ⎦

per stellis

9h.43′   9h.46′. Altitudo canis minoris 19.56′ by my cathol. Astrolabe. not yet a right line but almost

        10h.5′   not yet a right line

        10h.20′   very nere, but not yet perfect

        10h.45′.   yet doubtful to be perfect

        10h.52′.   As I judge now unsensibly a right line, ww enidimball rag or two, at & nere lower corner being obstructed. But others say not yet perfect.

11h.15′.　yet a right line & not contrary, but is not right rather wanting by the lower corner.

11h.30′.　yet continuing. others say waning [wanting?]

11h.39′+11h.47′.　Altitudo cap. II australiaris. 20.0′. As before.

12h.0′.　all say it is in a right line. at 12h.0′

12h.15′.　I described the apperence as soon as I could by my instrument of 32/1.

12h.30′.　Unsensibly different. And then we departed to bed.

Sr Nicholas Sanders & Christopher were with me & also observed in my Garret.

Instruments　10/1.　　15/1.　　32/1.　　11/1.

　　　　　　　　two.　　one.　　one.　　one.

The next morning about 8h½ my watch was to forward frō the sonne by a¼h & somewhat more.

The writing of *The History of the World,* in the Tower, that extraordinary piece of writing, bringing together long sweeps of history and opinion cast out fresh, long hauls from those friends who supported his arms to hold life while he made this master-work which might get him his freedom since it spoke for his beliefs — this book has been called "probably the greatest work ever produced in captivity, except Don Quixote." Said to us from an earlier period; in our time, it reminds us of Nehru's *History,* that personal work in the form of letters to his daughter from the British jail in India.

To Ralegh came those friends on whom he could count, in this work as in everything, for sustained and pointed work of detail, working as though it were a book of each his own : Hariot, Hughes and Warner; Robert Burhill, the scholar; Ben Jonson who claimed that he had contributed to the work; and Sir John Hoskins, set up high, a known poet in his day, and supposed to have made contributions and settled questions of style. The periods are Ralegh's own, and are echoed in his speech on the block. There are echoes here from poems. In Ralegh's writing, many things return; and here he not only takes from the books and calculations of his world, making them all his own by another alchemy, but he summons up — he is old, he has a crippling stroke and gets past it — echoes, many echoes of poems, in other muscles now of formal prose. The notebooks for *The History of the World* can still be seen and have been quoted by Oakeshott; and there are papers of Hariot's which have direct bearing on this book.

Ralegh had scarcely four years on this book; "but," says Stevens, "he had at command a Hariot, a sort of winged Mercury."

Isaac D'Israeli, the father of Benjamin, in his six volumes of *Literary Curiosities,* has an essay called "Literary Unions," the secret history of Ralegh's *History of the World* and Vasari's *Lives.* D'Israeli says of the life in the Tower :

> But in that imprisonment it singularly happened that he lived among literary characters, with the most intimate friendship. There he joined the Earl of Northumberland . . . and Hoskins . . . The truth is, that the collection of the materials of this history was the labour of several persons, who have not all been discovered. It has been ascertained that Ben Jonson was a considerable contributor; and there was an English philosopher from whom Descartes, it is said, even by his own countrymen, borrowed largely — Thomas Hariot . . .
>
> And Dr. Robert Burrel, Rector of Northwald, in the county of Norfolk, who was a great favourite of Sir Walter Rawleigh, and had been his chaplain.

In Braynford, he saw a child misshapen to a degree of extreme interest. This was in February, 1615; interest, sadness irremediable then or now, when we attempt much sculpture with the knife, and sometimes can come down to the formed child under the wild growth.

This child Hariot drew; he stares up at us from the page,

his goggle-eyes lifted wide and high in his head, over the horizon of the top of his head; his ears right down among his shoulders, even if his head does not grow actually beneath his shoulders; his broad nose, broad mouth, the shapes of breasts, and a rear view showing a Caliban, head hunched down and a tuft of flesh or hair like a queue over the brain-stem. Hariot has noted of the child's left hand : "2 thumbes + 2 fingers clinched up," and of his right : "this hand perfect," and, on the rear view : "All the body downward as of other children."

There is one sign of Southampton here. One asks the question about him, for he must enter somewhere, as Shakespeare must, and close there in his fascination. He does appear, but in a bleak and tantalizing label :

> Broomefeild my lo :
> Southhamptons man

and then, in another hand :

> A Catalogue of bookes of fortification
> for my L. of Southhampton

Two poems of Hariot's have come down to us. Only two; but in work-sheets, so that the steps of the writing are there. The haunting, suggestive, beautiful title he gives this poem is *Three Sea Marriages*. However, the name was written over the poem at the last. Hariot began :

> Many marriadges do I see

crossed the line out, and wrote

> Three marriadges here are made

then, between the first and second words, wrote "new" —

> one of staffe & in line Astrolabe

and here he gives us clearly his use of "staff" — no walking-staff, but the cross-staff, with its zenith and altitude distance scales, its sliding piece, by which it could be used as a sextant, and the divisions made "with the aid of a table of 10,000 equal parts."

The sea astrolabe was still in use far into the seventeenth century, past the lifetime of Hariot. It was held by the ring with a finger, and used with two scales.

Hariot added to the line. Now it reads

> one of the staffe and sea Astrolabe

and then, written and lightly crossed out

> card & compasse is an other
> one is sister tothers a brother.

He changes this. He keeps the sister and brother; this is curious for card and compass; and more curious in a poem of marriages. He moves from the sea-card, which Captain John Smith had listed among the necessary equipment for young seamen, with a cross-staff and back-staff. Hariot moves to another marriage, of the sea indeed, but of all else too :

> Of the Sonne & Starre is an other
> which now agree like sister & brother.

The sun and star, seen as sister and brother. Does this come out of his own life, his relation with his sister who married Yates? The sisters and brothers he knew, in their faithful attachments — Elizabeth Ralegh and her brother, Dorothy Percy and Essex? Or the Bible? Or the concord of strings? Surely this tells us very much of Hariot; and it tells us, as poetry does, things various, multiplied, in contradiction, ambiguous.

Does it say that he was married? Or was never married? Why is it not "brother and brother"? Or the other possible rhyming relationships? The poem goes on :

> And charde and compasse which were at bate,
> will now agree like a master & mate.

The work-sheet says "charde" and this was a time when the card was giving way to the chart as we know it, with its developments for careful recording of the ship's position, its distinct mapping of coastlines in elevation. This line has been transcribed as "which now of late," which does not accord with the poem on the page, nor make a unity in the poem.

Now the final six lines of the poem,

> If you use them well in this your iorny
> They will make you a . . . .'s Atomy

rewritten to

> They will be the King of Spaynes Atomy
> To bring you to silver & Indian gold
> Which will keep you in age frō hunger & cold
> God speed you well & send you fayre weather
> And that agayne we may meet to gether.

In these lines, the brief simple statement of the pride and lusting of the expedition; and then, I think, the line that dates the poem, if I read the "hunger & cold" right, I would place it, not as the wish of preservation of the desperate man we see, white-haired, limping ever since Cadiz, freed from the Tower for one exploit, but as the full strong Ralegh gathered together in life at Sherborne and the western ports, sailing to Guiana in 1595.

The poem is on a folio page with diagrams of parallels show-ing congruent angles, diagrams of angles over concentric circles and arcs (instrument-reading?) and, upside down, part of a passage about Nonius as observer and practicer, "besides the difficulties and insufficiencies in observing the meanes to the conclusions we sought."

Ralegh, who wrote of the durable fire and of the change in love from woe to wrath, from wrath to woe, and whose long marriage brought both constancy and the robbing, or removing, of his body from the bond, never wrote in terms of marriage. But it is of him one thinks, and of the many marriages, the sea marriages Hariot knew.

The poem can stand up after being taken apart line by line.

THREE SEA MARRIAGES

Three new marriages here are made
one of the staff and sea astrolabe
card and compass is another
(*crossed-out*) one is sister thothers a brother.
Of the sun and star is another
which now agree like sister and brother.

And chart and compass which were at bate
will now agree like master and mate.

If you use them well in this your journey
They will be the King of Spain's atomy
To bring you to silver and Indian gold
Which will keep you in age from hunger and cold
God speed you well and send you fair weather
And that again we may meet together.

A word might be said about the greeting of "God speed" — not used by itself as currency of salutation, but in full in a line of verse.

What does the poem declare of Hariot's emotional thinking? Of his experience, outward lifetime experience or inner concentration? One cannot derive the biographical in factual statement from any poem; but one can say what absorbed and evoked the life of these fusions in the poet. For the poem is not "emotional thinking" nor any other putting together of the split terms of our usage, that culturally tried to force us to say, "physical," "emotional," "spiritual," "psychic." All the splinters of the kind of thinking that the most whole of the Elizabethans have shown us we never need accept. From their joining of poetry and science, we can trace the buried life and bring it through in ourselves. It has existed always. We have it fully in Biblical man, and the best words for the joining are in King David's prayer for his son Solomon :

". . . the thoughts of the imagination of the heart."

Among Hariot's papers which his friend Nathaniel Torporley left to Sion College are the two versions of *The Gates of Alchemy,* by George Ripley, containing this verse :

> And furthermore the preparation of this conversion
> from thinge to thinge, from one state to another
> is don onlye by kindelie and discrete operation
> of nature, as is oft sperme within the mother
> for sperme and heate as sister be and brother
> which be converted within them self as nature can
> by action and passion at laste to perfecte man.

Here too is the core of the belief in the way of transformation. Here is seen the "sister and brother" of Hariot's poem, *Three Sea Marriages,* and the way these meanings are open to his time and to us.

The most primitive of numeration systems, the binary system, is found in usage among peoples of Africa and Australia. It has been contrasted with the systems based on ten, which are thought to refer to the ten fingers as counting apparatus. Even a sophisticated witness in our own time will say, "It is interesting to speculate what turns the history of culture would have taken if instead of fingers man had had just two 'inarticulate' stumps. If any system of numeration could at all have developed under such circumstances, it would have probably been of the binary type."

This system did of course develop, and is the base of present computer operations, and the Yes and No mode of thinking which has reduced so many political and man-in-the-street answers to falsity. But it is surprising that the base of the two-number system should be assigned a reason which is a chopping down.

Hariot makes several notes on a binary system. He does not

list his figures as zero and one, but makes his base clear. Here is the range :

```
−  −  −  −
−  −  −  +
−  −  +  −
−  −  +  +
−  +  −  −
−  +  −  +
+  −  −  −
─────────
+  −  +  −
+  −  +  +
+  +  +  −
```

The physical base for the plus and minus of the universe might be seen in human electrical systems, or in human bilateral symmetry. A later philosopher, Leibnitz, moved by the "mystic elegance of the binary system" exclaimed : *"Omnibus ex nihil ducendis sufficit unum."* (One is enough to derive all out of nothing.) Or perhaps he was moved by all and nothing to see the mystic elegance of the intellectual system.

There is a portrait of Northumberland, as he was late in life. This has some of the mystery of the other portraits, for we take the miniatures by Hilliard to be Henry Percy. This is a posthumous portrait by Van Dyke, now at Petworth House. The full mature, more-than-nature, deep eyes look out fram a face that may be slightly idealized. The head rests, as the young head rested, on the right hand. Among the dark richness of banded velvet, empty sword-bands, curtains, the heavy chair, the face over its plain collar looks and looks at the witness, oneself. This time he is identified : a legend in the dimness says Henry Earl of Northumberland. At a table under his elbow, as the book used to rest in the two Hilliard portraits, stands an hourglass, and his elbow pins down a paper on which a fragment of Latin speaks of weight. The diagram on the sheet carries two weights, one very large in the foreground, and then the fulcrum and farther off the small counterpiece in balance.

It is the diagrammatic representation of the emblem in that mysterious Hilliard painting of the young man, sometimes taken for a poet or man of letters, lying in summer against a pale-blue sky, the trees of that summer day seen in their delicate and shaded leaves, and the world forever hanging over against a word, a feather.

TANTI

Margett, April 15th, 1613.

Good Mr. Harriotts — Bycause I have no other newes to send you, you shall only receave the bare relacion of our voyage from Chatham to Margett att the North Forland, which I can tell you in breiffe, though it was to us (new seamen) very tedious. For wee went on board the sixt of April, and are but now arrived att the Foreland the 15., which you will say is very longe, but that you know the danger of the sands, and contrarie winds too, if yours att Sion agree with ours att sea. I have learned here certaine strange words amonge our mariners, which to interpret will require some tyme. If we had bene at Vlushinge, I mought perhaps have told you more, but I could forbeare writinge to you noe longer, though to little purpose, savinge only to lett you understand that wheresoever I am, I am bound to remember you, and soe rest

Your very loyteringe,
but lovinge skollar,
Thomas Aylesburie.

I must not forgett to tell you, your glasses have fitted my Lord excellentlie well; and soe, as I feare you will leese them both, but not without your owne consent, I have noe auctoritie to promise till you give leave.

June 9th, 1615.

Sir, — As by experience I have found your singular humaintie by our late conferences, to make good the noble fame of your great learning, so hath itt emboldened me by this my letter, to request that you would send me word by this bearer what the variation of the needle is about Mosco. For at this present I have such an ympediment fallen into my toes, that I cannot walke abroade, otherwise I had beene the presenter of this my request unto you myselfe, which, if it might have beene, I should then have moved some other questions, viz. whether it is probable that the variation can be in any place of the world 180 degrees, or the north point of the needle stand directly to the south. Allso whether a shippe sailing right east or west by the compasse, keepes upon a parallell, as the common received opinion amongst maryners is, which I thinke not, because the east and west of the compasse is a tangent to the parallell, but how little soever it so continues in sailing, it is a portion or arch of the great circle of the east and west, and therefore (I conceive) cannot but decline from the parallell. But ceasing to trouble you with these manner of questions, I crave perdon for this my boldnes, resting

Att your command,
John Rudston.

To his very good frend, Mr. Haryott in
Black-fryars, be these delivered.

Fifteen years before, Ralegh had sold all his Irish property to Richard Boyle — all except the Castle of Inchiquin Ralegh, which went to the Old Countess of Desmond, the legendary Countess who was born ten miles from Molanna a hundred years before, they said; and died in 1604, falling out of a cherry tree, they said. Richard Boyle bought all the rest, for a thousand pounds, over Lady Ralegh's objection that it would be worth two thousand pounds a year. Not to Ralegh, who had been robbed, he complained to the managing director, Henry Pine, and was in "endless disputes" with his tenants.

Now Richard Boyle, related to Spenser's wife Elizabeth Boyle, was the great Lord of Cork, last year created, and Baron of Youghal; he welcomed these ships, three times driven — once back into Plymouth, then into Falmouth, and then from west of the Scilly Isles, where a pinnace had sunk.

They were seven ships of war and two pinnaces as they

dropped anchor at Kinsale. The little port, at the mouth of the Bandon, had been fought over with the Irish and the Spaniards in 1601, but retaken; and his thousand men went ashore. Ralegh went on the few miles to Cork, and a great welcome. He stayed 24 days, invested in Irish copper, flew his hawks; best, he made his peace about the lands with Lord Boyle, who entertained him, and with whom he rode back to Lismore. Lord Boyle supplied the expedition with oxen, biscuit, beer, and iron, and gave Ralegh a 32-gallon cask of whisky, and £350.

This was the lord great in children (Aubrey says 13, the Britannica 14), of whom the last child, born in 1627, was the scientist Robert Boyle, who visited Galileo, become a member of the "Invisible College" which developed into the Royal Society, discovered the law named for him, and opened a vast body of knowledge on sound, on crystals, on specific gravities and refractive powers, and beyond all these, on chemical analysis. Among his early tracts are : "Urim and Thummim," "Sir George Ripley's Epistle to King Edward Unfolded"; "Caveat for Alchymists"; and "A Conference Concerning the Phylosophers Stone." He is supposed to have had Ralegh's papers on chemistry, and this may have included papers of Hariot's. He passed the latter part of his life in the home of his sister, Lady Ranelagh, in Pall Mall near St. James's, where in 1692, Boyle's library was sold. The following were remembered to have been represented : "Galileo, Borelli on the telescope; Gilbert, Digges, etc."

Boyle's papers were filed in a large case, on top of which an enormous pot of vitriol was set. One day, the pot smashed and the papers were mutilated beyond saving. Boyle's natural history collections were left to the Royal Society.

On August 19, 1617, the expedition sailed, by way of the Canary Islands where they were taken for Barbary pirates and attacked. Ralegh did not take vengeance; but one of his captains, Bailey (who was set by the government to spy on Ralegh for Spain), deserted and reported in England that Ralegh was going to do exactly what Spain and the anti-Ralegh faction — almost everyone in England — had predicted.

Bacon had said to Ralegh, "What will you do if, after all this expenditure, you miss of the gold mine?"

Ralegh answered : "We will look after the Plate Fleet, to be sure."

"But then," said Bacon, "you will be pirates!"

"Ah," Ralegh cried out, "Whoever heard of men being pirates for millions!"

Gondomar reported to the King of Spain concerning James : "The King promises he will do whatever we like to remedy and redress . . . so atrocious a wickedness as this." It was at this time that Gondomar suggested that a Spanish fleet capture Ralegh's expedition and kill all but Ralegh himself and his officers. They would be taken to Seville and executed.

Every part of the crossing was open to Gondomar. The early part was benign, with a friendly landing at Gomera, where the Governor's wife was half-English, and where the Governor gave Ralegh a commendatory note for Gondomar and some bread and fruit.

Then the disaster of the crossing, long, dismal; Ralegh was 64, an unpardoned man, ill probably with pneumonia; "But for the fruit," he says in a letter to his wife, "I could not have lived."

At one time the ship was surrounded with darkness.

Off Trinidad one day, they saw 15 rainbows.

They came to the mouths of the Orinoco.

The man is dead in law, since he has had no pardon. He goes out to Guiana again on a great throw of the dice. His older son, his lieutenant, his ships, whatever money he could raise; while Gondomar waits for one misstep, and James has promised Ralegh's head that it happens.

It closes in fast. Fever, Spaniards, and a raiding party sent inland, up the Orinoco, while Ralegh waits off the coast. On February 14, 1618, the letter reaches Ralegh. There had been the fight at San Thome, the longed-for battle which both sides, perhaps, precipitated. The English party said that this was the only way to enter the city; young Wat Ralegh threw himself on the fight and was killed; it was Keymis who was left alive to write the letter.

Ralegh writes to his wife : "Comfort your heart, dearest Bess; I shall sorrow for us both." He sees, up the page, his own words looking at him : "God knows I never knew what sorrow meant till now." He adds : "And I shall sorrow the less because I have not long to sorrow, because I have not long to live." He refers his wife to Winwood's letter from him. Winwood is his hope, but nothing is left. "My brains are broken and 'tis a torment to me to write, especially of misery."

He sails up the Atlantic. He hopes that he can find the lost colony and redeem his venture. But his men are deserting him, and he returns to England, to arrest at Plymouth, the chemicals to wreck him and turn him purple in his weltering at Salisbury (where he writes his *Apology*), and prison again and the final death-sentence and Hariot with him in the Gatehouse prison after the last cries of the Spaniards and the English, the last farewells, the last poem.

Hariot has left a page of notes, which by its crossings-out seems to have been made before the beheading of Ralegh. It is a list of the matters of which Ralegh spoke on the scaffold, the morning of the 29th of October : his two shaking fits; his calling God to witness he spoke justly and truly; and then the answer to all the charges made against him by Sir Lewis Stukeley, by whom he had been charged with treasons, attempts to escape, uses of money, being a French agent; he clears Lord Carew and Doncaster, the link with Northumberland. He speaks of his company "used ill in the voyadge" [says Hariot] and of the "spotting of his face" in the feigned sickness. And at last he comes to the old enmity, the hatred that has scaffolds in it. He speaks of Essex, "The E. of Essex," Hariot writes, clearing himself of Essex' death and of the rumor that he, Ralegh, had rejoiced. And asks the crowd to join him in prayer. And is axed to death.

That autumn, a sequence of three comets swept like three dreams across the sky : the first while the Queen pleaded for Ralegh; the second, three weeks after his death, when Hariot was back in his tiled house at Syon; and the third, at the end of November, under the northern scale of the Balance. Hariot made his observations on the quick succession. Galileo and Kepler, Grassi and Garducci in Italy, wrote notable and clashing essays on the movement of these comets. What bound down Hariot? His illness was far advanced, but he had some years. What drove in upon him? The train of Ralegh's spurting death, moving on everyone for fifteen years? No gold, no comet. The lost son. And Ralegh, the Ocean, chopped away. Lost. Three comets only streaked the sky; night after night, he made his notes of these.

Newmarkett, January 19th, 1618-9.

Sir, — Though I have bene yet soe little a while att Newmarkett, that I have not any thing of moment to ymport, yet I thinke it not amisse to write a bare salutations, and let you know, that in theise wearie journeys I am oftentimes comforted with the remembrance of your kind love and paynes bestowed on your loytering scholar, whose little credit in the way of learning is allwaies underpropped with the name of soe worthie a maister. The comet being spent, the talke of it still runnes current here. The King's Majesty before my comming spake with one of Cambridg called Olarentia (a name able to beget beleefe of some extraordinarie qualities), but what satisfaction he gave I cannot yet learne; here are papers out of Spayne about it, yea and from Roome, which I will endeavour to gett, and meane that you shall partake of the newes as tyme.

Cura ut valeas et me ames, who am ever trulie and unfaynedly yours att command,

Thomas Aylesburie.

To my right woorthie frend, Mr. Thomas
Harriot, att Syon, theise.

Hariot speaks in his will of Christ Church Hospital in London. There is no way now of knowing whether he was treated here nor of knowing of the progress of his disease. We do know, however, of a parallel story of sixteen years of "discomfort, distress, and pain" caused by cancer of the face — in this case, originating in the upper jaw and palate. The second story is in our own century, and is well documented : it is the last illness of Freud.

The long grief of Thomas Hariot lasted from 1605 to 1621; that of Freud, from 1923 — the date of the first operation — to 1939. Through the removal of the whole upper jaw and palate, with the defective speech and the deafness on the right side, the prosthesis (his "monster" which had to be modified every few days) and the statement of the early part of the illness : "I find living *for* one's health unbearable" : down through the years of suffering and the attempts to alleviate it, to the new operations, with their new hope and the statement in a letter to Ernest Jones, "What a contrast a bearable prosthesis would be, one that didn't clamor to be the main object of one's existence."

Three years from death, Freud had two exceptionally painful operations. Until now, the tissue had been classified as precancerous; now, it was unmistakably cancer. "I carry on with my analyses by changing a hot-water bottle every half-hour to hold by my cheek." In the last year, it was inoperable and incurable. The clawing, all the signs, were frightful. The odor from the wound made his favorite chow "shrink into the far corner of the room."

People said of Freud, as they did of Hariot, that his patience and goodness were extreme. Jones writes of Freud : "With all this agony, there was never the slightest sign of impatience or irritability." At last, he reminded his doctor and friend of his promise, and was given the morphine that let him die.

Syon, June 13th, 1619.

Sir, — When Mr. Warner and Mr. Hues were last at Sion, it happened that I was perfecting my auntient notes of the doctrine of reflections of bodies, unto whom I imparted the mysteries thereof, to the end to make your lordship acquainted with them as occasion served. And least that some particulars might be mistaken or forgotten, I thought best since to set them down in writing, whereby also nowe at times of leasure, when your minde is free from matters of greater waight, you may thinke and consider of them, if you please. It had been very convenient, I confess, to have written of this doctrine more at large, and particularly to have set downe the first principles, with such other of elementall propositions, as all doubtes might have been prevented; but my infirmitie is yet so troublesome, that I am forced, as well that as other traits, to let alone till time of better abilitie. In the meane time I have made choyce of these propositions, in whose explication you shall find, I hope, the summe of all that of this argument is reasonable to be delivered. And if any doubtes doe arise either of the hypothesis therein used, or of the concomitants and consequences therein also intimated, although upon due consideration onely they may be resolved, yet because I am beforehand in consideration of these matters, I shall be ready when I have notice of them to give your lordship full satisfaction for your ease. And seeing that my purpose, God willing, is within a few days to see your lordship, I cease from more wordes, resting, & c.

T. Harriot.

Hariot, writing :

> The truth when it is seen
> is knowne without other evidence.

The value set on action has always been emphasized; the life of action continually being set against the life of expression in other ways. People have spoken glorifying the life of the intellect, too, as if it could be set off against the exploration of the world in other ways. Hariot is the pilgrim of the joined life. He ventured, never allowing a split between "body" and "mind," the split for which the ruff and the Renaissance both stood.

Hariot wrote :

A man of wordes and not of deedes is like a garden full of weedes

This is a proverb known to English children since the middle
of the seventeenth century, taught to them by their parents and
nurses with the insistence of the nursery religion. It was first
recorded in 1659, by James Howell, in his collection of proverbs.

But here it is, fifty years earlier, in Hariot's papers. He looked
at it :

A man of wordes and not of deedes is like a garden full of weedes

and added :

A man of deedes and not of wordes is like a privie full of tourdes

Donne came to Frankfurt in June of 1619, with a flotilla of
boats dragged by horses against the stream, part of the embassy
of Lord Doncaster. After his illnesses, his closeness to death,
Donne's life had turned over. He had married

> those loves, which in youth scattered be
> On fame, wit, hopes — false mistresses — to Thee.

But the journey was in a magnificence of talk and wine and
diplomacy, and Donne was writing the sermons as chaplain to
James I. Doncaster was married to Lucy Percy, Northumber-
land's daughter; he was on his way to Heidelberg to the
Electress Elizabeth, who called the Elector Palatine from the
Congress of the Princes of the Union. The English suite, at
Doncaster's choice, ordered lodgings in the town, in spite of
Princess Elizabeth's invitation. She countermanded that order
with a proclamation forbidding anyone in any Heidelberg
market to supply any member of the English Embassy.

But the embassy was not in any way an effective one. Through
torrents, they pushed close to Frankfurt, but were not allowed
in, because the elections had gone badly for the Palatinate party.
Ferdinand was emperor. Doncaster withdrew to Spa, and wrote

to James asking leave to come home. This was refused. On the last day of August, Donne wrote to Dudley Carleton, beginning

> I present to your Lordship here a hand which I think you never saw, and a name which carries nonsuch merit with it as that it should be well known to you . . .

and announcing that Doncaster's suite were on their way to Holland, where Carleton was Ambassador.

In September they were in Frankfurt at last, and Donne stayed there all month while Doncaster made excursions. They started for Venice at the beginning of November, following Bruno's route; but, that late in the year, the passes were closed by snow.

Healthy, "with his sorrows moderated," Donne and the embassy were back in England early the next year. In a letter of this period, Donne writes :

"We hear nothing of my Lord of Doncaster, nor have we any way to send to him. I have not seen my Lady Doncaster, for she crossed to Penhurst and from thence to Petworth . . ." He goes to Bedington, to his brother-in-law, Sir Nicholas Carew, "and Chelsea, and Highgate."

By now, Hariot had come to the end of his illness.

When Hariot was deep in illness, ships were sent to Virginia to forward all the plans with men and provisions : 1 in January, the *Duty* of 70 tons with 51 persons; 3 in February; 2 in March; another in April and another in August; making "about foure and twenty hundred Soules" in Virginia. Of these, 100 were "tenants for the Colledges land."

That year, 1619, the first legislative assembly that ever convened on the American continent met in the church at Jamestown. The burgesses were elected, 2 from each plantation; the assembly consisted of the governor, Yeardley, 6 councillors, and 20 burgesses.

The secretary of the colony — and also the speaker — was
John Pory, a member of the assembly by virtue of being a
member of the council. This was the hard-drinking friend of
John Donne, whose life had paralleled Donne's in many ways;
and, more than that, had met it at many points. Now he had
the position which Donne had wanted, and for which he had
applied ten years before. He was, besides, an active cartographer
who had "worked assiduously for Hakluyt," says Gosse. He
must have known Hariot, his book and more than his book.
He refers to Hariot once; it is surprising that it is only once.

First there was a prayer from Rev. Richard Buck, of Jamestown, an Oxford man who had come out to Virginia in 1610,
and married Pocahontas to John Rolfe four years later. Rolfe
reported that he was a "verie good preacher." After the prayer,
the assembly sat for 6 days of concentrated business, in the choir
of the church. The orders against crimes — against, for instance,
outrages against the Indians, taking corn from canoes when
Indians refused to sell — were dealt with, and briefly, since
John Pory "for a long time has bene extreame sickly."

Several matters are of sharp interest. One petition is toward
the erecting of the University and College, at Henrico. This had
always been planned; it may be seen as an extension of that
school which was formed loosely in London, and called The
School of Night in mockery. It was to be made on ten thousand
acres at Henrico, the city of Henricus, named for Prince Henry
and all the hopes. It was here that Pocahontas had been
educated. This petition asked the Company to send, "when they
shall think it most convenient, workmen of all sortes, fitt for
that purpose." Workmen were sent over in the last year of
Hariot's life, lands were laid out, a rector was elected, and work
was begun on the college. Even Powhatan's death had not
wounded the peace between the English and Indians. Even the
clashes and the burnings, the raidings back and forth — a replica
inwardly of the border clashes stopped by James on the line,
now drawn in peace, between Scotland and Northumberland
— did not end this truce, although in our time white historians

271

speak of the skillfully concealed aggressive designs of the Indian leaders.

The fact was that the new chief of the Powhatan confederacy sent word to Jamestown that "so firmly was peace established that the sky 'should sooner fall than it dissolve.'"

At the time of Hariot's death, peace was ratified and sworn, the plaque stamped in brass, and fastened to one of the "oakes of note." The massacre fell on the following year.

But now, the assembly counsels those of the colony neither "utterly to reject them" (the better disposed of the Indians) "nor yet to drawe them to come in."

It was enacted by this assembly that each town, city, borough, and plantation "do obtaine unto themselves by just means a certine number of the natives' children to be educated by them in true religion and civile course of life — of which children the most towardly boyes in witt and graces of nature to be brought up by them in the first elements of literature, so to be fitted for the Colledge intended for them that from thence they may be sente to that worke of conversion."

And mulberry trees; and "Silke-flaxe," each man to plant and dress 100 plants. This is later spoken of as "Silk-grasse, whereof Master Hariot in his booke 1587 makes relation who then brought home some of it, with which a piece of Grogeran [grosgrain] was made, and given to Quene Elizabeth."

And hemp; and vines, 10 vines planted and maintained by each householder yearly until they have "attained to the art and experience of dressing a Vineyard either by their owne industry or by the Instruction of some Vigneron." These were vine-growers from Languedoc, brought to Virginia, a memory of the time long ago when Walter Ralegh fought in France, and in Languedoc saw not only the heretics smoked to death in the caves, but, curved over the hills, the vineyards of the south, and drank the wines, sweet wines and muscat. Reminder of these was the waves of grapes to the surge of the sea, by Barlow and Amadas seen, never by Ralegh, but always to be given his name, as this land is.

And the punishments: that Thomas Garnett, a servant of

Captain Powell's, for wantonness with a woman and neglect of his business, stand 4 days with his ears nailed to the pillory, and then 3 days more, and be every one of those days publicly whipped.

The next day of assembly, August 4th, was so hot and the day to follow likely to be so too, that they finished quickly. No man was to give any "piece shott or poulder, or any other armes, offensive or defensive" to the Indians upon pain of hanging. The Indians were considered comparatively harmless while they depended on bows and arrows. And reforms, and ordinances, and the unfinished business whose records had been sent to England in the *Prosperus*.

Among all of these was a petition to allow the "male children of those brought to Virginia, being the onely hope of a posterity, a single share a piece, and shares for their issues or for themselves, because that in a newe plantation it is not knowen whether man or woman be more necessary."

The hundred boys and girls from London came, and the indentured servants. Among these are the "20 and odd Negroes" who were brought in a Dutch man-of-war about the last of August. They had probably been bought in the West Indies, where the ship had been cruising, and were exchanged for victuals for the ship. They were servants, but by the middle of the century blacks and their children were usually held in servitude for life. Slavery.

New patents were granted — one among these was to Thomas Buckner — to transport persons and cattle to Virginia. As early as the end of August, 1619, a Dutch ship brought in 20-odd Negroes as indentured servants.

This was human life to be turned into a product.

News of another product, soon to be the chief and mainstay of this territory, and in spite of everything King James had done to ban it, protected in England; for within the next two years, Spanish tobacco was banned from England.

Tobacco was already the great thing — a bride-price was 120, and later 150, pounds of the best leaf-tobacco. The market was wide open, and exploding. By this year the life of the Colony seemed to depend on tobacco, and there was already an attempt to diversify crops, that never took hold. Captain John Smith pointed out that with tobacco selling at three shillings a pound, and grain at only two and six a bushel, a man's labor in tobacco was worth six times the other.

John Pory was completely recovered in September. On the 30th, he wrote to Sir Dudley Carleton: "At my first coming hither the solitary uncouthness of this place, compared with those partes of Christendome or Turky where I had bene; and likewise my being sequestred from all occurrents and passages which are so rife there, did not a little vexe me. And yet in these five moneths of my continuance here, there have come at one time or another eleven saile of ships into this river; but fraighted more with ignorance, than with any other merchandize. At length being hardened to this custom of abstinence from curiosity, I am resolved wholly to minde my business here, and nexte after my penne, to have some good book always in store being in solitude the best and choicest company. Besides among these christall rivers, and odoriferous woods I doe escape muche expense, envye, contempte, vanity, and vexation of minde."

It was not for 3 years more that the Indians of the 32 kingdoms, on the James, the York, and the Rappahannock, struck back at the 80 English settlements. They struck all together throughout the Colony, sometimes with a show of force, an aimless firing of a gun. It was the beginning of an attempt to repossess the land lying between the sea shores and the mountains; it went on with sniping, burning of houses, killing of cattle, destruction of crops — all the ways of an agricultural people at a weapon-level different from that of the invaders. As in Vietnam.

The colonists deserted many of the plantations including the college lands.

The Virginia Company requested help from London. It

came from the Tower of London — a supply of arms and armor that was a history of England : coats of mail, "iron skulls," bows and sheaves of arrows, short pistols. No plantation was ever to be left unguarded, and was to be kept with sufficient arms and ammunition.

The ways of living in peace with the Indians were forgotten. The college was abandoned — no, the Virginians were given orders to reoccupy the plantations which had been deserted in panic, to go on with the abandoned ironworks and the projected college.

They were to make war relentlessly against the Indians.

The King still hated tobacco, and there was interference with prices, at customs, in the trade of cattle and tobacco with Ireland. When John Pory, who had gone back to England, returned to Virginia in 1624, he reported to the Privy Council the utter failure of the Virginia Company and the colonists, "both as adventurers and as planters."

Hariot's Virginia hardly lasted his lifetime. Its rebirth, and the birth of the university, the College of William and Mary, came long after.

A turning-point in the history of these ideas came in the depth of winter to a young man, who "advanced the theory of equations, as did Hariot, an Englishman." He had been serving as a volunteer in the army of Denmark after an apprenticeship in mathematics with the chief men in France, and now, wandering through Poland and Hungary, Austria and Bohemia, was near Ulm on the night that he was to call The Olympica, November 10, 1619.

This is the young Descartes. He is twenty-three. Born in Touraine, he has gone to school under Chauveau de Melun, who became a passionate cartesian; had found Le Clerc, and — most important of all — Mersenne; worked with Claude Mydorge, the successor to Vieta, with a parallel reputation as the first mathematician of France. Then Descartes had gone on with Mersenne, until after long seclusion he went to Holland in 1618, and late in the year volunteered to fight Spain. He left after the election of the Elector Palatine as King of Bohemia. With Ferdinand as Emperor, all of Europe was changed. Descartes' outward view of his possibilities, along with those of Europe, had to be thought through again. And not thought only, he had to make a new life. He was in Prague, that city full of imaginings and rumors of invention of every kind, where Tycho had been when Descartes was a small boy. Here he joined Maximilian's army, and did his first work on the *Methode* in a soldier's camp. Then, away from fighting finally, two days after the battle of Prague, Descartes asked himself, "What road shall I pursue in life?" He was drinking, says one biographer, it was St. Martin's Eve, and young men are drunk then. No, Descartes says, I had had no wine for three months. This night was the turning-point in Descartes' life.

The night was a night of three dreams, a chain of dreams of interest in themselves, but of significance because they are what Descartes took into his life, worked on to interpret for himself, and took immediately in his own analysis as a guide to his own thought from that waking on.

The chain of dreams is an accretion of cumulative power, noted by many writers, but in the perspective in relation to Hariot and the buried history, of overwhelming and tragic power. They unfold the clue to a drama beyond theatre as we yet know it.

Here is the first dream. These have appeared in a footnote to a letter by Freud, and in two essays, one by J. O. Wisdom and one by Bertram Lewin. Baillet says in his biography of Descartes that he saw Descartes' paper on the night, The Olympica; but the paper has since been lost, and we recover the dreams only in Baillet's synopsis (and here in Norman Kemp Smith's translation).

The dream had to a great extent been excluded, as the child was excluded, from the literature of consciousness. Descartes said that this chain of dreams was a revelation from God, and marked the turning-point of his thought. They begin with Descartes' waking resolution to examine one and all of the beliefs which he had hitherto been holding, and to make this examination the basis of all his science.

After he had fallen asleep his imagination was strongly impressed with certain phantoms which appeared before him and terrified him in such wise that, while walking, as he fancied, through the streets, he was obliged to turn himself over to his left side so as to be able to advance to the place where he wished to go, feeling, as he did, a great weakness in his right side which disabled him from leaning on it. Ashamed of walking in that manner he makes an effort to straighten himself, but feels an impetuous wind which, catching him up in a kind of whirlwind, makes him revolve three or four times on his left foot. But what really frightens him is something more; the difficulty he has in dragging himself along makes him think he is falling at every step.

Then, perceiving on his path a college whose gate was open, the dreamer entered, "seeking there a refuge and a remedy for his trouble."

The bilateral lopsided life is there : left side letting him move, right side weak and lame and making shame. When he straightened, the wind caught him, he spins on his left foot in fear and falling. He tries to reach the church of the college before him,

his thought being to go there for prayer, but perceiving that he had passed a man of his acquaintence without saluting him, he tries to return on his steps to make due acknowledgment and is flung violently against the church by the wind.

At that moment, someone in the middle of the quad calls him by name, and says that if he will go in search of Monsieur N., this man has something to give him. The dreamer supposes that it is a melon brought from a foreign country.

But what surprises him still more is to see that those who together with this person are gathering round him for conversation stand on their feet straight and steady, whereas he himself on this same ground is bowed and staggering.

The wind has become less strong. With all this in mind, he wakes.

The melon . . . own unique distress, with everyone else stable . . . the possible sexual interpretation of weakness, straightness, refuge; these are underpainting of a work of very dense a reality. He awoke and

> feels a pain that causes him to fear that all this is the work of some evil genius bent on seducing him. He turns at once to his right side, his *other side*. He prays, begging to be protected and preserved, recognizing his sins — even though his life "might hitherto have been" irreproachable "in the eyes of men."

Two hours passed, in "thoughts of various kinds on all the good and evil in this world."

> He fell asleep again, and dreamed the second dream, in which he believes he hears a sharp and piercing noise which he takes for a clap of thunder, and opening his eyes, he perceives a large number of fiery sparks all around him in the room.

He knew these sparks. Often Descartes woke in the night, and found his eyes sparkling so brilliantly as to light the objects nearest him. Now he opened and closed his eyes; he saw things around him, reassuring objects; "his fear was dissipated, and it was in a reasonably tranquil condition that he fell asleep again."

As soon as he fell asleep, the third dream started. Unlike the two earlier dreams, this "had nothing terrifying in it."

> . . . He finds a book on his table, without knowing who put it there. He opens it, and seeing it is a dictionary, he is delighted, hoping that he might find it useful.

The delight is the key.

> At the same instant, he happens on another book, no less of a surprise to him than the first, not knowing how it had come there. He finds it to be a collection of poems entitled *Corpus Poetarum* etc.

He was curious and wanted to read. He opened the book to the line *Quod vitae sectabor iter?* What life-path shall I follow?

> At the same moment he perceives a man he does not know, who presents him with some verses beginning with the words *Est et Non.* These he recommends highly, insisting on the excellence of the poem.

The dreamer told him that he knew "what the piece was," recognizing it as among the Eclogues of Ausonius, a poet among those in the anthology. The man asks him, as he begins searching for a poem, where he had got the book; but the dreamer is still unable to say where it had come from, and now the dictionary has disappeared. As he said this, the dictionary is visible at the other end of the table; but changed.

> Meantime he comes upon the poems of Ausonius in the collection of poems he was handling *and being unable to find the piece beginning with the words* Est et Non, *he says to the man that he knows another passage of the same poet even finer, and that it begins with the words,* Quod vitae sectabor iter?*

The unknown sources : the man, the book, the melon, these go on. The man asks to see the preferred poem. Descartes begins to look for it, when he comes upon several portrait engravings and realizes that the edition is not one he knows. At this moment, man and books vanish while Descartes goes on dreaming; and in his dream, he knows that it is a dream and goes into its last stage : he interprets the dream before he wakes.

He makes an allegory of the dream, saying that the dictionary stands for all the sciences, the anthology of poems stands for "the union of philosophy and wisdom — for poets, due to the divine nature of inspiration, are often wiser than professional philosophers. The verse about the choice of a path in life represented a sage's advice, or possibly, moral theology. These ideas came to him while he was still asleep.

"He awoke and still meditating, interpreted the poets in the

* Italics mine — M.R.

anthology as signifying 'revelation and inspiration.' *Est et Non* were the Yes and No of Pythagoras and referred to truth and error in human knowledge and the sciences." His pleasure at fitting these pieces together, his success, convinced him that it was the Angel of Truth who had revealed to him the treasures of "all the sciences." There was no place for the portraits, but when he saw an artist the next day, that place seemed to be satisfied; its unanswered question dissolved away.

He saw the first two dreams as admonitions. The melon is linked with solitary pleasure; the wind with force that he willingly would allow to push him. God would not let him; but God drew him toward the church. Terror and thunder in the second dream were both accepted and interpreted as remorse and the presence of the Angel of Truth. He prayed and remembered now the excitement and enthusiasm that he had felt to be forerunner of a crisis, which these dreams expressed. He vowed to the Virgin a pilgrimage to her shrine at Loreto, "part of the way on foot and clad in lowly garb." The rapture was ended after a few days; he did fulfill his vow, four years later.

Freud, in writing of Descartes' crisis, warns us to accept the dreamer's comments as relevant to the interpretation of dreams, but he says that psychoanalysts would not be able to interpret it. He needs more of the associations of Descartes. Who is the man? Monsieur N.? What is the melon, to Descartes? The portraits?

Wisdom, using "universal symbolism," makes conventional suggestions in terms of sexuality. Lewin offers the suggestion that an illness has set up autonomous electric circuits in the brain, accounting for the scintillations; he works on the basis of a sleep-threatening and sleep-protecting struggle, and sees these dreams as not very effective preservers of Descartes' sleep. He purposely, he says, shifted his attention "to the matter of intellectual and scientific creation. For when one learns from Descartes that he believed this dream revealed to him that the physical world can be completely formulated in mathematical terms, and when one compares this remarkable assertion to the dilettante *Deuterei* that followed the dream, one cannot suppress astonishment."

The relation of the observer to the observed in these dreams were the relations that influenced Europe from then on; the scientific observer viewing the scientifically observed and observable in waking life; the separated mind and matter which became the Cartesian mind, *res cogitans,* and Cartesian matter, *res extensa;* the old formulation to which Descartes returned for an explanation, the vortices which are so like the spinning in which he lived while the other personages of his first dream were not spinning and not buffeted; except for close-packing — the particles are packed so tightly that they move in relationship, one of them communicates movement to the rest. The notion comes to us in another and political manner as the domino theory.

But I suggest that this dream is cumulative. The interpreters stop short, but the last choice is the choice that determined the dreamer's thinking, or rather gave the theatre of confirmation in which Descartes' thinking could now be acted out.

The choice is within the two poems, and Descartes chose duality, the split of mind and matter, setting his will on the path before him and letting go the world of *Est* and *Non,* which he saw as *Est* or *Non,* to be *or* not to be, as it has been seen by the entire stream of influential imagining men and women identified with the main and general stream of acceptance. There is, of course, another stream, going through Empedocles, Heraclitus, Bruno, Hariot, the recurrent imaging work for the unifying process that sees *Est* and *Non est,* joins them, sees the point around which they turn, and lives, in history and imagination, from that pivotal place.

Descartes was dreaming of Ausonius' Eclogues, II and IV. There are further clues to the nature of his dreaming, I believe, in the two poems. The Second Eclogue is a Latin version

of the Greek poem in the Palatine Anthology, 9.359, possibly
by Posidippus :

What road in life shall I take? the courts
are full of tumult; home is raked by care;
in travel, the troubles of home follow;
the merchant can always expect fresh losses,
fear of poverty's shame keeps him from sleep;
the farmer is worn out with work, shipwreck
makes a horror of the sea; celibate life
has its own pains, but even worse
the watch and ward kept by a jealous husband;
the work of war is bloody; and filthy money's
exactions, and usury's, slaughter the needy.
Every phase of life bears its brunt, no one
is glad of his own age; there is no understanding
in infants at the breast, and boys learn
stringent lessons, and adolescents the rash time.
Hazards beset the full-grown man, war, the sea,
anger and deceit, or the long chain of work always being
    exchanged
for one still heavier. Old age itself,
long hoped-for with mean prayers,
lays open the body lacerated with less disease.
Unanimously we despise the present;
some do not even want to become as gods.
Juturna cries out : "Who gave me enternal life?
Why is the condition of death
taken from me?" Under the crag of Caucasus,
Prometheus is a witness against Saturn's son
and never stops cursing Jove for giving him
endless life. Look at the modes of the mind. See how
Hippolytus the chaste was destroyed by tragic
care for his chastity. And against that,
how one who delights in a life stained
with looseness should contemplate the penalties
of sinful kings, incestuous Tereus
of soft Sardanapalus. The three Punic wars
warn us about betrayal, but

the destruction of Saguntum forbids us to keep faith.
Live, cleave to friendship forever —
that was the crime
that got the college of Pythagorean sages down.
Fearing this penalty, make no friendships . . .
Ambiguous desires always besiege and divide our minds . . .
    therefore
the proverb of the Greeks is best : they say
Good not to be born, but if you are, die quickly.

The Fourth Eclogue begins . . . but I cannot translate "Est et Non" — that certainly means Yes and No, but the sense of *Is,* of *To be* is so strong in that *Est* that it cannot pull apart, even though we know that Est was used for Yes. It is the Yes of existence.

Est and Non : The entire world uses these well-known syllables. Take them away, there's nothing for the language of man to be used on. Everything's in them, from them comes everything : business or leisure, whatever, tempest and calm —

to the piercing last line, after all dispute :

Qualis vita hominum, duo quam monosyllaba versant!
What a thing, the life of man, put in play by two syllables!

". . . a short story which Dr. John Pell lately told me he had from Sir Charles Cavendish, only brother to William then Earl, since first Duke of Newcastle; a Person of Honour, (well-skilled in the Mathematicks), who about that time lived in Paris. He discoursing there with Monsieur Roberval, concerning that piece of Descartes then lately published : I admire (saith M. Roberval) that notion in Descartes of putting over the whole equation to one side, making it equal to Nothing, and how he lighted upon it. The reason why you admire it (saith Sir Charles) is because you are a French-man; for if you were an English-man, you would not admire it. Why so? (saith M. Roberval) Because (saith Sir Charles) we in England know whence he had it; namely from Hariot's Algebra. What Book is that? (saith M. Roberval) I never saw it. Next time you come to my Chamber (saith Sir Charles) I will shew it you. Which a while after he did : And upon perusal of it, M. Roberval exclaimed with Admiration : (Il l'a veu! Il l'a veu!) He had seen it! He had seen it!) Finding all that in Hariot which he had before admired in Descartes; and not doubting but that Descartes had it from thence."

Descartes wrote, of his concerns :

> The sciences are now masked from us; the masks off, they will appear in all their beauty. To him who perceives the links of the sciences (catenam scientiarum) it will prove no more difficult to retain them in mind than to retain the number-series!

And, in *Cogitationes privatae* :

> As a comedian puts on his mask so as not to show the shame on his face; so I, about to step on the stage of this world where until now I have been only a spectator, I will appear masked.

Eric Temple Bell has pointed out that Hariot closed a long gap from the Babylonians to the sixteenth century, being "one of the first Europeans to duplicate the ancient feat of permitting a negative number to stand as one side, one member, of an equation."

It is his way of discovery and experience that distinguishes Hariot. For surely one of the great steps is the conscious discovery of the problem, whether it lie in history or mathematics or any other part of life seen as a field.

During this same period, the mathematician closely linked to Hariot through inclination and their common link Torporley — Francois Vieta — also rejected negative roots. It was not until 1659 that Hudde (1628-1704) used a letter to denote a negative or a positive number, with no discrimination regarding sign, and made it usable.

Dr. Alexander Rhead knew Hariot for only a short time at the end of his life. He had known of that "famous Mathematician" in relation to the Noble Earle of Northumberland, and Hariot's friendship and working closeness with Mr. Hughes "who wrote of the Globes, Mr. Warner and Mr. Turperley." Rhead prescribed the "curations" for cancer which were in use, the decoctions and waters, moist, he says, *actu,* but *potentia,* drying; the unguents with which to dress the ulcers twice a day, with their silver, their lead and white wax; the cauteries used as the "second externall meane in the curing of an Ozaena," and only used in cases "rebellious to powerful ordinary meanes; and the water "in this griefe," with its oils and oak extract, rose water and distilled water, to be injected into the nose, and also to be used in wet dressings morning and evening.

The terrible wounds of man to man had been escaped by Hariot. He had not been hurt in the rioting at Oxford, he had not been killed when Indians had turned on English after the first villages had been burned in Virginia; he had lived through the fighting in Ireland; his head had not been axed from his body.

He had escaped death by tempest, death by drowning.

He had lived through the plague years of stench and bell.

He had not been tortured for being an athiest, being a magician, a "juggler."

But here was the other violation, the long slow last violation that came on for many years.

We know a heroic response to this mode of death in our own

time with the long suffering and death of Freud. His biographer, Ernest Jones, has recorded the suffering, the brutal prosthesis put where his palate had been, and the clumsiness, hideous pain, and bravery of this time in which Freud went on with his work, refusing morphine until, at the end, he called for drug and death. Hariot was heroic here.

Hariot in his will leaves to Mistress Buckner, wife of Thomas Buckner, in whose house he lived during the last period of his life, fifteen pounds for reparations of certain damages, or for other uses. What were these damages?

We know, further, of his illness, that his case was used by Dr. Rhead in the lectures on cancer. The reference to Hariot is to be found in the 26th lecture, published in Part Two of "A Treatise of Ulcers."

In our time, there is still ignorance as to the causes of cancer and that curious relationship between the host and the disease that allows a wild growth to proliferate. There have been three speculations as to the cause of cancer in Hariot. Again, in our time there is the attack and defense of tobacco that existed in the time of Ralegh and King James, subsiding just after the lifetime of James and Hariot, when it was clear that it was tobacco, not gold, that would make the fortunes of Virginia. There was no connection made in 1621 relating tobacco to cancer. The gossip was that Hariot's cancer began because he was in the habit of holding his brass instruments in his mouth while he made his calculations.

As for the third cause given, it came from the enemies of his thought, who said, as Anthony à Wood does, that Hariot could never believe the position *Ex nihilo nihil fit.* In the end, they said, a *nihil* killed him.

The last piece of writing we have of Thomas Hariot's was written in the home of his friend Thomas Buckner, in Threadneedle Street. Buckner was Hariot's companion in that faraway voyage to Virginia; his name is listed down the list of seamen. Now he is a mercer, and a vestryman of St. Christopher le Stocks. It is in his house that Hariot closes his long illness, for which they mocked his thunderings about Nihil, and his reconciling strength that allowed all paradox, and with great malice, said, "But in the end, it was a little Nothing that killed him."

With his ruined face, dying, at the home of his friend where great breakage had taken place, Hariot wrote his extraordinary will, dated June 29, 1621. It can be seen at the Guildhall Library.

There are clues to the furnishing of his house. He speaks of the box of "drawne mappes standing nowe at the northeast window of that Roome" which is called the parlor "at my house in Syon."

He leaves his furnaces, one to Torporley, and two to Christopher Tooke, his friend and lens-grinder, the maker of instruments who had lived with him for many years, "my servaunte Christopher Tooke," with 100 pounds. A gift of maps and charts, books and "One wooden Boxe full or neere full of drawne Mappes standing now at the Northest windowe of that Roome wch is called the plo^r at my house in Syon" goes to the Earl of Northumberland, who he hopes will have him buried at Isleworth if he dies there; but if he die in London, Hariot hopes that he be buried in the parish church of the house where he lies.

He gives his papers "nowe vppon the table in my Library at Syon, conteyning fiue quires of paper, more or lesse wch were written by the last Lord Harrington, and Coppyed out of some of my Mathematicall papers for his instruction" to Sir Robert Sidney, Viscount Lisle, the "Robin" who was the brother of Philip Sidney. He notes instructions to return to Lord Lisle the two globes which Hariot borrowed of him. The bequests continue : a furnace to John Protheroe, one to Torporley, two to Tooke.

And to Mistress Buckner, "wife unto Thomas Buckner Mercer at whose house being in St. Christophers pishe I nowe lye," fifteen pounds toward the reparation of "some damages I have made" in the last stages of his illness. To their son, and to his own cousin "John Harriotte" living in Church peene, and married, there are bequests of fifty pounds each. To his servant John Sheller; his servant Joane; his servant under her, Jane; to Christopher Kellett "a Lymning paynter dwelling neare Petty Fraunce in Westminster"; to Joan Chapman living in Braynford; to his brewer in Braynford; to John Bill stationer a debt of forty pounds or so for books; and Christopher Ingram of Syon 3600 billets of wood. And manuscripts to be returned to Allen, "Thomas Allen of Gloster Hall in Oxford M^r of Artes."

Now the equipment: to the Earl of Northumberland "my two pspectiue trunckes wherewth I vse espetially to see Venus horned like the Moone and the Spottes in the Sonne The glasses of wch trunckes I desire to haue remooved into two other of the fayrest trunckes by my said servaunte Christopher Tooke." And to each of his executors, he instructs Christopher to give a telescope "of the best glasses and th^e fayrest trunckes" — Christopher to get all the residue of telescopes "wth the other glasses of his own making," except for two great long telescopes consisting of many parts which are to go to the Earl of Northumberland to remain in his library.

Christopher is to get the lens-making equipment, the dishes of iron, and the other lenses for telescopes. Mayerne is to be paid for drugs, and Wheatly, another apothecary who lived near the Stocks at the east end of Cheapside, is also to be paid (this is a larger debt, undoubtedly for the medicines used near the end).

Money from the sale of books and other goods is to be used for the poor of the parish, and for the poor of "the hospitall in Christes Church in Lond," where he may have lain; for the poor of Isleworth near Syon, and for Hariot's executors. Beyond this money, he wishes the value of the rest to go to "Sr Thomas Bodleyes Library in Oxford" or to such Charitable & pious uses as they shall thincke best, after the books have been appraised by Robert Hughes.

Then Hariot comes to his real wishes about his writings, the scraps of which have come to us in our time. "I order and Constitute the aforesaid Nathaniel Thorperley first to be Ouseer of my Mathematicall Writinges to be receiued of my Executors to pvse and order and to sepate the Cheife of them from my waste papers" [these are the papers we have], "to the end that after hee doth vunderstand them hee may make vse in penninge such doctrine that belonges vnto them for publique vses as it shall be thought Convenient by my Executors and him selfe And if it happen that some manner of Notacons or writinges of the said papers shall not be vnderstood by him then my desire is that it will please him to Conferre wth Mr Warner or Mr Hughes Attendants on the aforesaid Earle Concerning the aforesaid doubte. And if hee be not resolued by either of them That then hee Conferre wth the aforesaid John Protheroe Esquior or the aforesaid Thomas Alesbury Esquior." The papers, after such use, are to be put into a locked trunk and kept in Northumberland's library, with the key left in the Earl's hands. There is a provision that Torporley be allowed to have the papers again as he needs them.

Further than this, in the will, which is now in the Guildhall, Torporley is designated as overseer of "other written bookes and papers" as the executors and he shall think convenient.

Following this is the item containing order for the destruction of papers : "diuers waste papers (of wch some are in a Canvas bagge) of my Accompte to Sr Walter Rawley for all wch I haue discharges or acquitances lying in some boxes or other my desire is that they may bee all burnte. Also there is an other Canvas bagge of papers concerning Irishe Accompte (the psons whome they Concerne are dead many years since in the raigne of queene Elizabeth) wch I desire alsoe may be burnte as likewise many Idle paps and Cancelled Deedes wch are good for noe use."

Of the endless destruction of evidence by drowning, by burning, by selling for waste papers, by making into the lining of pie-pans — much of the treasure of Elizabethan manuscripts went in this indirect way into food; of the two fires of which twentieth-century librarians speak today : "You know we had the Fire of 1666 and Hitler's fire"; of the two floods; of the sales of great libraries in England and to Americans (see Sotheby's catalogues); of the possible evidence still in libraries and attics, not found because of the lack of interest that causes people to look in other directions; there is also the ordered destruction, as there is here, with Hariot bidding the burning of the clues, thinking them "good for noe vse."

But his desire we know. We know that he wanted to publish; that the next book after the *Brief and True Report of Virginia* and the *Arcticon* (lost now) and the *Regiment* (lost) is to be his mathematical doctrine.

Ten years after Hariot's death, a book was published in his name, the *Artis Analyticae Praxis,* containing his theory of equations, his work on conic sections and helices, and parts of his algebraic work. But it appeared after a tortured time in which Torporley seems to have undergone conflicts about the work with Vieta and the work with Hariot. In the preface, Cardanus and Stevinus are evoked, and the work with cubes and biquadratic equations is credited to Hariot. The preface ends with the praise of his simplicity, his treatment of mutation, his skill in *Logistices,* his great analytical work.

Hariot died on July 2nd, and was buried in the church of St. Christopher. That year, according to Stow's Survey of London, the church was put in repair and beautified. The following year, the monument which Northumberland wanted built to Hariot was made.

For James' fifty-seventh birthday, he liberated three of the great nobles, the princes, from the Tower, where, says Fonblanque, "in the exercise of his royal pleasure he had confined them." For that same pleasure, it was his new favorite, Buckingham, who brought the word to them.

Chamberlain writes to Dudley Carleton on July 18, 1622, "Buckingham appeared in the Tower, and conveyed to the Earls of Northumberland, Southampton, and Oxford, the King's command for their liberation on his birthday . . .

"On Sunday afternoon the Earl of Northumberland was released from his long imprisonment in the Tower, whence the Lord of Doncaster went to fetch him to his house with a coach and six horses."

The six horses, two more than Buckingham's fashionable four, were gossiped about as if the idea had been Northumberland's. But this was Hay's parade of welcome at this crisis of his life, when it was of chief importance to him and to his wife Lucy Percy to bring through the marriage which had been so hated by Northumberland. Chamberlain's letter goes on :

"The warders of the Tower make great moan that they have lost such a benefactor." The keeper of the Tower at this time is again Sir George More, the father-in-law of John Donne; it is to Donne that Hay now turns.

"All the lords and great men about this town go to visit and congratulate the Earl . . . Lord Arundel supper with him the first night, and dined there the next day, whither came likewise, unbidden, the Spanish Ambassador. The Earl continues at Syon for ten days, then goes to Petworth, thence to Penshurst, to see his daughter Lisle, and so on, when he thinks good, within his precincts." Chamberlain is writing four days after the other letter to Dudley Carleton.

For James had added a rider to Northumberland's liberation. Remembering the Border, remembering always his work and his wishes to dominate forever the north country, the fierce feuds and claims of the boundary, and the love and wealth that would bring the Percies home to the north, James had confined Northumberland for life to thirty miles' range around Petworth.

Bent, broken and grey, troubled constantly because of his eyes, Northumberland drove away from the Tower with the air booming under a salute of guns ordered by the King. The coach and six horses crossed the drawbridge and went up the hill. It turned left into London changed, bright, and roaring; for all the streets of his way were crowded with people come to see the prisoner freed. They were cheering as he passed, sixteen years of people, a generation who knew he was innocent of the charges against him and had shown their children that a prince might be framed for a lifetime.

Hariot was dead, Northumberland free. He would raise a monument, and make his life with the friends who had been with him then and now, with his children.

His children, and the marriage which had been so deep a goad to him, tantalizing him with the hated promise of a pardon to an innocent who could not tolerate any pardon, and loathed a Scottish one. James Hay, Lord Doncaster, about to be Lord Carlisle, turned to his friend of many years, the poet Jack Donne, now John Donne, Dean of St. Paul's, who twenty-one years ago had asked Northumberland to intercede so that his own marriage might not be cursed and doomed. Northumberland failed with Egerton; but the world had changed phase since then.

Donne came to Hanworth, and on August 25, 1622, preached before Hay and Lucy, and the company, "being the Earles of Northumberland, and Buckingham, &c," on a text from the Book of Job : EVERY MAN MAY SEE IT, MAN MAY BEHOLD IT AFAR OFF.

> The passage in Job is spoken by Elihu, and describes the greatness of God in terms of the tempest,
>> the spreading of the clouds,
>> the crashings of His pavilion.
> Behold, He spreadeth His light upon it.

Donne, with a glancing blow at the Jews, begins, showing the words of poets become the word of God, and goes on to ask for "roome for diver branches" for "The first part is a discovery, a manifestation of God to man; though that be undeniably true, *Posuit tenebras latibulum, God hath made darknesse his secret place,* yet it is as true, which proceeds from the same mouth, and the same pen, *Amictus tanquam pallio,* God covers himselfe *with light as with a garment,* he will be seene through his *works* : As we shall stand naked to one another, and not be ashamed of our *scars,* or *morphews,* in the sight of God, so God stands naked to the eyes of man, and is not ashamed of that humiliation, *Every man may see it, man may behold it afar off."* This proposition, this discovery, says Donne, will be the first part.

This is Donne as he had not been in many of the later poems, Donne remembering, the Donne of *tenebras,* of the great early portrait, long, fine, beautiful, with the Spanish hat and lace, serving to call us to the marvelous face of thought and attraction and the fine long hand.

Then the attack on those who deny a creation, who deny thus any God, and then "make a worse *God.*" And comes to works — works and books. "This world then is a *work,* a limited, a determined, a circumscribed work . . ." and "Every man hath a delight, and complacency in *knowledge,* and is ashamed of *ignorance,* even in booklearning . . . His house is not well furnished, he is not well furnished, without bookes."

Northumberland was in the world again. In a great house, hearing this preacher, the wild young man who stood in the court of York House following Essex with his eyes, with Northumberland's wife, raging and fiery as her brother standing there, and his own father murdered and falsely accused of the sin that would condemn him eternally in his eyes. False accusings : his own not yet arrived. A lifetime past.

"Dost thou love learning," the Dean's voice was concentrating, "as it is contracted, brought to a quintessence, wrought to a spirit, by *Philosophers?* the eldest of them in that whole book" (and he was quoting Trismegistus — Northumberland looked up startled) *"Quod Deus latens, simul & patens est,* testifies all that, and nothing but that, that as there is nothing so dark, so there is nothing so cleare, nothing so remote, nothing so neare us, as God.

"Dost thou love learning," Donne continued, "as it is

sweetned and set to musique by *Poets?* the King of the Poets
testifies the same, *Mens agitat molem, & magno se corpore
miscet* . . . a great, an universall spirit, that moves, a generall
soule, that animates, and agitates every peece of this world . . .
Saint Paul says," heard Northumberland sharply, for Donne
was speaking directly to him, *"The invisible things of God, are
seen by things which are made;* and thereby man is made in-
excuseable : Moses is an ancienter *Philosopher,* then *Trismegistus;* and his picture of God, is the Creation of the world."

Trismegistus, creation, Hariot writing, again and again, in
Latin, in Hebrew, in English, in that curling cipher of his, In
the beginning God made heaven and earth.

Donne had reached a clanging place, *"Levate oculos,* Lifte
up your eyes, on high . . ."

"But who knowes the volumes of this Author?

"Hast thou not room, hast thou not money, hast thou not
understanding, hast thou not leisure, for great volumes, for the
bookes of heaven, (for the *Mathematiques*) nor for the books
of Courts, (the Politiques) take but the *Georgigues,* the consideration of the *Earthe,* a farme, a garden, nay seven foot of
earth, a grave, and that will be book enough. Goe lower . . ."

Our eyes, he was saying, coming up out of the grave and the
worms, our eyes see only quantities, no substance.

That man may see God, he was saying. And God is the God
of Peace, and reconciles the two : "not, every man *may,* but
every man *hath* seen God . . .

"We have divers names for *man* in Hebrew, at least *foure;*
This that makes him but earth, Adam, is the meanest, and yet
Col-Adam, Every man may see God.

"David cals us to the contemplation of the heavens, *Coeli
enarrant,* and *Job* to the contemplation of the *firmament,*
of the *Pleiades,* and *Orion,* and *Arcturus,* and the ordinances
of heaven; but it is not onely the Mathematician that sees God,
Domini terra, the *earth* is the Lords, and *all that dwell therein;*
all, in all corners of the earth, may see him. *David* tells us, *They
that go down to the sea, in ships, they see the works* of the

Lord, and his wonders in the deep; but it is not onely the Mariner, the discoverer, that discovers God : but he that *puts his hand to the plough, and looks not back,* may see God there."

Ralegh. Hariot. The star-captains. All his men.

"Let him be *filius terrae.*" Donne spoke, and Northumberland caught the flash as he remembered what Donne had been called when they tried to deny him his degree : *filius noctis —* "*filius terrae,* the sonne of the earth, without noble extraction, without knowne place, of uncertaine parents, (even *Melchisedeck* was so) Let him be *filius percussionis,* the sonne of affliction, a man that hath inward heavy sentences, and heavy executions of the law; Let him be *filius mortis,* the sonne of death (as *Saul* said to *Jonathan* of *David*) a man designed to dye; nay let him be *filius Belial,* the sonne of iniquity, and of erlasting perdition, there is no lownesse, no natural, no spiritual dejection so low, but that that low man may see God.

"Let him be *filius terrae,* the sonne of the earth, and of no body else, let him be *Dominus terrae,* Lord of the earth, busied upon the earth, and nothing else, let him be *hospes terrae,* a guest, a tenant, an inmate of the earth, halfe of him in the earth, and the rest no where else, this poore man, this worldly man, this dying man, may see God."

All of us, I myself, gaunt Donne, closing in on the eagle sensitivity of his last illness, Hariot in earth. All.

"To end this, you can place the spheare in no position, in no position, in no station, in which the earth can eclipse the Sun; you can place this clod of earth, *man,* in no *ignorance,* in no *melancholy,* in no *oppression,* in no *sinne,* but that he *may,* but that he *does* see God. The Marigold opens to the Sunne, though it have no tongue to say so, the Atheist does see God, though he have not grace to confesse it."

Now he comes to another faculty. He has spoken of knowing, and of man as Adam. He comes to seeing, and to man as Enosh, who having tasted God's corrections, having considered the miseries of this world . . .

We think we see far; but "he that will see this objectt, must lye low; it is best discerned in the dark, in a heavy, and a calamitous fortune."

In accretion alone, what is there? "If I adde number to number, a span, a mile long, if at the end of all that long line of numbers, there be nothing that notes, *pounds,* or *crownes,* or *shillings,* what's that long number, but so many killions of millions of nothing?

"God made the Sun, and Moon, and Stars, glorious lights for man to see by; but mans infirmity requires spectacles," Donne says to Northumberland, "and affliction does that office. Gods meaning was, that by the sun-shine of prosperity, and by the beames of honour, and temporall blessings, a man should see farre into him; but I know not how he is come to need *spectacles;* scarce any man sees much in this matter, till affliction shew it to him."

Eye-salve, he says, affliction. But then darkness comes in its gifts. "Man *sees* best in the light, but *meditates* best in the dark . . ." You of the Court, you are the Court exemplified, you have beheld God in his spectacle of Crosses and affliction. He ends with the Song of the Three Children, *Blesse ye the Lord, praise him, and magnifie him for ever.*

Northumberland caused the monument to Hariot to be set in the chancel of St. Christopher's.

The inscription began:

SISTE, VIATOR, LEVITER PREME . . .

In English:

> Stay, traveller, tread lightly,
> Near here lies that which was mortal
> Of that most famous man
> Thomas Hariot,
> He was that most learned Hariot
> Of Syon on the river Thames,
> His birthplace and school
> Oxford
> He cultivated all knowledges

And excelled in all,
Mathematics, Philosophy, Science, Theology.
Most eager explorer, he studied truth
Devoutly he adored the triune God
Sixty years old, or thereabouts,
His farewell was to mortality, not life.
July 2, A.D. 1621

In the Great Fire of 1666, this monument was destroyed with most of this part of London, and it is left to us only as a recorded inscription in Stow. There is a drawing among Hariot's papers, of a heavy, formalized, coffin-shaped stone monument with only the letters D.O.M. on it and the spaces for an inscription indicated by dashes, with no clue on the page as to what or whose monument this might be.

The church endured for over a hundred years, while the Bank of England grew beside it on Threadneedle Street. Indeed, part of the church escaped the Great Fire and was repaired by Sir Christopher Wren in 1671. It was again "repaired and beautified" in 1696. The last burial here was that of Jenkins, a bank clerk, known for his great height of seven feet six inches.

In 1781, the expansion of the Bank of England required the taking down of this church. A garden with a fountain marked the site of the burial-ground attached to St. Christopher le Stocks. As the bank grew and was rebuilt, the garden became completely surrounded. Stevens speaks of it as "the loveliest spot in London."

It is today a place of intense stillness and greenness, completely surrounded by money. As if it were speaking for one aspect of the green New World and the wild hope for gold that by this century has been realized in many ways, through many disciplines, this garden stands over death, in life, in privacy. Standing here, by courtesy, I felt many forces.

It is very likely that Hariot's bones do not lie here. In 1867, the United Cemeteries at Nunhead received from the Bank of England several cases of human remains which were recorded as having been removed from under the Bank of England "being the old vaults of St. Christopher-le-Stocks." This is all the knowledge they have, they say, of the contents; there were also cases received by them in 1933, and of these they know only that they were removed from under the Bank of England.

The Bank of England reports that three catacomb vaults were purchased by the Bank; they are number 9396, 9397 and 9398, and are in the south wing of the Eastern Catacombs. During excavations in 1933, a further vault, 38322, was acquired.

But outside the garden, just within the wall, there is something very curious. There is nothing to declare here; it is again a matter of raising a question.

You see the flash of this image from outside the wall of the Bank of England, at the busy corner of Princes and Threadneedle Streets. It is a gold flying figure poised on one foot, high over the wall, based on a small dome. *London for Everyman* says, "Above is a charming figure of Ariel."

If you ask the bobby at the corner, he may say, as he did to me, "It's just a figger, 's far 's we're concerned."

Up the street, at the entrance, a tall Bank of England guard in a pink coat said, "It's a figure like Eros in Piccadilly Circus . . . It's Mercury."

I telephoned the general information service of the *Daily Telegraph,* wondering what a popular explanation might be. It was closed at night, but a boy at the city desk said he might help. There were boys' voices behind his. "It's a grasshopper," the voice said after conferring. No, it's not, I answered him. "Who told you it's not a grasshopper?" said the boy.

Next morning, the information room was open. "It's a modern representation of Brittania," they brought back information.

One of the officials at the Bank of England came back to the first answer. "It's a figure of Ariel, by Sir Charles Wheeler. I'm afraid I couldn't tell you why it's there."

But the curator of their museum said that there are four Ariels — drawings — in the Bank of England museum, and that for some reason Ariel has been a traditional figure to them.

Another official said that Sir Herbert Baker and Sir Charles

Wheeler, now the president of the Royal Academy, decided on the figure that now stands, gold, fleet, on the dome of a modified temple of Soane's Tivoli.

Sir Charles Wheeler has graciously written, "Sir Herbert Baker thought of the idea of Ariel for the dome of the Bank of England. We used to speak of the then Governour, Montague Norman, as a magician who, like Prospero in The Tempest, had Ariel as his messenger to all parts of the world.

"Ariel he regarded as a variant of Mercury, the messenger of the gods, and Mercury had been used as a symbol of bankers. Therefore he thought Ariel not inappropriate to symbolize the activities of the Bank of England.

"I hope this answers your question sufficiently."

The official at the Bank of England writes of the figure. "This is generally known by the names of Ariel, after the Spirit of the Air in Shakespeare's 'Tempest,' and could be taken to symbolize the spirit of the Bank carrying credit and trust around the world."

Traces of a lifetime. The freshness in which a man feels that he can find anything out, the opening of the world to deed and word, the ways in which the poetry, the science, all exploration, a personal relation to the unknown, are claimed and lived. The place where the country of Est and the country of Non Est are seen to meet and be alive, as a door to a continually opening new world.

The flying figure over the wall, a wall that seems fixed and defended, as of a bank, as of a prison. And beyond it, the city of the world. And beyond that, the sky of night and day, the lights of both. And beyond that, the universe of maximum and minimum, the infinities.

IN THE PRESENT:

The Search
for Thomas Hariot

*A*gain and again, reading Ralegh's poems, I came on slanting references to his loss and to the world he had found, a world of pilgrimage and creation

> Knowinge shee cann renew, and cann create
> Green from the grounds, and floures, yeven out of stone,
> By vertu lastinge over tyme and date,
>
> Levinge vs only woe, which like the moss,
> Havinge cumpassion of unburied bones
> Cleaves to mischance, and unrepayred loss.
>
> For tender stalkes —

In the bitter certainty in which he knew the lie, and gave the world the lie, and was accused forever of the lie; and disdain turning to despair; and voyaging and pilgrimage; and finally coming to that great stop that was Elizabeth's monster horror, death by the axe, by the sword — always there was a connection of loyalty that was the same as learning. We know of his wife's loyalty, but there was another, mentioned always with Ralegh : Hariot, whom he sent to the New World in place of himself, to see, to write and to bring about, to be scientist, describer and discoverer of that Virginia which is always associated both with Elizabeth and with Ralegh.

One wishes to avoid this kind of feeling, but as one goes further, it is impossible not to see some kind of bringing to birth by these two strange parents in this new world which Hariot saw : Hariot, as the "child" of Ralegh and Elizabeth.

But who was he? Where is he to be found? I read Ralegh's poems again with students, and I would set both them and my-

303

self to the question. The *Dictionary of National Biography* carried a brief note, full of puzzles and mysteries, and Jaffe's *Men of Science in America* had a splendid chapter called by his name but only partly about him. There was Henry Stevens' book published privately in 1900, to be found in the Rare Book Room of the Public Library, and its ramifying clues and excitements made it clear that Hariot, in his work and his friends, went far through the roots of our own time. But that was all. Except his own book, the first book in English about America, *A Brief and True Report.*

As I began to ask the questions about the signs in our own times that such a life had ever been lived, I also began to want to read about Hariot. I began to speak to people who were eminently qualified to deal with Hariot, his skills, his age, the great nets of the Renaissance in arts and science and political drama : Hiram Haydn, Henry Guerlac, and then to almost every writer I encountered. Each time I spoke of Hariot, the same thing happened. They would turn that look on me that told me I myself was getting in deeper. I read Ralegh's poems again with my students at Sarah Lawrence. In the few poems whose attribution is at all agreed upon, and in the river-flow of *The History of the World,* I began to see a man rather different from the glittering arrogant figure of the biographies (I except Waldman, Magnus, and a few others). In Hermann Hesse's key book, *The Journey to the East,* the two main characters, the defeated searcher and the servant of the lost expedition, who at the end of the story is revealed as the still existent leader, are both seen as the sides of one figure, or statue, or something like a glass vase shaped in the likeness of the two men; and it can be seen through the glass that there is a kind of smoke, as if it were their identities, that in a pouring movement is circulating through the two, so that ambiguities and weaknesses are joined into something stronger that is common to both. I began to see Ralegh — the glory and broken pride, writer, lover, commander, and man on the block of execution — and Hariot — the forgotten lost discoverer, the unverified man with whatever private life he may have had, his links, provable and un-provable, with the scientists, the poets, the technicians and lords of his day — as two figures joined.

Then I began to prepare to search for the papers and the materials in England. By a curious living link, a friend sent me on the way. Sir Martin Charteris, whom I had not yet met, very kindly spoke of my work, done and planned, to the Duke of Northumberland, the inheritor of much of the Hariot tradition and of Hariot's patron, the Ninth Earl, who had been kept pris-oner in the Tower of London for the years between the Gun-powder Plot and Hariot's death.

Through one of those chains of bad fortune by which hotels do not give a forwarding address and a new telephone number, Sir Martin could not reach me in London. I read at the British Museum and at Public Records while I lived across from that Hall at Clifford's Inn, and waited to hear. Finally, on my last day — no longer in England, but on the west coast of Ireland, on Valentia Island — the letter from the Duke came, with his invitation. It was two years before I could return.

In that time, the corridors to Hariot began to open; the range of his explorations grew more visible, the questions deepened; but there were doors that stayed obdurately shut. The confusion and even the authorship of the papers were puzzles. What I was saying about Hariot was unverifiable until his papers should be published; and they had been rejected over a hundred years ago by the Oxford University Press. My publishing arrangements at one moment depended on the advice asked from one of our prime authorities, who wrote an amazing letter for a scholar. He told the publisher that I would not be working with the manuscripts, and therefore my book should not be printed. I have a copy of that letter, which for a while ended my hopes. A man who had never met me and had no idea what work I was doing or might do, made this judgment. I went on working with the microfilms of the Hariot papers, brought back from the British Museum; and found another publisher.

Two years later, I was back in England, hoping now to perse-

vere to Alnwick, the castle of the Percies, with its great library
and muniment room, at last to accept the Duke of Northumberland's invitation. But not so fast; the letter from his secretary
said that His Grace was away for six weeks, and she regretted
that a visit would have to be put off until his return.

A few days later, my son and I left Well Walk in Hampstead
and took the morning train north to Newcastle. My son went
with me on the train-journey to Newcastle upon Tyne. I was
seething with nerves. I knew quite well that my invitation was
two years old, and that I had been told the Duke was not there.
Not to come. The whole thing was a folly, out of character, and
would end disastrously. But I was driven by now. What had I
been told long before? "By now, it is an obsession with you,
and these obsessive things sometimes turn out well." This could
not turn out at all, said the train wheels.

At Newcastle, I hired a car, and drove to Alnwick, through
the Hotspur Gate, and Outgate and Ingate and past the Hotspur
Motor School to the wide cobblestoned road before the castle.
The scarlet phone-booth.

When the voice of the secretary sounded, clear and distinct
with its softness as an undersong, I lied; I said that I "happened
to be" in the neighborhood. "Where are you now?" she asked.
"At the Barbican Gate," I told her. "Well, if you're that keen,
you'd better come along," she said. "Tell them you have an
appointment with Miss Heriot and they'll let you through."

She was standing at the foot of the inner stairs, a smiling red-
haired Scotswoman with the same name as the unknown. She
led us in. Since His Grace had invited me to see the library, she
said, I might just begin to look around today, and she brought
me to that high room, vibrating in gold, with its very long blue-
leather lectern, where I began to read. You might just stay in
the vicinity, suggested Miss Heriot, although tomorrow it will
be the housekeeper's decision. I had already seen the copy of
The History of the World given by Ralegh to the Ninth Earl,
and the tall books of the family papers; and glimpses of end-
lessness.

No rooms in Alnwick; no rooms in Alnmouth, at the coast. But twenty miles away there was an inn. When I telephoned the next morning, Miss Heriot answered. "Either it's because you're that keen, or because of luck," she said, "but the housekeeper has gone with His Grace's chauffeur to Newcastle to see *Lawrence of Arabia.*"

I had seen that movie; I knew it was one of the longest films ever made; and we drove back to the last turns of the road, where Alnwick Castle stood across the river and the field of horses. After that day, I was a *fait accompli,* and the reading went on.

Hariot began to fade in and out as I walked around and around him in the reading. There was very little directly about this man, but almost everything was related to him, and pieced something together, stroke by stroke. Except that at times he almost disappeared; did disappear. And then John Shirley's two reprints brought some details clear; Professor Batho's essays rose again; Vaughan's watercolors of the stages of the transformation opened that world.

The tourists in their processions moved behind the red rope barriers. Sometimes, as they went through the doorways, they would put up their hands in a furtive gesture and peel a long strip of brocade for a souvenir. The staff kept bolts of the brocade with which the walls were covered.

The great day came when they gave me the key to the tower — "If we're going to trust you, we must trust you completely, mustn't we?" and I began my work in the Muniment Room, that high, cool stone room of manuscripts and account rolls. Mr. Graham, the agent, had built a high ladder, a seagoing man's ladder of twenty rungs going up into the top shelves. My young son ran up and down that ladder, and finally rigged a rope device by which to let a case of papers down. I came to the rolls of the Ninth Earl's paymasters, and the great houses, the journeys by Thames and into the Low Countries, the captain's expenses and the expenses of life in the Tower of London, began to appear. And Hotspur's widow, sent for to claim the head of her husband and the four quarters of his body, which after execution were shown from the gates of four cities of England — she was told to come and claim these pieces of a rebel and give them Christian burial.

There was a morning when the Duke's flag was flying. They told me he would visit me that day in the Muniment Room. And finally we heard his foot on the stone stair, coming up that spiral. He came toward us, and I began to show him the papers of his family with which I was working. I told him some of what I was after. He put his head on one side, with its legendary red hair, and the turning-point of all my endeavor came. He said, "It's very much like fox-hunting."

A little later, he said, "I wish I could put my hand on two papers. I know they're in the library somewhere."

My son, speaking for the first time, said, "I think I can bring them to you."

Now, week by week, sometimes in and near London, sometimes in the north again, I began to understand the game played by the English superbly, often with research people — mostly Americans — and largely in the summer. The game goes like this: you are admitted to the room in which you have hoped to be, to start your hunt. You declare yourself, saying what you hope, what you want. The person on the other side of the desk slumps down a bit — one vertebra, say — and answers, "No." Many writers . . . scholars . . . Americans . . . turn raspberry-color then, all their hopes blasted; or go very hostile; or go to the National Portrait Gallery and cry.

But if you do none of these; if you meet this moment with your own enjoyment of the game, and stop asking for something, and instead begin to produce what you have — and I had the good fortune to be able to show, now, a glimpse of Hariot — you will see something take place. The man across from you changes. He becomes excited somehow, and somehow almost grateful; charming and kind. This is someone unknown or almost unknown to him. This is a link between two peoples, and between himself and you, however gypsy, however she-poet you appear to him.

308

At the Tower of London, the Governor said, "I have told you it is impossible to do what you ask. No writer, no historian may have permission to go there."

I said, "I understand what you are saying, and I will ask for nothing. I only want to tell you where I am in my work; and that from this prison men have cast out, not only to the new world, not only to the Northwest Passage, but to the moon."

The Governor rose, squared-off, military, with his clipped moustache, and said to the Guard, "Show this lady anything she wishes to see."

At Syon House, there were the portraits, and the maps, the building plans, the books, the mulberry tree, the marvelous building made of glass and air, a structure like the Crystal Palace (only smaller) that is the Duke of Northumberland's greenhouse. And somewhere along the wall — exactly how many feet we can read in the account rolls — there must be the foundation of Hariot's house.

The American Embassy very kindly provided aerial photographs made by the Air Force, and we may yet find the line of earth, slightly different in tone, that will indicate this place.

At Petworth, among the Turners, the great rooms of paintings and the Molyneux globe, the secret white room upstairs where the books that came back from the Tower after the Ninth Earl's captivity were shown me in the glimpse of one day that I shall never forget — and the children's toys of generations, the posters of trains and buffaloes and a lost West. There were celestial globes and Bruno's *De Immenso,* at last. And far in the north, another book of Bruno's, with that mark that is so moving to see, the mark on a diagram four hundred years old, the dent of the compass foot.

Downstairs, at Petworth, I went through the papers that have been kept there, although the trunk in which they were given was found to be so worm-eaten that they burned it years ago. The search for the map of America; the papers that fitted at last with the papers of the British Museum. And a note, after a day there, from Lancelot Whyte, whose thinking is central to many of these meanings.

309

And the archivist who walked with me under another lordly mulberry-tree. We stood on ground stained purple. She said to me, "I never noticed this tree before." I looked at her, startled. And she said, in acid friendliness, "I'm not a silkworm, I'm a bookworm."

Sion College, where Torporley's papers are, the two copies of George Ripley, and the great losses: "Two fires — the Great Fire and Hitler's fire — and two floods. But most went to the Americans." What happened here was that the religious books were kept and the scientific books were sold. There is a line on the application form at this library that says, "Curacy." There is a manuscript of *Britain's Ida* here, with its first line that echoes Spenser's line about Arlo-hill; this too among Torporley's papers.

And all the rest in London — the Bank of England, Somerset House and the wills, Guildhall and Hariot's will, walking through Blackfriars and the small streets and St. Paul's dome smiting. Public Records and the round room, the State papers and the helpful staff. The Chancery case found brilliantly by John Shirley, and his careful work in giving us the facts in full detail.

Often I longed for a book on Hariot. There was only Stevens', printed privately in 1900. Why did not Shirley publish? Surely Rowse must be writing on Hariot? Or Frances Yates, whose marvelous work on Bruno is a key to anyone with such concerns? Or M. R. Bradbrook, who has worked far past *The School of Night?*

I kept on, with Hariot fading in and fading out.

At Sherborne, there was another scene, Ralegh's heaven on Sleep Hill. The great painting of Elizabeth in procession with all her courtiers and gentlemen; and is Hariot looking from one of those high windows, or obscured in the crowd? There is one portrait, that used to be called by Hariot's name; but David Piper, of the National Portrait Gallery and *The English Face,* is of the opinion that it is probably a Dutch subject, painted by a Dutch artist.

The tobacconist in Sherborne, speaking of Ralegh's trial and imprisonment, "Properly framed, he was."

Nag's Head in Dorset. The Cerne Giant. Cerne Abbas and Up Cerne, where Ralegh hunted.

Returned to the States, another Nag's Head — on the Outer Banks, this time. And everything seems to be named for Ralegh in North Carolina : the Raleigh Bar and Grill, the city of Raleigh. I sit in the home of the historian, David Stick, on Collington Island, and we talk about the objects salvaged by Bankers to make weight for their nets. The weirs of the Indians were just outside, in the shallow water of the Sound. Where does he suppose the pinnace with Hariot's instruments and notes mght have been lightened? "Where are you staying?" he asks, and I name the motel. "Just about there, allowing for the shifting of the sand," he says, looking at me.

Working in the little cave of the microfilm reader on the Hariot papers. Swinging its head around so that I can look long at the line with the two dots for Est and Non Est, the line joining them, and the strong dot in the middle.

Other stories : the search for John Protheroe "an ingenious young man that accompanies me here often and loves you," wrote Sir William Lower to Hariot from Carmarthenshire, where he and Protheroe watched the sky through a telescope. Inquiries to Major Francis Jones, a chief authority on Wales and County Archivist of Carmarthenshire, brought very little until he knew that I had read Protheroe's will in Somerset House and knew that he was Torpoley's patron. Then Major Jones changed character: "It happens that I am interested in John Protheroe because he is an ancestor of mine . . . I am descended from Frances Protheroe, younger daughter of John Protheroe."

And in a room in Philadelphia, Mr. Clive Driver was showing me the little book of Gabriel Harvey's writings, with its curious reference to Hariot and what a poet should be. I came in my speaking to him to the inevitable moment when one remembers Lady Ralegh, in her long bravery and patience, standing

311

to beg for Sherborne and her rights at James's court. Mr. Driver stood at his full lean height. "I am descended from Lady Ralegh," he said.

The squiggles upside down on the folio pages seen as microfilm : Forgive me my sinne, and the small printer's device on *A Brief and True Report.* PERIIT ET INVENTA EST.

A strong unbreakable living link came from another source. A package came from Spain, the book of the plan of Philip II, published in 1957, by the Duke of Maura. The copy sent to me carries the stamp of the Library of the Duke of Medina Sidonia, and suddenly that horned crescent of ships is before us, the Captain General of the Ocean Sea is having his sacred banner hoisted; the Fleet engages, the English attacking in a long wing formation, single file; to the end of the day, when the Duke leans on the rail of the poop deck, eating his cheese and a crust. But the dedication of this book brings the scene to our time. In English it goes :

> To Luisa Isabel Alvarez de Toledo and Maura, twentieth titular head of the dukedom of Medina Sidonia, guardian of the documents of the archives, the source of this book which is dedicated to her with the appreciation of a historian and the affection of a grandfather.

With the book came the invitation from a mutual friend who knew that I needed the "other side" of that story and that war, and who sent a graceful message saying that it might be possible to enter those archives.

I did go to Madrid. I did go south for the first time, into that light of Andalusia, through those vineyards and to the Palace, very high over the green roofs of San Lucar de Barrameda, where the salt shores make their white edge to the river-mouth that opens an entire world. The Guadalquivir spreads green and blue, freighters sailing out to the Mediterranean and Africa, out to America, where Columbus and Magellan sailed.

On the highest story of the Palace, the papers. Holding it together, with the fearless rational eyes of the Duke (as he is in his portrait, wearing the Golden Fleece) this Duchess (who is the present Duke). The consciousness of prison soon to close on her, the immediacy of her concerns — her people and her children, what is happening to Spain, what is happening between the people of Spain and of the United States — this woman is a clue to the life that Hariot and Ralegh lived, with its irony and glories, its risks and profound nobility, its horsemanship of life and the frightfulness of its penalties. In showing me the "other side," she showed me the great sources of the present and the greatness with which the present may be met.

In England again, I came to the structure of air and white strokes that is another kind of palace, the glass structure that is a small version of the Crystal Palace and is the greenhouse of Syon House. In 1968, it is used by the Syon Garden Project, and we began to talk of another link, the possible planting of a Hariot Trail here, so that the plants and trees which Hariot describes in *A Brief and True Report* and which have been set out in a walk from Fort Ralegh to the Sound in North Carolina might also be set out where Hariot lived so much of his life, at the site of his house.

And all the time, the plans to reach the moon were going ahead. Blast-off at Cape Canaveral, now called Kennedy. And his work in helices and conic section, spherical triangles and early observations of the moon, built in to the history of this casting-out. As his sailing with Grenville, Ralph Lane, Thomas Cavendish, and leaving Ralegh in silver at the door of the Council Chamber, is built into the poems, the lives, the tries for the moon and beyond to the moons of Jupiter and beyond.

Hariot's mathematics, the forming of algebra and Descartes' dreams, the long line from Telesio through Bruno, Della Porta, Campanella, to the working out of a unity between consciousness and the universe; the world as animal, *sanctum, sacrum, venerabile,* all enter into this our moment.

It was not that he did not acknowledge defeat.

Each time he dived, deep under defeat. And whatever is under is also over. They dive into the universe, at the opening on the line that joins being and non-being.

He speaks to us, in our faith and lack of faith, longing for abundant traces of him in the John Wallis archives — it all must be there, for this man loved his memory — hoping for a metal finder that will rake up his instruments in the sand of the Outer Banks where his drowned notes lie faceless, for a shovel that can dig the earth of Molanna in Ireland. But longing for the present too, for this moment when we live and the traces of Hariot live, past the penalties, past the end, into the life of mankind, that's womankind too, and the language past the end, the language of transformations.

The contemporary statement has been put very well by Rozsa Peter, who says: "There are therefore connexions between statements occurring in them, i.e. independently not only of the contents but even of the logical values of the statements. They are true entirely by virtue of their logical structure; they are called logical identities . . ."

She moves now to the "dangerous operations" and applies them to the logical functions.

"These new operations have brought with them the transfinite elements. 'Something is true for *all* elements of the universe of discourse'; if the universe of discourse is infinite, as is the case with natural numbers or with the set of points in a plane, then we talk about the infinite as though it were something finished and closed in our hands. 'There is an X in an infinite universe of discourse.'"

We are reminded of the method, well-known to experimental physicists, of catching a lion in the Sahara. Pour everything into a sieve; what goes through is sand, the rest is the lion. Or : divide — as the mathematician does — the Sahara in half, and keep dividing until you can put a cage over your lion.

Unless the lion is moving.

Our lion is Hariot. He is moving.

He moves into the country of perception. This time, perception is projected to infinity, with infinite processes going on everywhere. But this is the present, in which we live, and we can be sure that "the methods used up to now will not be sufficient to prove the freedom from contradiction of analysis." Here is another NON SUFFICIT; it takes us into the future.

Or, rather, it takes us fully into the present.

He fades in and out many times. Often it is a torment to go any further. This is too uncertain. Where are the astronomers, the navigation people, the mathematicians of infinity?

There is a moment in that book of Hermann Hesse's of which I have already spoken, *The Journey to the East,* when the narrator tells of the flat frightful time in which he could no longer deal with life, in which he knew that the company with whom he had started on that journey no longer existed, that faith had been finally broken in the gorge of Morbio Inferiore. He knew that the betrayal had been complete. He knew that he could not go on with the task he had set himself — to write the history of the journey — for he had no records, he had no archive. Only he was left, and he was barren.

I had turned in the great part of my book, but the holes that were left to be filled could any single one contain any hope of mine, and myself too. I was exhausted. I called up Catherine Drinker Bowen, and told her of this nightmare structure, made of silvery strokes, shining strokes, with long ranges of air between them, gaps I could never fill. She laughed a practical laugh. "Write the strokes," she said, "and don't write the gaps!"

The desolation went on. The manuscript, lost by the publisher. The illustrations, lost by the publisher, and very difficult to replace. The long delays for the book, which I finally saw as Hariot's long story of delay and failure.

One day, in the mail, there was a letter from England. I opened it and saw the letterhead : The Thomas Hariot Seminar. At Oxford, at that moment, they were meeting. In a panelled room? In their sweaters? The historians, the astronomers, the men and women of spherical triangles, of helices, the Bruno scholars, Rowse, Shirley, Dr. Ethel Seaton who had cracked the ciper used by Hariot, Major Jones who knew about Lower and Protheroe, Dr. Wright who had wanted this work to go ahead — were they all there, gathered, piecing this story together, with all knowledge, all invention, all the skills we need to find the past which is the present?

And where is Hariot? He is here, he is everywhere, standing at the ends of all corridors, waiting to be found.

"Lost, Foundered and Found"

*T*he device on the title-page of
A Brief and True Report, fortuitously as it may be seen to come
to Hariot through his printer and the widow that printer
married, takes on further definition as Hariot's life goes on into
our own time. PERIIT ET INVENTA EST. Perire carries the meanings
of to go through, to be lost, and also to die, to perish, and to
waste away with love, to be undone, to founder, to be ruined
politically, and also to vanish.

Invenire is to come upon, to light upon, to find, to meet with.
It is also to come upon in reading; to find out, to discover; to
learn, to find out from others; and also to bring about.

Lost, Employed in discovering. Found.
It is a transformation of which Ralegh wrote :

She is gone, she is lost! She is found, she is ever fair.

Transformation, and beyond transformation, it is identity of
the states of change, the phases that Keats and Chapman,
Shakespeare, Ralegh and all discoverers — among whom Hariot
takes his place — have known and have given to us.

ACKNOWLEDGMENT

My thanks to the Duke of Northumberland, who in kindness opened to me the Library and Muniment Room at Alnwick Castle, giving me the most free access to these and to the Muniment Room and other materials and the library at Syon House; also Miss Elizabeth Heriot, His Grace's secretary, and Mr. D. P. Graham of the Alnwick Estate Office, and Miss Mathieson, at Syon House, for help and courtesies.

My deep thanks to the Duchess of Medina Sidonia for great kindness in Madrid and at the Palace of Medina Sidonia at San Lucar de Barrameda, for her stories and for opening to me the Medina Sidonia Archive and my first sight of Andalusia;

To the British Museum for the use of the Hariot Papers;

To Sir Martin Charteris, private secretary to Queen Elizabeth II, and Lady Charteris, for kindness and belief in the possibilities;

To Lord Egremont for kind permission to use certain materials at Petworth; to Miss D. Beatrice Harris, Secretary to Petworth House; to Mr. Francis Steer, West Sussex County Archivist, and his assistants, Miss G. M. A. Beck and Miss Elizabeth Barrie;

To Major Simon Wingfield Digby, M.P., for access to Sherborne, and to Mr. E. W. T. Malcolm, Estate Agent at Sherborne;

To Mr. Francis S. Mason, Deputy Cultural Attaché, and to Miss Margaret Haferd, of the American Embassy in London, for their kind help and for air photographs;

To Colonel T. P. Butler, Resident Governor and Major of the Tower of London, and to the Yeoman Warders of the Tower;

To R. A. Woods, of the Bank of England, and to its museum staff;

To Major Francis Jones, C. V. C. and archivist of Carmarthenshire;

321

To Marie de L. Welch for long-sustained faith and help;

To Ursula Winant; to Eric Mottram; to Miriam S. Reik;

To Henriette de S. Lehman for unquestioning help;

To the American Council of Learned Societies, for a grant that enabled me to go to England, Spain, and the Outer Banks;

To the National Council for the Arts, for a grant during the early period of writing;

To the New Hope Foundation, for a grant that helped me to reach the completion of one part of the search; to Lenore Marshall;

To the staffs of many libraries, particularly the staff of the British Museum; of the New York Public Library, especially Philomena Houlihan; of the Office of Public Records in London; of Sion College Library; of Roanoke, particularly Louise M. Meekins and Bruce Black; of the Sarah Lawrence Library, particularly Elizabeth Seely, who allowed me to keep books unforgivably long; A. H. Hall of the Guildhall Library; the Hispanic Society Library; the American Geographical Society Library;

To Katherine H. Cole, who went on a journey; to David Stick;

To Helen M. Lynd for her help and her long concern for discovery, and for Keats, for her reading of the manuscript and for her valuable notes;

To Lancelot L. Whyte, a hero of this kind of process, for an early reading of the manuscript;

To Hiram Haydn, for his work in the counter-renaissance and his encouragement;

To William L. Rukeyser, for unflagging cheerful help and filial courage all up and down the mountain range of this search;

To the staff of the Hayden Planetarium, to James S. Pickering and Dr. Kenneth Franklin, and Mrs. Cecily Scherer of the library;

To Miss Gee, of the Keats Library (Heath Library, Hampstead);

To Miss Jean Bratton and Mr. Peter Feibleman, for help in Spain;

To Ella Winter, for transcribing at Petworth;

To Messrs. Philip and Lionel Robinson, who kindly brought Ralegh's notebook out of the vault;

To Mr. David Cohen of the Argosy Bookshop, for a copy of Ralegh's *History of the World,* and for many kindnesses; J. W. Steedman, Bookseller, of Newcastle upon Tyne;

To David Piper, Curator of the National Portrait Gallery, for examining the portrait supposed to be of Hariot;

To Sir Arthur Norrington, the President of Trinity, for having the portrait in the President's lodgings conveyed to London, and to his secretary, Miss H. L. Gargies for her kindness to me at Oxford;

To the staff of the Library of the University of California at Berkeley; to the staff of the Folger Library; to the staff of the Vassar Library, and Miss Ethel Plum;

To Robert Payne; to William A. Reuben, who asked a question; to Mrs. Monroe Friedman; to Mrs. Herbert Spiesberger;

To Mr. E. A. Rudd, of May, May, and Deacon;

To Mr. Clive Driver, of the Rosenbach Foundation, Philadelphia;

To Mrs. Joan St. G. Saunders, particularly for her help in replacing the lost illustrations;

To Frances G. Wickes, for her confidence in the unknown possibilities in this history;

To Cyril S. Smith; to Henry Guerlac;

To all those whose help, in interviews and correspondence, built stroke by stroke the structure of Hariot in his surround; to Dr. John Nelson; to those who assisted me, particularly Uri Soviv, Marice Counsell, and Frances Ricketts, who read the cipher; to Dr. Edward Lurie;

To Susan Woolfson, for her work in Washington, and the recovery of the Notes;

To Fran and Charles Buchholtz, for a search that they thought failed in Bermuda;

To Walt Wheeling, for his idea for the design of the jacket of this book;

To Lucy Lowe for skillful and encouraging typing of the manuscript, and to her staff; to Jacqueline Butler for typing, early and late; and her work on the Notes;

To the Thomas Harriot Seminar, Museum of the History of Science, Broad Street, Oxford, for their existence and their work (and I here use the spelling that they favor and ask that we use, hoping that they will understand why, thinking of Ariel, I chose "Hariot" and give all spellings);

To the Harriot Seminar in America; my work is, in its way, a preface to the long search for Hariot which they are instigating.

To Sarah Lawrence College and to my students there, whom I first set the errand of searching with me for the traces of Thomas Hariot.

To those unknown to me who will go on with the discoveries.

NOTES

All the material for the 1585-86 expedition is derived from Thomas Hariot's *A Brief and True Report of The New Found Land of Virginia,* Facsimile Edition of the 1588 Quarto, Introduction by Randolph G. Adams, New York, 1951, and the Ralph Lane account in Hakluyt (I have also consulted the Lenox Copy in the New York Public Library, and the de Bry-Hariot of 1590, also there); from the John White drawings, in the British Museum, and for a while on loan to the Morgan Library in New York City. For reproductions of these, and for their captions, I have used Stefan Lorant, *The New World,* a full collection of the first pictures of America, rev. ed., New York, 1965.

For masterful work on the papers, see D. B. Quinn, *The Roanoke Voyages 1584-1590,* 2 vols., London, 1955. See also the work of John Shirley on the Hariot papers — soon to be published, I hope — the books of A. H. Rowse, particularly *Sir Walter Ralegh* and *The Elizabethans in America;* and those of Louis B. Wright, particularly *Middle-Class Culture in Elizabethan England.*

The Spanish material comes from the Museo Naval in Madrid, Col. Navarrete, Vol. XXV, 48, fols. 190-193, from the original in the Archivo General de Indias de Sevilla; Vol. XXV, 49, fols. 194-195; Vol XXV, 53, fols. 202-204. (Some of it appears in translation in Rowse's *Grenville.*) My informant says that nothing is known of Hariot in Spain but that he was *un pirata.* Also consulted: Spanish printed sources on Ralegh, Drake, and Grenville.

The illustrations used here come from White's watercolors and map, the Molyneux globe in Petworth House; the detail of the cascades at London Bridge from a collection of poems of Charles d'Orleans 125 years before, reproduced in A. P. Herbert, *The*

Thames, London, 1966. The memories of England are all taken from references in the writings of Hariot and Ralph Lane. I have assumed on several authorities that Hariot is responsible for the captions to White's drawings.

Source material dealing with the Outer Banks and Tidewater Virginia has been consulted, and such secondary material as Richard L. Morton's *Colonial Virginia,* 2 vols., published for The Virginia Historical Society, Chapel Hill, 1960, and Douglas L. Rights, *The American Indian in North Carolina,* 2nd ed., Winston-Salem, 1957. David Stick, the historian of the Outer Banks, has been of help, as has his book, *The Outer Banks;* and I wish particularly to thank the staff of the Roanoke Museum, the caretakers of the Hariot Trail, a path through the woods along which can be found the trees and plants named and described in *A Brief and True Report.*

No manuscript of Hariot's American writings, or American notes, survives; or perhaps we can still say, No manuscript has been found. This book will serve a purpose if it can help the search for this material.

A — Manuscripts at Alnwick Castle, Northumberland, in the library; mss and account rolls in the Muniment Room

BM — British Museum

Med — The archives of the Dukes of Medina Sidonia, San Lucar de Barrameda

NYPL — Collections of the New York Public Library

PH — Petworth House, Sussex

PR — Public Records, London

SC — Sion College, London

SH — Syon House, Isleworth

SP — Calendar of State papers, listed as Domestic, Colonial, Ireland

TH — Thomas Hariot, Mathematical Papers, British museum

page
22 ... *into the woods."*

     All these quotations from Hakluyt, *The English Voyages,* Vol. VI, p. 132 passim.

Information from John White's drawings in Stefan Lorant, *The New World*, New York, 1946.

27 ... *(ait ille)."*
Jordani Bruno Nolani, *Opera Latine Conscripta*, Naples, Dom, Morano, 1879. Vol. I, Pars II, *De Immenso et Innumerabilis*, p. 228.

27 ...*in wonderful admiration."*
Thomas Hariot, *A Brief and True Report*, facsimile ed., pp. unnumb.

35 ...*into the field*.
The material is moving from Hariot's book and captions to Lane's account, and freely among all of these.

36 ...*man's assay*
Almost certainly Joachim Ganz, says Quinn.

36 ...*of ore*.
Planning.

43 ...*his course*.
See Donald Mackenzie, *The Migration of Symbols*, New York, 1926; and Fernando Ortiz, *El Huracan*, Mexico, Fondo de Cultura Economica, 1947.

44 ...*to sea*.
See Hakluyt, Ralph Lane's Report; Sir Francis Drake's West Indian Voyage. See David Stick, *The Outer Banks*, Chapel Hill, N.C., 1958, Ch. 7.

46 ...*and in them*.
See David Stick; and Hart Crane, "The Hurricane," in *Collected Poems*, New York, 1930.

48 ... See Hariot, Lane, Drake.

51 ...*the university*.
Ency. Brit., 11th ed., Oxford.

52 ...*Queen's supremacy."*
State Papers and Addenda, Vol. CV, p. 186.

52 ...*had lapsed;*
State Papers, *op. cit.*, p. 402.

52 ...*the fiery coals."*
Ibid., p. 500.

53 ...*set on fire."*
Edith Sitwell quoting Burnet and Neale, in *The Queens and the Hive*, London, Macmillan, 1962. Ch. 22, pp. 166-67.

53 ...*to ecclesiastical dignityes."*
State Papers and Addenda, Vol. CXL, p. 515.

54 ...*the plague."*
Ibid., p. 575.

54 ...*muses in 1560."*
His follower and defender, John Wallis, was archivist of Oxford in the year after 1658. His friend and colleague, Robert Hues, was at Oxford with Hariot, and later again as tutor to young Algernon Percy. In the papers of these men, and of Brian Twyne, may very well be the memoirs that would light up this obliterated story. I hope to go on searching, and it is my earnest hope that others will take up this search.

56 ...*Known as Drake's Bay,*
Drake's Plate, now at the University of California, Berkeley, commemorates this.

57 ...*night at Syon."*
Material from Cal. S.O. Sp.; Elizabeth Jenkins, *Elizabeth the Great;* London, 1958. Harrison, *Tudor England;* Cal. Hist. Soc.; and A.P. Herbert, *The Thames,* London, 1966.
Herbert, *The Thames,* London, 1966.

58 ...*in the Caribbean.*
Material for this section is based on or taken directly from *Sir Francis Drake's West Indian Voyage, begun in the yeere 1585,* published by M. Thomas Cates; in Hakluyt's *Voyages.* Also *Ency. Brit.,* 11th ed.

59 ...*"fearful about everything."*
Philleo Nash, Commissioner for Indian Affairs 1962-66, in conversation with the author, September, 1967.
...*planned deculturation,*
Ibid.

60 ...*to his glorye.*
BM, Lansdowne 51/14. The order of the text altered.

61 ...*cannot be remembered."*
Material from Collingwood, *The Idea of History,* Oxford, Clarendon Press, 1946, pp. 58, 154.

62 ...*world of ideas."*
Collingwood, *op. cit.,* pp. 151-59, is talking about the ideas of Michael Oakeshott in *Experience and Its Modes,* Cambridge, 1933.

63 ...*of their office."*

Cabala, sive Scrinia Sacra, *Mysteries of State and Government in Letters,* London, 1663. King Charles ... to the Vice-Chancellor of Cambridge, March 4, 1629, p. 124.

64 ...*done after him."*

The Lives of the Alchemystical Philosophers, Anonymous, 1815. Reprinted, London, 1955, p. 16.

64 ...*alchemy, science.*

Ency. Brit., 11th ed., Roger Bacon.

...*and Specula Mathematica.*

Ibid.

67 ...*and took his manors.*

Martin Hume, *Sir Walter Ralegh;* Arthur Mee, *Devon,* London, 1965.

69 ...*he was in Oxford.*

McIntyre, *Giordano Bruno,* p. 21. Jane S. Semple, *Bruno in England* (unpublished thesis), Smith College, Northampton, Mass., passim. Boulting, *Giordano Bruno,* passim. Singer, *Giordano Bruno,* Bruno, *De Immenso.* Bruno, *Cause, Principle and Unity;* Translation, int. and notes by Jack Lindsay.

70 ...*some "troubles" in 1584.*

E. J. Worman, and McKerrow's *Dictionary of Printers* (see Semple, *op. cit.* n. App. A, p. ii).

70 ...*'in these parts.'*

McIntrye, *op. cit.,* pp. 34-35.

71 ...*". . . all science had its spring."*

Florio, in his preface to his translation of Montaigne.

72 ...*"the other received the rest of us."*

Bruno, *Cena de la Ceneri,* after Elton.

See Semple; and Elton, passim.

73 ...*Sir Thomas Perrott. . . .*

Son of Sir John Perrott, who escaped hanging by dying in the Tower of natural causes. He was said to be the natural son of Henry VIII; his resemblance to the King was strong.

73 ...*Frances Yates . . .*

See Yates, *The French Academies of the Seventeenth Century,* 1947; and Yates, *Giordano Bruno and the Hermetic Tradition,* London, Routledge and Kegan Paul, 1964.

74 ... *"the strife of the concordant and the love of the opposed."*
For the background in science and philosophy, see also Jack Lindsay's introduction to his translation of the Causa, *op. cit.,* U.S. ed., International Publishers, 1964.

75 ... *the normal behavior of nature.*
See D. Singer; Badaloni; Lindsay; Boulting, Haydn; and, always, Bruno.

75 ... *where unified opposites meet.*
See Lindsay, *op. cit.,* Ch. 7, "Bruno and Science."

75 ... *the story goes ...*
The thread of this story is in Aubrey's *Brief Lives* : Walter Warner.

75 ... *on Donne ...*
See Lindsay on Donne and his relation to Bruno, on the many arguments Descartes borrowed from Bruno (particularly that of the relation between the finite and the infinite), on the identity between the scientific idea of low depraved matter and the "religious" idea of low depraved woman.

77 ... *two ships could be fitted out.*
Parkes, *Hakluyt,* p. 82 and App. II.

77 ... *"the knowledge of America already achieved elsewhere."* Ibid, p. 84.

77 ... The passage on Cavendish — see Dyke, Gwenyth, "Thomas Cavendish and the Roanoke Voyage 1585," *The Suffolk Review,* October 1956, pp. 33 ff.
Manuscript Division, New York Public Library, Hakluyt MSS; also see E.G.R. Taylor, *Original Writings and Correspondence of the Two Hakluyts,* London, 1935, pp. 211-236, & Vol. I, 33; and George Bruner Parks, *Richard Hakluyt and the English Voyages,* revised ed., N.Y., Frederick Ungar, 1961.

... *and out of us comes discovery.*
In *Cena di Cenere,* 1584; often credited not to Bruno, but to Francis Bacon. For a comparable inference of the female principle in space travel, cf. the contemporary film and book, *2001,* in which the astronaut on an all-male expedition to Jupiter arrives at the moment of diving into the "star-gate" and rebirth — or birth — out of the female universe as the new species, the Star Child.

78 ... *November 27, 1586.*

Syon House MSS at Alnwick Castle. See also G.R. Batho, *The Household Papers of Henry Percy,* London, Royal Historical Society, Camden Third Series, 1962.

78 ... *such entries.*
Account Rolls, Alnwick Castle; and Batho, *Household Papers of Henry Percy.*

78 ... *English Catholics."*
Edward Barrington de Fonblanque, *Annals of the House of Percy,* London, privately printed, 1887. 2 vols. Vol. II, p. 178.

79 ... *of his sovereign."*
Fonblanque, *op. cit.,* Vol. II, p. 167.

80 ... *ninth Earl of Northumberland(?).*
Postcard, the Fitzwilliam; and Erna Auerbach, *Nicholas Hilliard,* London, 1961, Plate 95. "This version, which is of great beauty, came originally from the collection of Lord Delisle and Dudley" (p. 120).

80 ... *ninth Earl of Northumberland(?).*
Ibid., Plate 94, and pp. 119-20.

81 ... *casting a horoscope.*
Singer et al., *History of Technology,* Vol. III, p. 617.

84 ... *the Spanish Main.*
Contemporary Spanish sources compare Tudor England with Stalinist Russia and her allies. Cf. Duque de Maura, *El Designio de Felipe II,* Madrid, 1957, p. 141 passim.

84 ... *of the English continue.*
Letters and copies in the Archive of the Dukes of Medina Sidonia, San Lucar.

85 ... *15 February 1587* ... Instituto Historico de Marina. Coleccion de Diarios y Relaciones para la Historia de los Viajos y Descubrimientos. IV. Madrid, 1944.

88 ... *Never before imprinted.'"*
Alexander C. Judson, *The Life of Edmund Spenser,* Baltimore, 1945. A volume in *The Works of Edmund Spenser.*

90 ... *near to Muskery Quirke*
L. Russell Muirhead, *Ireland,* 2nd ed., New York, reprinted 1952.

90 ... *the Glen of Aherlow."*
Judson, op. cit.

331

90 ... *says Sebastian Evans,*
   In *The Works of Edmund Spenser,* VI, pp. 150-51.
   ... *to be felt;*
   Edwin Greenlaw, *ibid.,* VI, p. 394.
92 ... *by a causeway."*
   Muirhead, *op. cit.,* p. 220.
93 ... *legally operative.*
   A. L. Rowse, *Sir Walter Ralegh,* New York, 1962, p. 248.
93 ... *had made £200.*
   Ibid.
94 ... *"silence the company."*
   C.F. Tucker Brooke, ed., *The Works of Christopher Marlowe,* Oxford, 1920. See Wraight and Stern, *In Search of Christopher Marlowe;* and biographies by Charles Norman, Frederick Boas, John Bakeless; and Leslie Hotson's books on Marlowe.
95 ... *man more excellent.*
   A version of the Talmudic dispute over which is greater, wheat or bread. The answer says : Bread, for God alone made wheat, but God and man together make bread.
99 ... *science and magic.*
   Arturo Castiglioni, *Adventures of the Mind,* New York, 1946, p. 261.
99 .. *to be seen by them.*
   Natural Magick, by John Baptista Porta. I am quoting from the 1658 edition, London, Thomas Young and Samuel Speed; to be sold at the Three Pigeons, and at the Angel in St. Paul's Churchyard. Hariot will have known the earlier Latin version.
101 .. *as Hariot was.*
   Luis de Góngora, born in the same year as Hariot, 1561-1627. See his *Poesias Completas;* Gerald Brenan, *The Literature of the Spanish People,* Cambridge, 1951; Robinson Jeffers, *Poetry, Gongorism and a Thousand Years.* Los Angeles, 1949.
   .. *young Northumberland.*
   Portrait in *Nicholas Hilliard,* by Erna Auerbach.
102 .. *on his wavy plains.*
   Some of this translation is from Brenan.
103 .. *tue trezze piova!*

De la Armade que fue a Inglaterra. This is the poem of the fury and horror in Spain of the loss of the Fleet. The last is from Petrarch.

103 .. *sources in life?*
Both questions asked by Brenan.

106 .. *Mr. Hariot too."*
Aubrey's Brief Lives, George Clifford : Earl of Cumberland. See also Purchas's *Pilgrims.*

107 .. *of maidenlike modesty.*
In Quinn's edition, he gives the Latin also: *In virginei pudoris signum.*

107 .. *quieter people than they.*
All the delights are in the words of the captions, given most fully, with excellent notes, in Quinn, *The Roanoke Voyages,* Vol. I, John White's Drawings, pp. 398-463.

108 .. *"Toure ashes."*
TH, Addl. 6789, fol. 242.

109 .. See Singer, Boulting, quoting Sigwart and Spampanato.

110 .. *De Immenso,* Book VII, Ch. XVI and Fiorentino's introduction, xxxv-xxxvi.

112 .. *satisfied with him."*
After Bruno, in Doc. vii (Inquisition) in Boulting, *Giordano Bruno,* London, n.d., p. 225.

113 .. *credit and sway."*
Harrison, *Elizabethan Journals,* March 12, 22, 1591.

115 .. *John Dee.*
Sion College Library, MSS of Thomas Hariot given by Nathaniel Torporley. See *The Lives of the Alchemystical Philosophers,* 1815. From the 1678 ed. (Latin), London, 1955; and Eirenaeus Philalethes and others (including George Ripley), Collectanea Chemica, London, 1893, repub., 1963.

116 .. *in alchemical arts.*
Transcript of the Registers of the Company of Stationers in London; A Short Title Catalogue of Books Printed in England, Scotland and Ireland, in Harrison, *Elizabethan Journals,* for May 12, 1591.

125 .. *the next reign :*
Hariot, writing of "The prince 1610" (this is the *Prince Royal,*

named for Prince Henry) "launched Sept. 25, length 132 f, by the heele 21 rake of the poste 15
: = rake of the stem."

125 .. *was crushed.*

For description and use of the "peine forte et dure," see Victor Hugo, *The Man Who Laughs,* Book IV, Ch. VIII.

125 .. *were extremely slim."*

Wraight and Stern, *In Search of Christopher Marlowe,* pp. 285-86.

125 .. *Sir Thomas Walsingham.*

Where "17 large Indian pictures" were hanging over the White Staircase. These are thought to be John White's paintings of Virginia scenes. All that appears in this century are the seventeen watercolors.

126 .. *witness shalbe produced.*

Leslie Hotson made the crucial find of these documents in the Public Record Office in 1925. See his *The Death of Christopher Marlowe,* London; 1925, and *The First Night of Twelfth Night,* New York, 1954.

It is in the possession of Miriam Reik. It has his name in it and those of the de Riveras.

129 .. *made on June 1st.*

Discovered by Leslie Hotson in the Public Record Office, 1925.

130 .. *torture and release?*

See Wraight and Stern, pp. 296-97; and Charles Norman, *The Muses' Darling,* New York, 1946, Ch. XXIII.

130 .. *substituted another corpse."*

Wraight and Stern, *op. cit.,* p. 303.

130 .. *Another theory*

S.A. Tannenbaum's, in *The Assassination of Christopher Marlowe,* New York, 1928.

131 .. *yeare' 1593?"*

Wraight and Stern, Part V.

131 .. *the slightest trace.)*

Ibid., p. 315.

131 .. *or soothsayers.*

Daniel, II, 27.

132 .. *they understand not."*

These passages from Ralegh, *History of the World,* Ch. II, 2, 5.

132 .. *manifest representation."*

Ralegh's translation of Nicholas of Cusa, Com. Theolog., c.l.

132..May 10, 1593."

Wilson, F.P. *The Plague in Shakespeare's London*. Oxford University Press, 1963, pp. 77-95.

133..the East India Company."

Parks, George Bruner, *Richard Hakluyt,* p. 156, describing the Hakluyt manuscripts which passed from Selden's library to the Bodleian. These are the identities of "enemy researchs," English privateering and English profit, according to Parks.

134..*sitting in Cerne.*

A.O. Gibbons, *Cerne Abbas,* Dorchester, 1962, p. 79.

134..*contact with it."*

Ibid., p. 8.

134..*of the figure."*

Ibid., pp. 9-10.

134..*our historian writes).*

Ibid., p. 11n.

135..*In Harl. 6349, as:*

In *Revue Germanique,* "Notes et Documents," pp. 578-87.

137..*the hearsay evidence.*

The Cerne Abbas history here refers to G.B. Harrison, *Willobie his Avisa,* London, 1926, which contains an account of the hearing, as does Charles Norman's *The Muses' Darling.*

142.."captures the voices of the gods." Frances A. Yates, *Giordano Bruno and the Hermetic Tradition,* New York, Vintage Books, 1970.

142..*Guyana's wealth inviolate."*

Ronald Schiller, in *Latin American Report,* Vol. VI, No. 12, New Orleans.

143..*100,000 people;*

500,000 is the expected population by 1975; by 1980, 1,000,000.

143..*"instant Pittsburgh."*

"It is hoped," says *Reader's Digest* (July, 1968) "that from Guyana will come enough hydroelectric power, iron ore, steel, aluminum, lumber and wood pulp, manganese, sulphur, coal, nickel, chrome and other minerals to convert Venezuela into an industrial nation."

144..*and a mistress.*

See Percy's Advice to his Son; and Frances Yates, *A Study of Love's Labour's Lost,* app., Cambridge, 1936; and Robert Hugh

Kargon, Atomism in England from Hariot to Newton, Oxford,
1966, Ch. II.

145 .. Chapman's translation. Kenneth Burke, "Ode on a Grecian
Urn," from *A Grammar of Motives,* Englewood Cliffs, N.J.,
Prentice-Hall, 1945.

148 .. *'the school of night.'"*
Phyllis Brooks Bartlett, Introduction to *The Poems of George
Chapman,* New York, 1962, edited by her. This passage refers
to M.C. Bradbrook, *The School of Night,* Cambridge, 1936,
and Yates, *A Study of Love's Labour's Lost.*

148 .. *honored and reverenced.*
An echo of Chapman is in William Strachey's *The History of
Travel into Virginia Britannia.* Strachey says: ". . . especially
that which has been published by that true lover of virtue and
great learned professor of all arts and knowledges, Mr. Hariot,
who lived there in the time of the first colony, spoke the Indian
language, searched the country, and made many proofs of the
richness of the soil, and commodities thereof." This was dedicated to Sir Francis Bacon, Lord High Chancellor; another
copy was dedicated to Sir Allen Apsley, Lieutenant of the
Tower of London during some of the period when both
Ralegh and Northumberland were imprisoned there.

148 .. *I imparted."*
Did Keats see this edition of Chapman's *Homer*? Clarke speaks
of another edition only; his memory of the night was recorded
years later. This quotation, whose spelling and punctuation I
have slightly changed (against my habit), is in the edition
found in the Keats Collection at the Heath Library, Keats
Grove.

149 .. All quotations from Bacon's letter to the Earl of Devonshire
(Blount, created Earl 1603) in Cabala, London, 1663.

156 .. *from his notes;*
Petworth House MSS, 5 folios.

157 .. *little thin mist.*
When one or two words are illegible, I have generally indicated this.

.. *Hariot first named the sailors' watches of the day.*
BM, addl. 6783, VII, fol. 21. Waters, in *The Art of Navigation
in England in Elizabethan and Early Tudor Times,* New

Haven, 1958, p. 582, dates these notes as probably before 1595. I wish they were, but several pages on, Hariot says, "This is how tonnage is found for the King's shippes," setting the date for that page at least as after 1603. The word "later" is illegible to Mr. Waters; I hope words that I now find illegible will be clear to other readers of these fertile papers.

151 .. *the four lines* TH. BM IV, fol. 383v (384 missing).

.. *as he wrote* TH, BM III, fol. 321v.

153 .. *at other times."*

Harrison, *Elizabethan Journals,* Vol. II, p. 210.

159 .. *have disappeared.*

Disappeared! See Boulting, *op. cit.,* p. 295.

160 .. *universe occupies infinity . . ."*

Ibid., p. 120.

161 .. *"a way that is unspeakable."*

Taylor, *op. cit.*

In Kepler, Opera No. 403, Vienna, Nationalbibliothek, Cod

163 .. *problems in optics,*

10703, pp. 381-82.

164 .. *field of optics."*

Kargon, *Atomism in England from Hariot to Newton,* p. 26.

164 .. *Tyronian after him."*

D'Agapayeff, p. 16.

165 .. *Randall Knevett . . .*

Cf. Halliwell, p. 38.

168 .. *horse hire and horse meat . . .*

All this material from account rolls at Alnwick, U.I. 3(1). Spelling modified by author after seven lines.

170 .. his insatiable energy —

See Edmund Gosse, *Life and Letters of John Donne,* London, Heinemann. 2 vols., 1899. Works of John Donne. A. J. Kempe, *The Loseley Manuscripts,* London, 1835. Robinson Brothers, Catalogue 83. Rare Books and Manuscripts. London, 1953 (privately printed).

170 .. *"a dangerous passion."*

Gosse, *op. cit.,* I, p. 100.

172 .. *"to your leisure."*

Northumberland to Lord Cobham, 6 August 1602. State Papers. Also in Fonblanque, II, 224-25.

172..*and a lethargy."*
    Fonblanque, II, 238-39.
172..*means of friends."*
    Cabala, p. 25.
173..Plague material from F.P. Wilson, *The Plague in Shakespeare's London*, London, 1963, and S.O. Dom., *Jas. I*, Vol. III.
174..*of July 1603."*
    Public Record Office, S/K 105, SP 14/2. George More is the father-in-law of Donne.
174..*exclaim against him"*
    Waad to Cecil (as also above), S.O. Dom., *Jas. I*, and Martin A.S. Hume, *Sir Walter Ralegh*, London, 1906, p. 266.
175..*food and lodging.*
    Wilson, *op. cit.*, quoting John Milner, *History of Winchester*, i. 390.
175..*and sickness."*
    Material on the trial quoted and adapted from Ralegh, *The History of the World, with the Life and Tryal of the Author*, London, 1687; Williamson, *Sir Walter Raleigh;* Hume, *Sir Walter Ralegh.*
177..*eternity in Heaven.*
    In the 1687 account of the trial, there is a misprint for Hariot's name and a garbled sentence.
178..*glass to air.*
    TH (VII), fols. 148-415.
178..*now double."*
    Ibid., fol. 148.
179..*ratio calculi.*
    This cipher was first broken by Ethel Seaton. FrancesRicketts worked on it with me.
179..*close-packing diagrams.*
    TH (VII), fol. 166.
179..*from earlier observations).*
    Ibid., fol. 283.
179..*diameter of the eye.*
    Ibid., fol. 310. First "diameter" almost illegible to me.
181..Material on Ophiucus chiefly from conversation and writings by James Pickering, astronomer of the Hayden Planetarium and author of *1001 Questions About Astronomy;* and Max

Casper, *Kepler*, Translated and edited by C. Doris Hellman, London and New York, 1959.

182 ..*p. 58 seq."*
TH, Petworth Papers, Vol. II, p. 6. And "De Stella Cygnis," p. 187, iungitur Serpentarii.

185 ..Material from the Alnwick MSS; reprinted in Fonblanque; *Gunpowder Plot Book;* William Hepworth Dixon, *Her Majesty's Tower,* 4 vols., London, 1869; etc.

192 ..*during His Majesty's Pleasure."*
Star Chamber decree.

195 ..*were involved.*
Examination of Nathaniel Torperley, 27 November 1605. MS, Public Record Office.

196 ..*than her sister."*
David Harris Willson, *King James VI and I*, London, 1963, p. 87.

197 ..*abiit H.3."*
J.L.E. Dreyer, *Tycho Brahe,* New York, 1963, p. 203.

197 ..*says a 20th century chart.*
Wendy-Jane Thomas, Astro-Analysis of King James I of England, 15th October 1967, manuscript sent to author.

199 ..*Mr. Herriott's house.*
Robert Pratt covered the lime house with deal boards and he and William Staunton pulled down the colehouse in her La : garden and sett it upp in the newe orchard. Alnwick rolls : Ingram, 11Feb1608-12Feb1609.

199 ..*pantry, and kitchen.*
BM, Addl. 6786, fol. 426.

199 ..*rest of the page.*
TH (VII), fol. 392.

200 ..*the Jamestown Colony."*
Morton, *Colonial Virginia,* Vol. I, p. 4. See Quinn, *The Roanoke Voyages;* Andrews, *Our Earliest Colonial Settlements;* and Alexander Brown, *Genesis of the United States.*

201 ..*in those parts."*
Quoted in Morton, p. 7, from Rowse, Int. to George Hamor, *A True Discourse of the Present Estate of Virginia,* the letter written to Wharton, not preserved, but abridged and printed in 1625.

202 .. *George Percy*

He wrote this, later. Cf. Arber and Bradley, *Travels and Works of Captain John Smith*, I, lxxii. And Mrs. F.S. Henry Jorg, *A True Relation* of the Hon. Master George Percy, Williamsburg, Va., 1960.

202 .. *new discovered Virginia.*

Northumberland, from the Tower, backed his young brother George, the youngest of eight children. Northumberland's account rolls show that George Percy was given £75 a year, that his debts were paid: "to backers £14.20s"; that the following were sent to him on 13 July 1608 by Mr. Willm MclShaine knives, blawe beads, books, ink, wax, Biskey, butter, lights, starch, Boxes, caskes, a feather bedde, bolster, blanketts, and a covering of tapestrie." And again: mercerie for sutes, chamlett, perpetuano, silk mockado, fustian for doublet, cloth breeches, points, garters, stockings, boots, hats with silk and gold bands, colored Dutch hat edged edged with gold; monmouth cap (this is a plush cap worn by sailors and soldiers).

202 : . *so much gilded durt."*

Morton, quoting Arber and Bradley's *Smith,* in *Colonial Virginia,* I, 14.

203 .. *dim past reversed.*

From Hart Crane, *The Bridge,* "Cape Hatteras," p. 34, from *Complete Poems and Selected Letters and Prose of Hart Crane.* Reprinted by permission of Liveright Publishing Corp. Copyright 1933, © 1958, 1966 by Liveright Publishing Corp.

204 .... *if they could be procured."* Spedding, Vol. IV, p. 23.

208 .. *non contradicant."*

Thomas Hariot, Mathematical Papers, 3, fol. 375.

208 .. *inclined to experiments.*

Rossi 205; Bowen 120.

210 .. *manners and allegiance.*

This, and the following quotation, from David Harris Willson, *King James VI and I,* pp. 250, 256.

210 .. *take compassion on him."*

Ibid., p. 259.

211 .. *for Virginia.*

BM, Harl., fol. 523.

212 .. *Orinoco came after that.*
  and King James' *Counterblast.*
216 .. "*. . . of another world.*"
  Gosse, *op. cit.,* vol. 2, pp. 84-85.
219 .. *ride it out safely.*"
  John Donne, *Sermons,* Vol. IV. Sermon 10, pp. 280-82.
219 .. *Secretary for Virginia.*
  S.P. Dom. Corr. Jac. I, Vol. XLIII, Nos. 39 and 76, Cal., pp.
  487-92.
220 .. *So many historians.*
  Lucian, *Trips to the Moon,* London, 1893, p. 19. *Says Lucian.*
  Lucian, *op cit., The True History,* p. 76.
224 .. Material on Jupiter's moons, conversation of Dr. Kenneth
  Franklin, astronomer at the Hayden Planetarium; Owen Ging-
  rich, "A Model of Jupiter's Satellite Orbits," *Sky & Telescope,*
  May, 1959. Hariot material : TH, Petworth Papers, Vol. II,
  fol. 15, recto and verso.
227 .. *subdoer of necessities.*"
  Bacon, quoted by Farrington, in *Francis Bacon, Philosopher
  of Industrial Science,* London, 1951. (Excerpt mine)
228 .. *but have.*"
  Coleridge, in *Coleridge on the Seventeenth Century,* Rebecca
  Florence Brinkley, ed., Durham, N.C., 1955. From Monologues
  of S.T.C. and the letter to W. Sotheby, September 10, 1802.
229 .. *not thought to be realizable.*"
  Bernal, *op. cit.,* p. 292. Bernal adds here, of the telescope : "The
  means of making it had in fact been available for some 300
  years. It seems, however, to have required the more quanti-
  tative concentration of optical manufacture that went with the
  greater wealth of the sixteenth century to bring about its discovery by chance."
230 .. H.D. Thoreau, *Journals,* "A Week : Sunday," pp. 106-108.
232 .. the biography of imagination.
  Giorgio de Santillana, *The Crime of Galileo,* p. 30; Ludovico
  Geymonat, *Galileo Galilei,* p. 45.
243 .. *like a pocket.*"
  Aubrey's Brief Lives, Walter Warner. Isaac Walton told
  Aubrey that Warner lived near the Water-stairs in a lane not
  far from Northumberland House at Charing Cross. Warner

341

had a pension of forty pounds a year from Northumberland. Warner spent his summers with Sir Thomas Aylesbury in Windsor Park; he was known for his inverted logarithmic tables.

243 .. *in "a cell,"*

The Tempest, Act V, Sc. 1. "This cell's my court : here have I few attendants,/ And subjects none abroad."

243 .. *the end at last.*

Goethe, *Faust,* translated by George Madison Priest, New York, 1959.

245 .. *seen and heard."*

This passage after Strachey.

247 .. G. Wilson Knight, *The Shakespearian Tempest,* London, 1953, 3rd ed., Ch. V.

248 .. *themselves a music."*

Knight, *op. cit.,* p. xiv.

248 .. *could be seen?*

Also in use as "perspective glass" as Hariot used it, for telescope.

250 .. *4000 leaden soldyers."*

A. U.I, 3(1)

251 .. *Public Record Office.*

If this is the Chancery suit of Ralegh, Sanderson et al., Hariot was interrogated on November 11, 1611. Cf. Shirley.

253 .. *Don Quixote."*

Hume, *Ralegh,* p. 297.

254 .. *still be seen*

Robinson Brothers' collection, London, one such notebook.

254 .. *winged Mercury."*

Stevens, *op. cit.,* p. 127.

254 .. *his chaplain.*

I. D'Israeli, *Literary Curiosities,* London, 1834, 9th ed., Vol. V, pp. 234-35.

256 .. *10,000 equal parts."*

Material here from Waters, *The Art of Navigation in England in Elizabethan and Early Tudor Times,* and at the Museum of the City of New York.

256 .. *were at bate,*

"At bate" — in strife, struggle. *OED*

257 .. *poem on the page,*
    BM, Addl. 6788, fol. 490.
259 .. *containing this verse :*
    Sion College Library, George Ripley's Chemistry, 2 copies,
    with a note (in Hariot's hand?) "Opus nostrum fit ex vera
    radice, et ex duobus substantiis mercurialibus, condis. assumptis,
    et/ex minera tractis, puris et mundis &." There is also a copy
    of Sir Edward Kelly on the Philosopher's Stone.
259 .. *within the mother.*
    Mater, in the older version of *The Twelve Gates.* This is the
    alchemical base, the matrix, the mother; and both meanings
    — all meanings — of the word are here.
259 .. *the binary type."*
    Tobias Dantzig, *Number, The Language of Science,* New
    York, Macmillian, 1930.
260 .. *the range :*
    TH, BM Addl. 6786, fol. 284.
261 .. Portrait in Petworth House. Photo by Photo Studies Ltd., 3
    Cavendish Place, London.
261 .. *till you give leave.*
    Aylesbury is frequently mentioned as one of the scientific
    circle of Briggs, Hariot, Warner, and others. Some of his astro-
    nomical observations are preserved in MS. Birch, 4408, and are,
    as far as I know, the only remaining memorials of his attach-
    ment to science. But more may yet be found in Europe.
262 .. *John Rudston.*
    An astronomical treatise by John Rudston on the "great con-
    junction of Jupiter and Saturn" in 1623, is preserved in MS.
    Harl. 5211.
262 .. Materials from Stebbing, Williamson, and other lives of
    Ralegh; Aubrey; *Ency. Brit.;* Judson's *Life of Spenser;* John
    F. Eaton, *A Bibliography of the Honourable Robert Boule,* 2nd
    ed., Oxford, 1961.
264 .. *pirates for millions!"*
    Sir Thomas Wilson's note, from Stebbing, p. 303.
264 .. *a wickedness as this."*
    Williamson, p. 175.
264 .. *and executed.*
    Ibid.

264..*saw fifteen rainbows.*

BM, Ralegh's Journal.

267..*letter to Ernest Jones,*

The story is told in Vol. III of Jones' *Freud*, pp. 94-262.

268..*resting, &c.*

The Harl. MSS., generally ascribed to Hariot, and even by the late Professor Rigaud, are in the handwriting of Sir Charles Cavendish. In Harl. MS. 6083 is a paper in the autograph of Hariot, "de numeris triangularibus," which appears to have hitherto escaped the notice of his biographers. According to Aubrey, the Duke of Northumberland gave Hariot a pension of £400 per annum, and to Robert Hues and Walter Warner he gave £40 (*Lives,* p. 368). Hues was the author of a popular work, *de usu globorum,* which passed through several editions, and was also translated into English. I do not know whether a Mr. Hues, who is mentioned in Harl. MS. 4728, p. 5, as having been a chaplain at the Bermudas, be the same person. (Note from Halliwell, *op. cit.*)

268..*without other evidence.*

BM, Addl. 6783, VII, fol. 132.

269..*collection of proverbs.*

In Iona and Peter Opie, *Oxford Dictionary of Nursery Rhymes,* Oxford, 1951, p. 286.

270..*and twenty burgesses.*

SP Col. I, 1619; Narratives of Early Virginia; Proceedings of the Virginia Assembly, 1619.

272..*than it dissolve.'"*

Morton, *Colonial Virginia,* Vol. I, p. 73.

273..*Slavery.*

Morton, *op. cit.,* Vol. I, p. 70.

274..*six times the other.*

Kingsbury, Records, quoted in Morton, Vol. I, p. 93.

275..*against the Indians.*

Material from Morton, Ch. 5.

275..*an Englishman"*

Elizabeth Haldane, *Descartes,* London, 1905. Also see Baillet, Balz, Adam, Kemp Smith, on Descartes; Bontroux, *Imagination and Mathematics;* Bertram D. Lewin, *Dreams and the Uses of Regression,* 1958.

280 .. *and the sciences."*
   Lewin, p. 35.
281 .. *cannot suppress astonishment.*
   Ibid., pp. 48-49.
281 .. *Loeb Classical Library edition :*
   Ausonius. Loeb, Vol. I, pp. 160-67; 170-73. Cambridge, Mass.,
   1919, 1961.
284 .. *from thence."*
   John Wallis, *A Treatise of Algebra,* London, 1685, p. 198.
284 .. *I will appear masked*
   See Norman Kemp Smith, *New Studies in the Philosophy of
   Descartes,* London, 1952; and *Cogitationes privatae* (A.T.x, p.
   215) and *Oeuvres inedites de Descartes,* ed. by Foucher de
   Careil, i, p. 3. (Trans. by the author.)
284 .. *of an equation."*
   Eric Temple Bell, *The Development of Mathematics,* New
   York, 1940, p. 158.
293 .. *fine long hand.*
   Two of James' favorites were hearing this sermon. It was to
   Robert Carr, his "honorable and faithful friend," he left "that
   picture of mine which is taken in shadows and was made very
   many years before I was of this profession." Donne's will,
   Gosse, II, p. 363.
297 .. *"repaired and beautified"*
   Henry B. Wheatley, *London Past and Present,* London, 1891.
   3 vols.
298 .. *St. Christopher-le-Stocks."*
   Letter to the author from the Secretary of United Cemeteries,
   Ltd., November 1, 1963.
298 .. *figure of Ariel."*
   London for Everyman, rev. ed., London, 1961.
299 .. *sufficiently."*
   Letter to the author, November 17, 1963.
299 .. *around the world."*
   Letter from R.A. Wood to the author, October 28, 1968.

PARTIAL READING LIST*

The Age of Shakespeare. Ed. Boris Ford. Vol. II of The Pelican
Guide to English Literature. Harmondsworth, Middlesex :
Penguin Books, 1963.

An Almanacke . . . for the Year 1598. Made by Thomas Buckminster.
Intro. Eustace F. Bosanquet. Shakespeare Association Facsimile No. 8.

Ashley, Maurice. *England in the Seventeenth Century.* Vol. IV of
the Pelican History of England. Harmondsworth, Middlesex :
Penguin Books, 1954.

———. *The Stuarts in Love.* New York : The Macmillan Company,
1964.

Aubrey's Brief Lives. Ed. Oliver Lawson Dick. Ann Arbor Paper-
backs : The University of Michigan Press, 1962.

Auerbach, Erna. *Nicholas Hilliard.* London : Routledge and Kegan
Paul, 1961.

Bacon, Francis. *New Atlantis.* Ed. Alfred E. Gough. Oxford : Clarendon Press, 1924.

———. *The Complete Essays.* Intro. Henry Le Roy Finch. New
York : Washington Square Press, 1963.

Bagwell, Richard, *Ireland Under the Tudors.* 3 vols. London : Longmans Green, 1885-90.

Bakeless, John. *Tragicall History of Christopher Marlowe.* Cambridge, Mass. : Harvard Univsrity Press, 1942.

Baillet, Adrien. *Vie de Monsieur Descartes.* La Table Ronde.

Bamburgh Castle. Guide Book. Alnwick : H. C. Coates and Son,
1960.

*(To be read in connection with the *Notes* and with the complete works
of John Shirley and David Quinn which are indispensable to this search.)

Balz, Albert G. A. *Descartes and the Modern Mind*. New Haven :
    Yale University Press, 1952.

Boas, Frederick S. *Christopher Marlowe. A Biographical and Critical
    Study*. Oxford : Clarendon Press, 1960.

Bossut, John. *General History of Mathematics*. London, 1803.

Boulting, William. *Giordano Bruno : His Life, Thought, and Mar-
    tyrdom*. London : Kegan Paul, Trench, Trubner and Co., n.d.

Bowen, Catherine Drinker. *Francis Bacon*. Boston : Little, Brown,
    1963.

———. *The Lion and the Crown*. Boston : Little, Brown, 1965.

Bradbrook, M. C. Introduction to Beaumont & Fletcher, *Selected
    Plays*. London and New York : Dent and Dutton, Every-
    man's Library, 1962.

———. *The School of Night : A Study in the Literary Relationships
    of Sir Walter Ralegh*. Cambridge : University Press, 1936.

Brahe, Tycho. *Triangulorum Planorum et Sphaericorum — Praxis
    Arithmetica* (1591, 1595). Ed. Dr. F. I. Studnicka. Prague :
    Ios. Farsky, 1886.

Bronowski, J. and Mazlish, Bruce. *The Western Intellectual Tradi-
    tion*. New York : Harper Torchbooks, 1960.

Bruno, Giordano. *Cause, Principle and Unity*. Trans. Jack Lindsay.
    New York : International Publishers, 1964.

———. *Opere*. Milano : Riccardo Ricciardi (with the Opere of Cam-
    panella), n.d.

———. *The Expulsion of the Triumphant Beast*. Trans. and ed.
    Arthur D. Imerti. New Brunswick, N.J.: Rutgers University
    Press, 1964.

——— e Campanella, Tomaso. *Opere*. Ed. Augusto Guzzo and
    Romano Americo. Milano : Riccardo Ricciardi Editore, n.d.

Burtt, E. A. *The Metaphysical Foundations of Modern Science*. New
    York : Doubleday Anchor Books, 1955.

Butterfield, Herbert. *The Origins of Modern Science, 1300-1800*. New
    York : The Macmillan Company, 1960.

Buxton, John. *Elizabethan Taste*. London : Macmillan and Co., 1963.

Byrne, M. St. Clare. *Elizabethan Life in Town and Country*. Lon-
    don : University Paperbacks, 1961.

Cajoris, Florian. *History of Mathematics*. London : Macmillan,
    1895.

348

Chamberlain, John. *Letters*. Ed. Norman E. McClure. 2 vols. Philadelphia : The American Philosophical Society, 1939.

Chamberlin, Frederick. *The Private Character of Queen Elizabeth*. London : John Lane, The Bodley Head, 1922.

Chapman, George. *The Plays of George Chapman*. Ed. Thomas Marc Parrott. 2 vols. Tragedies; 2 vols. Comedies. New York : Russell and Russell, 1961.

Chomsky, Noam. *Cartesian Linguistics*. New York : Harper and Row, 1966.

Chute, Marchette. *Ben Jonson of Westminster*. New York : E. P. Dutton and Co., 1953.

——. *Shakespeare of London*. New York : E. P. Dutton and Co., 1950.

City of Chichester : The Sole Official Guide. 17th ed. The Chichester City Council, 1963.

Corbin, Henry. *Avicenna and the Visionary Recital*. Trans. William R. Trask. Bollingen Series LXVI. New York : Pantheon Books, 1960.

Coleridge, Samuel Taylor. *Letters*. Ed. Kathleen Raine. London : Grey Walls Press, 1950.

——. *The Inquiring Spirit*. Ed. Kathleen Coburn. New York : Pantheon Books, 1951.

——. *Notebooks*. Ed. Kathleen Coburn. New York : Pantheon, 1957.

——. *Table Talk and Omniana*. London, Oxford University Press, 1917.

——. *Unpublished Letters*. Ed. Earl L. Griggs. New Haven : Yale University Press, 1933.

Craig, Hardin. *The Literature of the English Renaissance, 1485-1660*. Vol. II of *A History of English Literature*. New York : Collier Books, 1962.

Crombie, A. C. *Medieval and Early Modern Science*. Vol. II : Science in the Later Middle Ages and Early Modern Times : XIII-XVII Centuries. New York : Doubleday Anchor Books, 1959.

Crowther, J. G. *Francis Bacon*. London : Cresset, 1960.

——. *The Social Relations of Science*. New York : The Macmillan Company, 1941.

349

d'Agapayeff, Alexander. *Codes and Cyphers*. London, Oxford Univ. Press. Rev. ed. 1949.

Davis, John. *Voyages and Works*. Ed. A. H. Markham. London : Hakluyt Society, 1880.

Davy, Humphrey. *Collected Works*. 9 vols. London, 1839-40.

de Fonblanque, Edward Barrington. *Annals of the House of Percy, from the Conquest to the Opening of the Nineteenth Century*. 2 vols. London : Richard Clay and Sons, 1887.

de Ford, Miriam Allen. *The Overbury Affair*. New York : Avon Book Division, 1960.

de Morgan, Augustus. *A Budget of Paradoxes*. London : Longmans, Green, 1872.

Descartes, René. *Correspondance*. Ed. Ch. Adam and G. Milhaud. Paris, 1941.

de Thou, Jacques Auguste. *Histoire Universelle, 1564-1607*. Suite de N. Rigault. London, 1729.

Devereux, W. B. *Lives and Letters of the Devereux, Earls of Essex*. 2 vols. London, 1853.

Diccionario Enciclopedico Hispano-Americano. Barcelona, 1893.

Donne, John. *The Complete Poetry and Selected Prose of John Donne*. Ed. Charles M. Coffin. New York : The Modern Library, 1952. *Sermons*. 6 vols.

Dixon, William Hepworth. *Her Majesty's Tower*. 4 vols. London : Hurst and Blackett, Publishers, 1869.

Dreyer, J. L. E. *Tycho Brahe*. New York : Dover Publications, 1963. Republication of 1890 edition.

Duque de Maura. *El Designo de Felipe II y el episidio de la Armada Invencible*. Madrid : Javier Morata, 1957.

Dyke, Gwenyth. "Thomas Cavendish : The Roanoke Voyage 1585." *The Suffolk Review*, October, 1956.

Edwards, Philip. *Sir Walter Ralegh*. London : Longmans, Green and Co., 1953.

The Elizabethan Journals. 2 vols. Ed. G. B. Harrison. New York : Doubleday Anchor Books, 1965.

Ellis, Havelock. *Chapman*. Bloomsbury : The Nonesuch Press, 1934.

England's Helicon. London : Shakespeare Head Press, 1925.

Geymonat, Ludovico. *Galileo Galilie.* New York : McGraw-Hill, Inc. 1965.

Gibbons, A. O. *Cerne Abbas : Notes and Speculations on a Dorset Village.* Dorchester : Friary Press, 1962.

Godwin, Francis. *The Man in the Moone : A Story of Space Travel in the Early 17th Century.* Hereford : The Hereford Times, 1959.

Gosse, Edmund. *Life and Letters of John Donne.* 2 vols. London : William Heinemann, 1899.

Greenberg, Sidney. *The Infinite in Giordano Bruno* (w. tr. of *Causa*). New York : King's Crown Press, 1950.

Gunther, R. W. T. *Early Science in Oxford.* 14 vols. Oxford : Oxford History Society for Publications, 1965.

Hakluyt, Richard. *A Selection of the Principal Voyages, Traffiques and Discoveries of the English Nation.* London : William Heinemann, 1927.

———. *Voyages.* 8 vols. London : Everyman's Library, 1962.

Haldane, Elizabeth. *Descartes.* London : John Murray, 1905.

Halliday, F. E. The Life of Shakespeare. Harmondsworth, Middlesex : Penguin Books, 1963.

Halliwell. *Letters on Scientific Subjects.*

Hariot, Thomas. *A Brief and True Report of the New Found Land of Virginia.* New York : The History Book Club, Inc., 1951. Facsimile edition.

———. *Artis Analyticae Praxis.* London, 1631.

Harrison, G. B. *Introducing Shakespeare.* Harmondsworth, Middlesex : Penguin Books, 1962.

Haydn, Hiram. *The Counter-Renaissance.* New York : Grove Press, 1960.

——— (ed.). *The Portable Elizabethan Reader.* New York : The Viking Press, 1959.

Heer, Friedrich. *The Intellectual History of Europe.* Tr. J. Steinberg. London : Weidenfeld and Nicholson, 1966.

Henley, Pauline. *Spenser in Ireland.* Cork : Cork University Press, 1928.

Herbert, George. *The Latin Poetry of George Herbert.* Ed. Mark and Paul R. Murphy. Columbus : Ohio University Press, 1965.

History of Technology. Ed. Charles Singer, *et al.* Vol. III : *From the*

Renaissance to the Industrial Revolution. New York and London : Oxford University Press, 1957.

The Household Papers of Henry Percy, Ninth Earl of Northumberland (1564-1632). Ed. G. R. Batho. London : Offices of the Royal Historical Society, 1962.

Hoyle, Fred. *Frontiers of Astronomy.* New York : A Signet Science Library Book, 1963.

Hues, Robert. *Tractatus de Globis et Eorum Usu* (1592). Ed. Clements R. Markham. London : Hakluyt Society, 1889.

Hume, Martin A. S. *Sir Walter Ralegh.* London : T. Fisher Unwin, 1906.

Illing, Robert. *A Dictionary of Music.* Harmondsworth, Middlesex : Penguin Books, 1951.

Irwin, Margaret. *That Great Lucifer : A Portrait of Sir Walter Ralegh.* London : Chatto and Windus, 1960.

James, D. G. *The Dream of Prospero.* Oxford : Clarendon Press, 1967.

Jonson, Ben. *The Complete Plays.* 2 vols. London : Everyman's Library, 1963.

———. *The Complete Poetry of Ben Jonson.* Ed. William B. Hunter, Jr. Garden City, N.Y. : Anchor Books, 1963.

———. *The Songs and Poems.* London : Philip Allan and Co., 1924.

Judson, A. C. *Spenser in Southern Ireland.* Bloomington, Ind. : Principia Press, 1933.

Judson Alexander C. *The Life of Edmund Spenser.* Vol. VIII of *The Works of Edmund Spenser.* Baltimore : The Johns Hopkins Press, 1945.

Kepler, Johannes. *Gesammelte Werke.* Eds. Walther von Dyck and Max Caspar. Munich : C. H. Beck, 1937–.

Kill Devil Hill National Memorial, North Carolina. Washington, D.C. : U. S. Government Printing Office, 1951.

King James I and VI. *A Counterblast against Tobacco* (1604).

Koestler, Arthur. *The Watershed : A Biography of Johannes Kepler.* New York : Anchor Books, 1960.

The Last Fight of the Revenge and the Death of Sir Richard

Grenville, related by Sir Walter Raleigh, *et al.* Ed. Edmund Goldsmith. Vol. II. Edinburgh : privately printed, 1886.

Leconfield, Lord. *Petworth Manor in the Seventeenth Century.* London : Oxford University Press, 1954.

Lettres, memoires et negociations du Chevalier Carleton. 3 vols. La Haye et a Leide, 1759.

Lorant, Stefan, *The New World.* Rev. ed. New York : Duell, Sloan & Pearce, 1965.

Lovejoy, Arthur O. *The Great Chain of Being.* New York : Harper Torchbooks, 1936.

Lucian. *Trips to the Moon.* Trans. Thomas Francklin. London : Cassell and Co., 1893.

Lucretius. *De Rerum Natura.* Trans. W. H. D. Rouse. London : William Heinemann, 1937.

Magnus, Philip. *Sir Walter Ralegh.* New York : The Macmillan Company, 1956.

Marlowe, Christopher. *Works.* Ed. C. F. Tucker Brooke. Oxford : Clarendon Press, 1957.

Martz, Louis L. *The Poetry of Meditation.* New Haven : Yale University Press, 1954.

Mason, Stephen F. *Main Currents of Scientific Thought : A History of the Sciences.* New York : Abelard-Schuman, 1956.

Mattingly, Garrett. *The Armada.* Boston : Houghton Mifflin Company, 1959.

Newgate Calendar. Ed. Edwin Valentine Mitchell. Garden City, N. Y. : Garden City Publishing Company, 1926. From Knapp and Baldwin, "Newgate Calendar," q. v. on Savage, based on Old Bailey records.

Nicolson, Marjorie. *Science and Imagination.* Ithaca, N. Y. : Great Seal Books, 1956.

Norman, Charles. *The Muses' Darling : The Life of Christopher Marlowe.* New York : Rinehart and Company, 1946.

Oakeshott, Walter. *The Queen and the Poet.* London : Faber and Faber, 1960.

O'Connor, Frank. *Shakespeare's Progress.* Cleveland and New York : World Publishing Company, 1960.

353

The Oxford Book of Sixteenth Century Verse. Ed. E. K. Chambers.
Oxford : Clarendon Press, 1955.
The Oxford Pocket Guide. Oxford : Alfred Savage.

Parks, George Bruner, *Richard Hakluyt and the English Voyages.*
New York : Frederick Ungar, 1961.
Petworth House, Sussex, A Property of the National Trust. Plaistow :
Curwen Press, 1960.
The Phoenix Nest. London : Shakespeare Head Press, 1926.
Piehler, H. A. *England for Everyman.* London : J. M. Dent and
Sons, 1960.
Poe, Edgar Allen. *Selected Prose and Poetry.* Introduction W. H.
Auden. New York : Rinehart and Company, 1954.
Polanyi, Michael. *Personal Knowledge.* Harper Torchbooks, 1964.
Purchas Samuel. *Purchas his Pilgrimes.* London; 1625.

Quinn, David Beers. *The Roanoke Voyages, 1584-1590.* 2 vols. Lon-
don : Hakluyt Society, 1955.
Quinn, David B., and Shirley, John W. "A Contemporary List of
Hariot References." *Renaissance Quarterly,* XXII, No. 1, 1969.

Ralegh, Sir Walter. *The Discoverie of . . . Guiana.* Ed. V. T. Harlow.
London : The Argonaut Press, 1928.
———. *History of the World.*
———. *The Poems.* Ed. Agnes Latham. Cambridge, Mass. : Harvard
University Press, 1951.
———. *The Works of Sir Walter Ralegh.* Oxford University Press,
1829.
Readings in the Literature of Science. Ed. William C. Dampier and
Margaret Dampier. New York : Harper Torchbooks, 1959.
Records of the Virginia Company.
The Riddle of Shakespeare's Sonnets, with essays by Edmond Hubler,
Northrop Frye, Leslie H. Fiedler, Stephen Spender and R. P.
Blackmur, with Oscar Wilde's "The Portrait of Dr. Witt."
New York : Basic Books, 1962.
Rossi, Paolo. *Francis Bacon — From Magic to Science.* Tr. Sacha
Rabinovitch. London : Routledge and Kegan Paul, 1968.
Rowse, A. L. *Christopher Marlowe, His Life and Work.* New York :
Harper and Row, 1964.
———. *The Elizabethans and America.* New York : Harper and
Brothers, 1959.

354

————. *The England of Elizabeth : The Structure of Society*. London : Macmillan and Company, 1961.

————. *Sir Richard Grenville of the Revenge*. London : Jonathan Cape, 1963.

————. *Sir Walter Ralegh : His Family and Private Life*. New York : Harper and Brothers, 1962.

————. *William Shakespeare,* A Biography. London : Macmillan and Company, 1963.

Ryan, Lawrence V. *Roger Ascham*. Palo Alto, Calif. : Stanford University Press, 1963.

Santillana, Giorgio de. *The Crime of Galileo*. Chicago : Phoenix Books, University of Chicago Press, 1955.

Seventeenth Century Studies Presented to Sir Herbert Grierson. Oxford : Clarendon Press, 1938.

Seznec, Jean. *The Survival of the Pagan Gods*. Trans. Barbara Sessions. New York : Harper and Brothers, 1961.

Shakespeare, William. *The Complete Works*. Ed. W. J. Craig. London : Oxford University Press, 1924.

————. *Four Great Comedies*. New York : The Pocket Library, 1960.

————. *The Tempest*. Vol. VII of The Penguin Shakespeare. Ed. G. B. Harrison. Harmondsworth, Middlesex : Penguin Books, 1958.

Shakespeare's Comedy of the Tempest. Ed. Richard Wilson. London : J. M. Dent and Sons, 1927.

Sherborne, Dorset. Official Guide. 7th ed. Surrey : The Home Publishing Company.

Sidney, Sir Philip. *The Countess of Pembroke's Arcadia*. London : Sampson Low, Son, and Marston, 1867.

Silver Poets of the Sixteenth Century. Ed. Gerald Bullett. London : J. M. Dent and Sons, 1947.

Singer, Dorothea Waley. *Giordano Bruno, His Life and Thought*. New York : Henry Schuman, 1950.

Smith, John. *History of Virginia*. 1626 ed. London : Hakluyt Society, 1880.

Smith, Norman Kemp. *New Studies in the Philosophy of Descartes*. London : Macmillan, 1952.

Spedding, James. *Letters and Life of Francis Bacon*. London, 1861.

Stebbing, William. *Sir Walter Ralegh*. Oxford : Clarendon Press, 1899.

Spencer, Edmund. *Complete Works*. Ed. R. Morris. London : Macmillan, 1929.

Stevens, Henry. *Hariot* 1900.

Stick, David. *Fabulous Dare : The Story of Dare County Past and Present*. Kitty Hawk, N. C. : The Dare Press, 1949.

————. *The Outer Banks of North Carolina*. Chapel Hill : The University of North Carolina Press, 1958.

Strathmann, Ernest A. *Sir Walter Ralegh : A Study in Elizabethan Skepticism*. New York : Columbia University Press, 1951.

Symbols of the Church. Ed Carroll E. Whittemore. Boston : Whittemore Associates, 1959.

Syon House. London : Syon House Estate, 1950.

Sypher, Wylie. *Four Stages of Renaissance Art*. New York : Anchor Books Original, 1955.

Taylor, E. G. R. *Late Tudor and Early Stuart Geography*. London : Methuen, 1934.

Taylor, Henry Osborn. *Thought and Expression in the Sixteenth Century*. 2 vols. New York : Frederick Ungar Publishing Company, 1959.

Thomson, S. Harrison. *Progress of Medieval and Renaissance Studies in the United States and Canada*. Bulletin No. 25. Boulder, Col. : University of Colorado, 1960.

Tillyard, E. M. W. *The Elizabethan World Picture*. New York : Avon Book Division, 1960.

Toward Modern Science. Vol. I. Ed. Robert M. Palter. New York : The Noonday Press, 1961.

The Tower of London, Ministry of Works Guide-book. London : H. M. S. Office, 1960.

The Transactions of the Honourable Society of Cymmrodocion. Session 1937. London, 1938.

The View of Fraunce (1604). Intro. W. P. Barrett. Shakespeare Association Facsimiles No. 13, 1936.

The Voyages and Colonising of Sir Humphrey Gilbert. Ed. David Beers Quinn. 2 vols. London : Hakluyt Society, 1940.

Waldman, Milton. *Sir Walter Raleigh*. London : Collins, 1943.

————. *Sir Walter Ralegh*. London : St. Jame's Library, 1950.

Wallis, John. *A Treatise of Algebra*. London : 1685

The Water Color Drawings of John White from the British Museum, 1965.

Waters, D. W. *The Art of Navigation in England in Elizabethan and Early Stuart Times*. New Haven : Yale University Press, 1958.

Watson, David Lindsay. *Scientists are Human*. London : Watts and Company, 1938.

Webster's Biographical Dictionary. Springfield, Mass. : Webster's Biographical Dictionary, 1943.

Webster and Tourneur. Introduction by John Addington Symonds. London : T. Fisher Unwin, n.d.

Williamson, Hugh Ross. *Sir Walter Raleigh*. London : Faber and Faber, 1951.

Willey, Basil. *The Seventeenth Century Background*. New York : Doubleday Anchor Books, 1953.

Willson, David Harris. *King James VI and I*. London : Jonathan Cape, 1963.

Wilson, John Dover. *Life in Shakespeare's England*. Harmondsworth, Middlesex : Penguin Books, 1959.

Wilson, F. P. *The Plague in Shakespeare's London*. London : Oxford University Press, 1963.

Winwood Papers.

Wolf, A. *A History of Science, Technology and Philosophy in the 16th and 17th Centuries*. 2 vols. New York : Harper Torchbooks, 1959.

Woollaston, Sir Gerald Woods. *Heraldry*. The Heraldry Society, 1960.

Work for Chimny-Sweepers or A Warning for Tobacconists, 1601. Introduction S. H. Atkins. Shakespeare Association Facsimile No. 11. London : Oxford University Press, 1936.

Wright, Louis B. *Middle-class Culture in Elizabethan England*. Ithaca, N. Y. : Cornell University Press, 1958.

Wyatt, Sir Thomas. *The Collected Poems*. Ed. Kenneth Muir. Cambridge, Mass. : Harvard University Press, 1950.

Yates, Frances A. *Giordano Bruno and the Hermetic Tradition*. London : Routledge and Kegan Paul, 1964.

INDEX

Britain's Ida, 310
Brooke, Francis, 25
Bruno, Giordano, 4-5, 6, 27, 65, 68, 69-76, 82, 88, 90, 108-13, 114, 141, 142, 158-61, 166, 216, 227, 228, 229, 232, 270, 309, 310, 313; *Ash-Wednesday Supper, The,* 73, 74; *Cabala of Pegasus, The,* 73; *Candle-man, The,* 69; *De Immenso,* 27, 65, 75-76, 108, 109-10, 112, 159, 166, 309; *De Monade,* 109; *De Triplici Minimo,* 109; *Expulsion of the Triumphant Beast, The,* 73, 75; *Heroic Ecstasies,* 73, 74; *Idiota Triumphans,* 141; *Insomnium,* 141; *Modern and Complete Art of Remembering, A,* 71; *On Cause, Principle and Unity,* 73; *On the Infinite Universe and Worlds,* 73, 74, 110; *Shadow of Ideas, The,* 71; *Spaccio,* 91
Brunswick, Duke of, 166, 196, 197
Bry, Theodore de, 105, 106-8, 110, 223
Buchanan, George, 197
Buckingham, George Villiers, Duke of, 290-91, 292
Buckner, Thomas, 13, 273, 286-88
Bull, Eleanor, 129, 130
Burghley, Lord, 60, 83, 92
Burhill, Robert, 253, 254
Burke, Kenneth, 145
Burroughs, Sir John, 122, 123-25
Bye-plot, 175

Cadiz, 61, 85, 101, 149, 169
Caesar, Sir Julius, 171
Caliban, 241-42, 243, 255
California, 56
Cambridge University, 52, 53-54, 77, 94
Camden, William, 152, 153, 155-56
Campanella, Tommaso, 108, 159
Campion, Edmund, 176
Campo, Richarte de Verde, *see* Grenville
Cancer, 11, 267, 285-86
Carew, Lord, 265
Carew, Sir George, 90, 123
Carew, Sir Nicholas, 166, 171, 270
Carew, Thomas, 75
Carleill, *see* Hay, James
Carleton, Dudley, 12, 186-87, 215, 231, 241, 270, 274, 291

Carlisle, Lord, *see* Hay, James
Cavendish, Sir Charles, 283-84
Cavendish, Thomas, 19, 21, 22, 25, 77-78, 313
Cecil, Sir William, 52, 79, 122, 123, 124, 154, 173-74, 187, 190, 193-4
Cerne, 134; Cerne Abbas, 133, 134, 135-39, 311; Cerne Giant, 11, 134, 311; Up Cerne, 133, 136, 311
Chamberlain, John, 215, 218, 291
Champernowne, Kat, *see* Ashley, Kat
Champernowne, Sir Richard, 67
Change, 88, 90-91
Chapman, George, 12, 15, 142, 144-49; *Achilles Shield,* 146; translation of Homer, 144-45, 148-49; *De Guiana,* 148-49; *Shadow of Night, The,* 147; *Sir Giles Goosecap,* 147
Charles I, 166
Charlewood, J., 73
Charteris, Sir Martin, 305
Chaucer, 81, 88, 198; *Astrolabe,* 81
Chesapeake, 29, 35
Ching, I, 75
Ciphers, 164-67
"Circle of the Secret Ones," 99
Ciudad Guyana, 143
Clarke, Charles Cowden, 25, 145
Clarke, Sir William, 171
Clifford, George, 77, 105-6, 122, 124
Close-packing, 10, 163, 179
Cobham, Henry, 78, 174, 175, 176, 204
Codes, 164-67
Coke, Lord, 153, 174-76, 210
Coleridge, S. T., iii, 55, 75, 228; *Omniana,* 75
College of the Fellowship for the Discovery of the North-West Passage, The, 139-41
Collingwood, R. G., 61
Columbus, Christopher, 59
Columbus, Diego, 211
Comets, 10, 27, 266
Compasses, 29
Cope, Sir Walter, 178, 201
Copernican theory, 159
Copernicus, 14, 112
Cork, Lord, *see* Boyle, Richard, 262
Corporations, 210-11
Corporación Venezolana de Guyana (C.V.G.), 143
Coryat, George, 52
Costa, Josephus a, 211

360

366

About the Author

Born in New York, where she now lives, MURIEL
RUKEYSER has published both poetry and prose, including *The Speed of Darkness, The Life of Poetry,* with
its chapter on "the rare union" of poetry and science,
and the biography *Willard Gibbs* which, like this latest
work, deals with another hero of the buried imagination.

She moved toward this book in England—in the British
Museum, the Tower, the Bank, and particularly in the
collections and gardens of the Duke of Northumberland,
descendant of the Wizard Earl, who, with Ralegh, was
one of Hariot's tragic patrons; in Spain, in the archives
of the Duchess of Medina Sidonia, descendant of the
commander of the Armada; and on the sandbars near
Hatteras where Ralegh sent his expedition—that landscape of imagination where the Wright Brothers and
Hariot found the real and potential new world.

Muriel Rukeyser is a member of the Institute of Arts
and Letters, of the Thomas Harriot Seminar at Oxford
(Harriot can be spelled as you will; she has chosen
"Hariot" for reasons that will be apparent in the book),
of the Society of American Historians and the History
of Science Society.